Come Home to Little House
Five Generations of Pioneer Girls

WHERE LITTLE HOUSE BEGAN
Martha Morse
Laura's great-grandmother
born 1782

BOSTON'S LITTLE HOUSE GIRL
Charlotte Tucker
Laura's grandmother
born 1809

SPIRIT OF THE WESTERN FRONTIER
Caroline Quiner
Laura's mother
born 1839

AMERICA'S ORIGINAL PIONEER GIRL
Laura Ingalls
born 1867

PIONEER FOR A NEW CENTURY
Rose Wilder
Laura's daughter
born 1886

The Little House

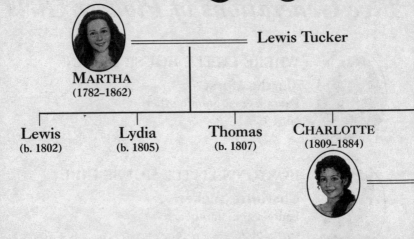

MARTHA
(1782–1862) ———————— Lewis Tucker

Lewis
(b. 1802)   **Lydia**
(b. 1805)   **Thomas**
(b. 1807)   **CHARLOTTE**
(1809–1884)

Joseph
(1834–1862)   **Henry**
(1835–1882)   **Martha**
(1837–1927)

Mary
(1865–1928)   **LAURA**
(1867–1957)

Family Tree &

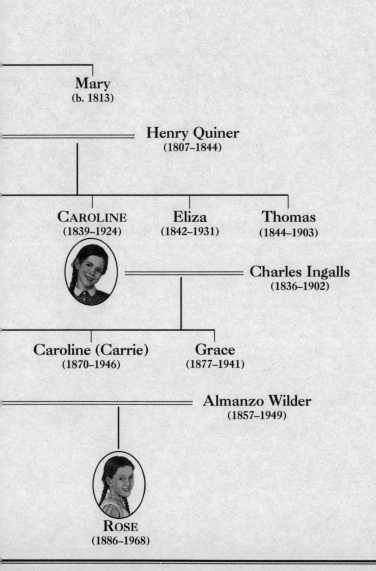

Mary
(b. 1813)

Henry Quiner
(1807–1844)

CAROLINE
(1839–1924)

Eliza
(1842–1931)

Thomas
(1844–1903)

Charles Ingalls
(1836–1902)

Caroline (Carrie)
(1870–1946)

Grace
(1877–1941)

Almanzo Wilder
(1857–1949)

ROSE
(1886–1968)

In the Land *of the* Big Red Apple

Roger Lea MacBride

Illustrated by David Gilleece

SCHOLASTIC INC.
New York Toronto London Auckland Sydney
Mexico City New Delhi Hong Kong

ISBN 0-439-15437-5

12 11 10 9 8 7 6 5 4 3 2 1   0 1 2 3 4 5/0

Printed in the U.S.A.   40

First Scholastic printing, January 2000

For my godchildren in order of appearance:
Slayton Dabney and Kaleigh Morrison

Contents

In the Land of the
Big Red Apple

Are We Poor?

Papa drove the rattling wagon slowly along the twisting road through the steep Ozark hills, so slowly that Rose wanted to jump off the wagon seat and run ahead. She silently tried to hurry along the mares, Pet and May. They would never get to Mr. Rippee's at this pace!

But the horses couldn't hear her, and even if they could, Papa would never let them run with the wagon on such a bumpy, rutted road.

Rose sighed and wriggled her bottom on the hard seat between Mama and Papa. Fido sat on Mama's lap, a contented look on his face, his little pink tongue hanging out. Every so often he raised his nose to catch a scent on the dusty fall breeze.

A pale ghost of the moon hovered over the treetops in a sky that glowed deep blue. The sunshine lay on Rose's shoulders like a cozy shawl, bright and warm. She inhaled deeply to catch a whiff of smoke from Papa's pipe mingling with the spicy smell of falling leaves.

Finally the team turned off the road into a wagon track that climbed a hillside. The forest fell away behind them and the horses bent their necks and grunted as they pulled the wagon into a great field that soared up and up in front of them. In that field were lines and lines of apple trees, more than anyone could possibly count. The trees marched across the sloping hillside like an army of bushy-headed soldiers. Each tree cast a patch of moving shadow on the golden grass.

Papa *whoa*ed the mares and pushed up his hat brim to see better. Fido whined and fidgeted to get down, but Mama held him tight.

Boughs laden with red-and-yellow fruit, as pretty and bright as Christmas balls, swayed and shook. Men, women, even children—some on ladders, some standing on the ground—swarmed over the branches, picking the fruit into baskets. The whole orchard quivered with motion.

This was their future, Rose thought, and the instant she thought it, Papa uttered a satisfied, "Mmm-mmm." He tapped out the ashes of his pipe on the side of the wagon.

"I don't think there's any crop as lovely as apples," sighed Mama.

"Mr. Rippee sets a nice orchard," Papa agreed. "In a couple years, our place'll look as fine as this, and full of pickers, too. Then, my prairie Rose, we'll be rich." He gave Rose a wink and smiled at Mama.

"Rich." Rose repeated the word in her thoughts. She couldn't imagine the spindly little apple trees in their own orchard ever growing big enough to be heavy with fruit. And she certainly couldn't imagine being rich.

Blanche Coday, a girl in Rose's school, was

rich. All the children said so. Blanche's father owned the drugstore in Mansfield. Blanche wore a different, beautifully lace-collared dress every day of the week. From her wrist dangled a gold-colored bracelet, and her black shoes shined like the inside of a nugget of split coal.

Rose wore the same dress every day, for a whole school session. Only when it became tattered, or so pinched in the shoulders that the seams might rip out—only then could Rose go with Mama to Reynolds' Store and pick out cloth to sew up a new one. No matter how scuffed and patched her heavy Brogan shoes might become, they also had to last a whole school session. And her set of hair ribbons, one for each of her braids, were meant to last as long as her dress, although Rose sometimes lost them playing.

Some of the town girls, in their lovely dresses, with nickels to spend for gum and candy, teased Rose. They called her "country girl." And because Rose was the best scholar in spelling, they called her "teacher's pet." Rose didn't mind being teacher's pet.

But she knew she wasn't really a country girl, at least not like the poor girls whose mothers sent them to school with dirty feet, unwashed, unbraided hair, and runny noses. It made Rose's neck burn with shame to be called a country girl.

Rose looked at Mr. Rippee's fine orchard and asked Mama and Papa, "Are we poor?"

Papa's eyes flickered at Rose as he tucked his pipe into the pocket of his overalls. Mama set Fido in the wagon box and drew her shawl closer around her shoulders. "I think you had better answer that, Manly. You're the one who put the thought in her head."

"Now, I wouldn't say we're poor, exactly," Papa said thoughtfully, twisting an end of his mustache. "We've got our own spread. Folks who have land have their freedom, which is a sight better than money any day. The land's thin and stony, but it's ours so long as we keep up the mortgage and taxes.

"We've got the mares, and the mules, Roy and Nellie. We had a good first growing season here in the Ozarks, with cash crops, and food left over to last the winter."

"And don't forget my hens, Manly," Mama added, puffing herself up a little. "It was my egg money that bought you the new plow."

"Nobody can make a chicken listen to reason the way you can, Bess," Papa chuckled. "If chickens could vote, you'd be president."

"All right then," Mama said in a satisfied voice. "No, I wouldn't say we're poor, Rose. But the going is rough for every farmer right now, what with the country run down, so many folks thrown off their land and their jobs. Things will get better again. It takes time.

"Besides," she added, "you know what your grandpa Ingalls always says about rich and poor."

"What?"

"The rich man gets his ice in the summer, and the poor man gets it in the winter. It all evens up in the end."

Now Mama and Papa looked at Mr. Rippee's orchard with searching, hopeful eyes. Rose knew they were all thinking the same thought. This was what had brought the family all that way, 650 long, hot, dusty miles, from the barren, burned-out prairie to the Land of the Big Red Apple in Missouri. They came to have a better life for themselves, to make a future.

Rose knew that in that future, their orchard would look just as beautiful as Mr. Rippee's. Whole families would travel from all around the countryside to pick the apples. And then women in houses far away in great cities would bake pies of them. When that day came, she and Mama and Papa would have everything they ever wanted.

A lightning shot of excitement ran through Rose. Some day Mama could have a new Sunday dress whenever she needed, Papa could have a buggy to take Mama for rides in the summer, and Rose could have hair ribbons in any color she wanted.

It had been a bit more than a year since they first came to the little town of Mansfield and bought the rough forty-acre place. They called it Rocky Ridge Farm, because it sat on a rocky ridge. How everything had changed in just that year! Rose realized with a start that she was growing up fast. She was nearly nine years old, old enough now to do most any chore on the farm.

And how the little farm had changed as well! The fall before, they had started out with a drafty log house, a sack of beans, a sack of cornmeal, and a piece of salt pork.

Now they had their own field of corn, and a harvest of potatoes, and onions, and cabbage, and a whole summer of wonderful eating from the garden. Papa had even managed to get a small crop of oats from the new ground he had plowed in between the deadened trees.

Best of all, they had the tender young apple saplings, nearly a thousand in all, that were left behind by the man who had sold them the farm. Papa had replanted them all in the spring. Now all they had to do was tend them a little and wait for their first harvest.

No, Rose decided. Papa was right. They weren't poor. But still, four years until the first apple crop seemed an eternity. Wheat and oats and corn grew from pitiful little seeds all the way to harvest in a few months. Trees grew so slowly!

In the orchard of Silas Rippee, the pickers harvested the fruit like hungry butting bees. Two boys flung rotten apples at each other, until a grown-up scolded them to get back to work. Scattered on the ground around the trees sat crates mounded up with the shining red-and-gold fruit. The air smelled winy sweet.

Some grown-ups were standing around a table. One of them dumped a crate of apples onto it. That was the culling table, said Papa, where the bruised and damaged apples were sorted from the best ones.

"Watch the team while your mother and I go talk to Mr. Rippee," he said.

The culling table was a big triangle with high sides on it, like a box, and tilted up at the flat end. When the pickers dumped a crate of apples into the high side, they rolled down toward the point of the triangle.

The bottom of the box was slatted, with open spaces for leaves and stems to fall through to the ground. Grown-ups stood all around the box, sorting out the reddest, plumpest apples and putting them in baskets on the ground. The culls that were bruised or cut or not quite red enough went into other baskets. Everyone talked and laughed as they worked, and ate apples. Rose's mouth watered.

When Mama and Papa came back, they drove the wagon next to a place where many crates sat on the ground. Then they all climbed down and walked slowly among the crates, looking carefully at each one. Rose and Mama followed Papa, watching him pick up an apple here and there and then peer at the apples hidden underneath.

"What are you doing, Papa?" asked Rose.

"You can't be too careful buying apples," he said. "An orchard man always puts the best, reddest apples on top. You have to make sure he isn't hiding culls underneath."

Papa knew a few things about apples. His father set an orchard when Papa was a little farmer boy, and Papa helped harvest the crop.

When Papa had picked the crates he wanted, an orchard worker helped dump the apples into the wagon box. Papa pulled out his leather sack with the drawstring and fished out four silver coins, which he handed to Mr. Rippee. Mr. Rippee shook Papa's hand and dropped the coins in his pocket. The pocket bulged with coins, and he jingled like sleigh bells when he moved. Mr. Rippee was rich.

"Here's a job for you, Rose," Papa said. "Climb up in there and spread them around 'til the pile is level. You're smaller and your feet won't hurt the apples. Mind you don't bang them up."

Rose carefully and gently pushed the growing pile of rosy-golden apples around each time another crate was dumped into the wagon. She waded carefully through the apples without lifting her feet, so she wouldn't step on a single one. Soon the whole wagon box was a sea of red and yellow, full almost to the top. She wanted to dive right in, it looked so inviting. She picked two of the reddest ones she could find, gave one to Mama, and they each took a bite.

"Delicious," said Mama through a mouthful, the juice running down her chin. "If there were no other food in the world, I think I could live on apples alone."

Hers was the sweetest apple Rose could ever remember eating.

They ate apples all the way home. Papa drove very slowly, so the bumps wouldn't bruise any. A bruised apple will rot, and a single rotten apple can ruin a whole load. Rose kept glancing back into the wagon box. She couldn't believe that the little sea of fruit really belonged to them.

Papa dug a hole for the apples, next to the mound where they had ground-stored the potatoes and onions. He lined it with straw, and Rose helped fill it with apples. Then he covered it up with more straw and a thick layer of earth. Now they would have fresh, crisp apples all through the winter.

After Papa was done, Rose helped Mama peel and slice the rest of the apples for drying. All that day and the next Mama peeled and Rose sliced. Each apple must be sliced into eight equal parts, not too thin and not too thick, with the seeds cut out.

"These Ben Davises are a good variety," Mama said as she munched on one. "The same as ours will be." Her deep-blue eyes sparkled with pleasure. "Crisp and sturdy. When we have our own apples, they should ship well. City people like a firm red apple."

"Mama, when we're rich, will I have different dresses to wear to school?"

Mama looked at Rose with a crooked grin and chuckled. "Your Papa talks a good game, Rose," she said, peeling another apple. Her quick hands flew around the apple and the sunlight raced up and down the knife blade as she turned the skin into a long curling ribbon that dropped into a pail. "He's a hopeful sort, and hope makes a nourishing breakfast. But it is a poor supper."

"What does that mean, hope is a poor supper?"

"Hope is what keeps a body climbing life's mountain," explained Mama. "Hope that it is better or easier when you reach the top. But it is best not to put our hopes up very high. Who can say what troubles we might meet along the way? We have never raised apples before.

"But when our orchard comes into bearing, we ought to be able to pay off the mortgage and have some clear money. It isn't being rich like rich folks. But for a farmer, it's rich."

Rose nodded, but she didn't really understand the difference.

They peeled and sliced until they had a big bowl of slices. Then Mama took an old sheet and spread it over some planks she had set in a sunny spot. The planks sat on blocks of wood to make a table. Mama showed Rose how to lay out the apple slices in rows, close together but not touching.

They sat on the porch where they could shoo away birds that might try to steal them. Rose brushed away bees with the branch of a bush. Mama threw the peelings near the henhouse for the chickens, to keep them distracted.

They peeled and sliced while the sunning apples soaked up the warmth, began to shrink, and turned crusty. At first the slices turned dark. But then the sunshine bleached them a creamy yellow.

They took up the sheet at sunset and put it out again in the morning, spreading out the slices as before. After three days, the apple slices had dried leathery soft and rattled like walnuts when the sheet was gathered up.

Then Mama put them all in a sack that she hung from a rafter in the kitchen. The heat from the stove would keep them dry all winter, ready to be made into her delicious fried apple pies. The sack of dried apples filled the kitchen with a wonderful fruity smell.

Harvest time on the farm was hard, never-ending work, from lamplight to lamplight. Sometimes they even worked by moonlight. It had to be done quickly to gather everything in and keep it safe from a killing frost and from the woods creatures.

And there were still the everyday chores to be done—clothes to be washed, bread to bake, the chickens to be watered and fed and their eggs gathered, the house to be swept each morning after breakfast, and wood to be gathered for the stove.

And still the harvest was not finished. Tomorrow, Papa said, they would go to the Stubbinses' farm with Abe Baird, Papa's hired hand, and Abe's little brother Swiney, to help Mr. Stubbins gather in his cane crop. Rose's heart leaped with joy. She had not seen her friend Alva Stubbins since school ended. She had so much to tell!

Sorghum Time

They got up early and ate a breakfast of reheated beans and cold potatoes to save time. Mama filled a small sack with the fried apple pies she had cooked the day before. Abe and Swiney, who was eight years old, appeared out of the thick morning fog like ghostriders, on Old Guts, their mule with the grumbling stomach. Then everyone got into Papa's wagon for the drive.

Papa had just settled onto the seat when Rose cried out, "Wait, Papa! I forgot something." She clambered down the wagon wheel and dashed into the house.

"Why, whatever in the world?" Mama's voice called after her.

Rose ran into the bedroom to the fireplace and took down from the mantel the autograph book Professor Kay had given her that summer for winning the final spelling contest. She tucked it under her arm, ran, and got back into the wagon.

"I want Alva to write something in it," Rose explained. She was so happy she had remembered to bring it along.

Then they made the short drive through the damp, cottony air to the Stubbinses' farm. The woods stood perfectly still and the fog seemed to drink up every sound, swallowing the wagon's creaking and rumbling, and muffling the ringing of the horses' shoes on the flinty rocks.

Swiney showed Rose an Indian arrowhead he had found along Fry Creek. It was the tiniest thing, very pointy and still sharp after all the years it must have lain in the mud. Rose made a picture in her head of the Indian who owned it, creeping along the creek bank, hunting a rabbit or a quail for his supper.

"I'd give anything to see wild Indians," Rose said.

"Me too," said Swiney. "I bet they was plenty a-living around here too. They's arrowheads everywhere, if you know where to look."

The fog was so thick that Rose didn't realize they had arrived until the horses snorted in surprise and stopped short with a jingle of harness. The faint shape of a barn rose up in front of them.

"Howdy!" Papa shouted. "Anyone about?"

A shadowy figure in a hat peered out of the barn door.

"Why, I'd know that team anywhere," a man's cheerful voice called out. "That'd be the Wilders' Morgans."

It was Mr. Stubbins, grinning ear to ear as he walked up to the wagon.

"Howdy, Mrs. Wilder. Abe, Swiney. Hello there, Rose. Alva's a-waiting you down in the sorghum patch."

Rose squirmed happily.

"You folks ready to cook up a batch of 'lasses?" he said cheerfully.

"Sure as shootin'," Papa said.

"You best let me lead your team down to the field," Mr. Stubbins said. "I wouldn't want them a-pulling your wagon into a ditch. Fog's mighty thick down the hollow."

Mr. Stubbins led the team past rows of sorghum stalks that looked like corn except they had no ears. On top of the stalks were dark brown clusters of seeds.

When they finally stopped, Rose could not see Alva, or anything else for that matter. The gray mist swallowed up everything except the nearest edge of the cane field. But she could hear the hushed voices of people talking and leaves rustling. Everyone was already in the field working.

Mr. Stubbins gave each of them a stick that was flat like a paddle. Mama and Papa and Rose had never stripped cane, so Mr. Stubbins showed them how to do it.

"You'uns go down the rows and knock off the leaves, just so," Mr. Stubbins said, knocking the leaves from a stalk with the stick. Then they each picked a row to themselves and began walking through the cane stalks. It was slow work. The paddle was heavy, and Rose had to hit each leaf twice to knock it off, and sometimes even more. And the top leaves were too high to reach.

In no time even Swiney had disappeared ahead of Rose into the ghostly mist until all she could hear was the *whack! whack!* of sticks all through the field. Working in the foggy cane field was like being inside a dream.

Rose got to the end of her row at the same time as Alva reached the end of the row she was stripping.

"This is hard," Rose huffed, dragging her paddle on the ground behind her. Her arms complained with aches.

"Just you wait 'til the cane's stripped and cut," Alva said. "That's when the fun gets a-going." She broke down one of the stalks and peeled off two strips of the sinewy cane. She handed one to Rose, stuck the other in her mouth and started chewing on it.

"Go on," she said through a mouthful of cane. "Smack down on it."

Rose bit the stringy piece. A deliciously sweet taste filled her mouth, lighter than molasses. The more she gnawed on it, the more the sweet juice came out.

They picked two rows next to each other and worked side by side all morning, chattering like sparrows and stopping now and then to chew a piece of cane. Rose told Alva all about school, the spelldown she'd won, the blacksnake that got loose from Harry Carnall's pocket, and Blanche Coday.

Alva laughed hard at the snake story, but she was quiet when Rose told about her new friend, Blanche. Alva did not like town girls. She thought they were stuck up. And Alva never wanted to go to school. She liked working on the farm with her father.

Then Rose taught Alva a song she had learned from the other girls at school. It was a ditty they sang when they jumped rope, but she sang it in rhythm with the swing of her stick against the cane leaves:

Katie Mariar jumped in the fire,
The fire was so hot, she jumped in the pot,
The pot was so black, she jumped in the crack,
The crack was so high, she jumped in the sky,
The sky was so blue, she jumped in a canoe,
The canoe was so shallow, she jumped in the
* tallow,*
The tallow was so soft, she jumped in the loft,
The loft was so rotten, she jumped in the cotton,
The cotton was so white, she stayed all night.

Then Alva told Rose about the candy breaking her older sister had given at their house.

"What's a candy breaking?"

"It's kissing games," said Alva, giggling.

Rose was shocked. "You kissed a boy?"

"I didn't kiss no boy," Alva said sharply, her face pinched in disgust. "I ain't never kissed no boy and I ain't a-aiming to neither. I already told you, Rose. I'm a-going to be an old maid when I'm growed. But my big sister Effie did. And I never did laugh so hard to see it."

"But why did she do it?" Rose asked in wonderment. She could not imagine ever kissing a boy, or wanting to. Kissing was for mothers and fathers, and for children to kiss them good night before they went to bed. Rose would never kiss a boy until she got married, and that was a long, long time off.

"My mama got a mess of stick candy at Reynolds' Store, all different pretty colors," Alva explained. "She busted 'em in half, and stirred up all the pieces in a bowl. Then my sister's girl friends came, all dressed up. And a bunch of boys came too, only they had to pay a nickel for the candy.

"They throwed a towel over the bowl and one of them boys reached in and picked him a piece. Then he told his favorite girl to try. If she picked the same color, the boy had to kiss the girl. If they was different, the next boy took his turn."

Alva put her hand to her mouth and started to giggle hard.

"But the boys cheated," she gurgled. "And they saved their pieces and traded 'em 'til they all had a piece of every color. Everybody was a-kissing everybody else. Oh, Rose, I never

24

seen nothing so foolish."

Alva puckered her lips and made smacking sounds, like kissing, and then she crumpled up with laughter, slumping to the ground with weakness. Alva's giggling so tickled Rose that she burst out laughing as well. Before long tears were running down both their cheeks and their faces were flushed and shiny.

"Rose!" Mama's voice came through the rustling cane. "That's enough play, now. Mind your work."

So they went back to stripping cane. But all the rest of the morning when they got bored they made smacking sounds that sent them both into fits of laughter.

By the time all the cane had been stripped, the sun had climbed high over the trees, the fog and mist had burned off, and the air was warm. Then the grown-ups walked through the field with sharp knives lopping off the seed heads and chopping down the cane.

Rose, Alva, Swiney, and the other children followed, gathering the bare stalks and dragging them out of the field. They piled the

stalks in an open place where Papa and Abe worked, near the cane mill.

The mill was a metal box with a wheel inside, perched on a tower of squared-off logs. A long pole stuck far out from the top. Harnessed to the end of it was one of Mr. Stubbins's mules, placidly munching oats in his feed bag.

As soon as they brought the first stalks in from the field, Abe showed Papa how to feed the mill. Then Abe gave the mule a pat and it began to walk in a great circle around the machine. The pole kept the mule from walking anywhere but in that great circle. The pole turned the wheel inside the box. Then Papa fed the cane stalks into the box.

Rose could hear the stalks crackling and crunching as the wheel smashed them flat. The flattened, shattered stalks came out the other side. And out of a spout at the bottom of the mill, like magic, poured a little stream of clear, greenish cane juice. It dribbled into a piece of cloth that had been draped over a large barrel, to strain out insects and bits of cane. Then the juice began to fill the barrel.

The patient mule plodded around and around in a circle, never going anywhere but making that machine squeeze juice out of the stalks.

Nearby Mr. Stubbins fed stove wood into a fire in a stone trough with a tall stone chimney at one end. Lying on the ground was a long, shallow copper pan.

"That there's the cooker," Alva said.

"What does it do?" asked Rose. "How does it make molasses?"

"You'll see," Alva said. "We best get the cane out of the field first. We got to keep the mill fed so there's always juice enough to keep a-cooking."

They hauled cane until a great mountain had grown by the mill, the stalks jackstrawed all over the ground. Rose's stomach growled emptily. Her arms ached and her legs quivered. Each armload seemed heavier than the last. Her hands and dress became sticky with cane juice, and bees buzzed greedily all about her. The mill crawled with them, and the mule's tail never stopped swishing them away.

Finally Rose heard the tinny sound of Mrs. Stubbins beating a pot with a stick. That was the signal for dinner. As tired as they all were, the children raced each other to the cooker where Mrs. Stubbins and Mama and Effie had laid out a great harvest banquet.

Baldknobbers

They ate until they were stuffed: fried chicken, biscuits, mashed sweet potatoes, boiled cabbage with bits of fried bacon, Mama's crispy fried apple pies, and tangy-sweet lemonade. The lemonade was extra good with a little of the fresh cane juice poured in. Rose couldn't remember when she had been so hungry, or when food had tasted so satisfying.

The grown-ups took turns at the cooker when they weren't eating, stirring the steaming juice to keep it from burning, and wiping the sweat from their faces with rags. When

Rose was done eating, Mama gave her a cup of lemonade to take to Papa.

The cooker's long copper tray lay atop the trough of fire. Little copper dams divided it into five smaller trays. One end of the tray sat a little bit higher than the other. Clouds of steam and smoke billowed into the still, hot air, and the heat from the fire turned faces and arms pink.

Mr. Stubbins poured fresh cane juice from the mill into the first section, closest to the chimney. Papa stirred and stirred the juice as it heated to boiling. Soon a greenish foam floated on top. Papa lifted the foam out with a flat skimmer that had holes in the bottom. He held it up until the juice ran through the holes. Then he dumped the skimmings into a barrel. Mr. Stubbins would feed the skimmings to his hogs.

Rose stuck her finger in the foam and licked it. The cooked juice was even sweeter than the juice in the stalks.

After the juice in the first section had cooked awhile, Papa pulled out a rag that was stuffed in a little hole in the dam that led into the next section. The partly cooked juice drained into the next section, and Papa began to stir it with a wooden spoon in his left hand.

Then he plugged the hole up and Mr. Stubbins poured a new batch in the first section. Papa stirred that batch with his right hand. He must keep stirring and skimming or the juice would scorch and taste bitter.

On the other side of the cooker, Abe stirred two more sections, and Alva's sister, Effie, stirred the last. Abe and Effie talked with each other in low, shy voices. Rose noticed that when Effie was busy stirring, Abe looked at her in a curious way from under a shock of the dark black hair that dangled over his smooth forehead.

The juice flowed from section to section all afternoon, cooking a little bit each time as the cookers skimmed off the foam. First it turned light yellow, and then a golden color. Finally, when the cooked juice had reached the last section, Effie tested it. Sometimes she let Abe have a taste. She held the spoon to his lips like feeding a baby, and he looked into her eyes as he sipped the steaming liquid. Rose thought she saw Effie blush once or twice, but it was hard to tell, her face was so shiny and bright from the heat.

Rose looked at Alva and saw that she was watching as well. Alva made a low kissing noise and they both burst out laughing. Effie shot a scowl at Alva, which only made Alva laugh harder.

Then Effie dipped a wooden spoon into the juice. If it made a thread when poured, she opened the last hole and a rich stream of thick reddish-gold molasses poured into a small barrel.

Rose wanted to taste the molasses, but Papa said she must wait until the last batch. Then they would all get a chance to sop the pan. Rose liked the sweet, dark smell of all that juice cooking. She watched the grown-ups work, and Papa even let her stir a few times to see what it was like.

"'Pears you folks are a-settling yourselves into these hills for good," Mr. Stubbins said to Papa and Mama.

"It's fine country," said Papa, skimming

some foam and dumping it into the barrel. He kept wiping his forehead to stop the sweat from running into his eyes. "It has its hardships like any land, the soil being so thin. But with hard work and Providence, I reckon we'll make out, once the orchard comes into bearing."

"We like it very much," Mama agreed. "Although I don't think I'll ever get used to the chiggers biting, and the summer heat wears me all out."

"I reckon it gets right hot at that," Mr. Stubbins agreed with a chuckle. He set down the bucket he was carrying, took off his hat, and mopped his forehead. "You ought to have been here a few years back. Got hot as Hades one summer. So hot, in fact, that the popcorn started a-popping right in the field."

Papa laughed and Mama grinned. Rose stifled a giggle.

"You may laugh, Wilder," Mr. Stubbins said, a twinkle in his eyes. "But it's a true tale. Fact is, the corn kept on a-popping until that popcorn was near two feet deep. It kept a-popping till it drifted up over the fences and into the fields. The whole country was knee-deep in popcorn.

"Now this one poor farmer's mules was a-grazing in the pasture. They seen all that popcorn and mistook it for snow. They started a-shivering and afore he knew it, them mules near froze to death. He got 'em up to his barn and had to build a fire and rub their ears to keep off the frostbite. Yessir. Now that's hot."

Rose laughed out loud. She loved tall tales, and she liked Mr. Stubbins. He was always cheerful and mischievous.

"You have got a knack for tale telling," Papa said.

"Oh, we always lie to newcomers," Mr. Stubbins said with a chuckle. "But we don't mean nothing by it. We ain't got much to do around here 'sides work ourselves half to death, and it ain't often we got someone to lie to. All us hill folks've heard them stories a hunnert times afore."

Mr. Stubbins pulled his pipe out of his overalls, filled it with tobacco, and lit it. "You folks are mighty good neighbors. It's good to have peaceful, hardworking farmers in this valley. Time was, not so far back, these hills was a-crawling with troublemakers. A lot of folks just up and left."

"That's right," Abe chimed in. "It lacks just a few years now since they convicted the last of them Baldknobbers down in Forsyth. Now they was an ornery bunch."

"What's a Baldknobber?" Rose piped up, forgetting her manners. But Mama did not seem to mind. She was looking at Abe, brushing a wisp of hair from her face, waiting for him to explain.

"The Baldknobbers was a vigilance committee," Abe said in his warm, throaty voice that Rose loved so well. His face was smooth and young, but his bushy black eyebrows, strong jaw, and deep voice belonged to a grown-up man. "Down by the White River, 'long the Arkansas line. After the War of the Rebellion there weren't much law hereabouts on account this was border country, right dab a-tween North and South.

"Some folks was for the Union and some for

the Confederacy. My pa told me a body had to know how to sing 'Dixie' and the 'Battle Hymn of the Republic' with the same fire. There was feuds, neighbor agin neighbor, brother agin brother. Like the Hatfields and McCoys, in Kentucky. When the war ended, there was bad feelings all around.

"My pa used to tell me there was a passel of outlaws that rode the hills, a-rustling folks's livestock. It was a bad time."

Abe brushed the shock of thick black hair from his forehead.

"Well, some proper folks got a-studying on it and aimed to make their own law. They had a meetin' in a secret place, on a bare hilltop they call a bald knob. Snapp's Bald it was, I think."

"Yep. That's right," said Mr. Stubbins. "They say there was more'n a hunnert of 'em. Standing on that bald knob, nothing on it but rock, they could see a rider a-coming for miles around. That way they could keep their plans secret. Afore long, folks took to calling 'em Baldknobbers."

"What did they do?" asked Mama. "Certainly the citizens of a place have a right to protect themselves from thieves and murderers. I have lived in lawless times, on the prairie, and no one found fault with any man who stood up to protect his family and livestock."

"Yes, ma'am," Abe said. "But it still weren't lawful. They snatched some of them criminals right out'n the jail and they weren't seen again in these parts.

"I reckon them Baldknobbers did run off a lot of them fellows that was a-terrorizing the people. But then they got big-headed and took up a-harassing their neighbors and a-taking the law to their own hands, a-settling scores and such.

"Once in a while some Baldknobber got a burr under his shirt agin one of his neighbors, or he aimed to jump some other fellow's land, and why, he'd make an accusation agin the man. Maybe say he'd rustled a cow, or butchered another man's hog, or some such. Even if it were a lie.

"Then this Baldknobber would get the rest of them Baldknobbers to go along one night in a posse. They wore frightful black masks with red yarn stitched around the eye holes, white stitching around the mouth, and two points sewed on to look like they was a-sprouting horns. Then they turned their coats inside out so nobody could say for sure who they was."

Swiney had come over to listen. He put his fists against his head and put up his forefingers like horns, and stuck out his tongue. Alva scowled at him and gave him a hard shove that sent him stumbling. Swiney was always clowning, and Alva liked to vex him.

"They'd come a-riding up in the dark of a night to the poor fellow's house, a-looking like the de— er, dickens," Abe went on. "They'd call that farmer out and throw down a bundle of sticks. They let him know he had as many days as they was sticks to pack up his family and belongings and get out of the county, or they'd come back and ride him out. And they'd do it, too."

"That's terrible," said Mama. "Where was

the sheriff? Couldn't he do something?"

Abe laughed. "Why, he was a Baldknobber hisself, ma'am. Their slogan was, 'Join the band or leave the land.' And plenty of folks did, too."

"But that's all past now, Mrs. Wilder," Mr. Stubbins said. "The government finally sent in some proper lawmen. They caught the culprits and put the last of them in jail a few years back."

A shiver ran up and down Rose's spine. She'd rather see Indians any day than Baldknobbers dressed in their horrible costumes.

"Well, I can't imagine a more peaceful place than these hills," said Mama, wiping her hands on her apron. "Thank goodness those days are gone."

All the rest of the afternoon the children played games they made up about Baldknobbers and swatted bees with cane sticks. The bees were too busy stealing cane juice to fight back, except one that stung Swiney over his eye, making it swell shut. It looked terrible, but Swiney didn't complain. He went around showing it to people, to see them gasp in shock. After that the children carried lemonade and water to the grown-ups at the cooker. Barrel after barrel of sweet molasses poured like liquid gold out of the cooker.

One of those barrels was the share for Papa, Mama, and Rose, one was the share for Abe and Swiney, and the rest was for Mr. Stubbins, for his family and to trade in town. No one would need to buy molasses that winter.

When Rose tired of playing, she remembered her autograph album. She fetched it, and her pencil, out of the wagon and proudly showed it to Alva. Alva flipped through the pages, her eyebrows knitted together in deep concentration. In the album was the saying Papa had written for Rose, and the poem Mama had made up for her, and the ditty that Blanche had written after Rose spelled her down in school.

"It's right pretty," Alva said, holding it out for Rose to take back.

"I want you to write something in it," Rose said, handing Alva the pencil. Alva just stared at the pencil a moment, and then her forehead wrinkled into a frown.

"I . . . I wouldn't know nothing to write," she stammered.

"Just anything at all," coaxed Rose. "I want you to. Won't you, please?"

"I cain't!" Alva said sharply.

"But . . . why not?"

"I just cain't. I mean, I cain't hardly write my name. I cain't write no fancy words like them town girls." A shadow seemed to pass over her face, like a curtain coming down. Her eyes flashed hurtfully. Rose shrunk to see it. Alva had never been cross with her before.

"Besides," she spat out, "what's the use of an old autograph book? It don't make you no smarter than me." She slammed the book shut and shoved it roughly into Rose's hands. Then she whirled and stalked off to watch her father stir the cane juice.

Rose tucked the book under her arm, her face burning with embarrassment, without knowing what to be embarrassed about. She hadn't meant to tease Alva or make her cross.

Rose was sorry, but then a little part of her got angry as well. Alva was always scoffing at the town girls. Rose thought that was no better than town girls scoffing at country girls.

Besides, since she had started school, Rose knew that some of the town girls were not stuck-up. Rose had liked Dora and Cora, the Hibbard twins who were so nice to her and shared their good chicken at dinnertime. And Rose hoped that she and Blanche might be friends when school took up again in December.

All of a sudden Rose felt all mixed up. She liked Alva. But she didn't really understand her, why she stayed out of school and why she hated town so much. Alva liked stories as much as Rose. Rose knew Alva would like reading books, too, if only she would try. And if only she would come to school, they could play together at recess and dinnertime.

Rose sighed as she walked somberly back to the wagon and tucked the autograph album in a sack. Then Papa asked her to help Swiney gather more wood for the cooker. The fun of that day had gone out for Rose, like a guttering candle. She went about her chores heavily, thinking and puzzling.

Mr. Stubbins's cane patch was stripped now. Only a carpet of brown leaves lay on the ground. Crows mingled with the geese and ducks, pecking at the fallen seed heads. Finally, when the sun was beginning to set, the last stalks had been milled and the last of the cooked molasses had dribbled into a barrel. Mr. Stubbins doused the fire, raising a great column of steam into the cooling fall air.

Then all the children crowded noisily around the cooker holding pieces of cane they had split and frayed at the end into a brush. They dabbed the frayed ends in the stiffening molasses and licked off the succulent, dark-tasting syrup, making satisfied humming noises as they did it. Then Mrs. Stubbins brought a bag of apples that they brushed with molasses and ate as well.

Rose stole glances at Alva, standing on the other side of the cooker, to see if she was still cross. But Alva's eyes refused to meet Rose's.

Alva chattered with her sisters, and worried Swiney with a blade of grass she kept poking in his ear. Swiney got her back by jerking her fiery-red braids. But Alva ignored Rose as if Rose had become invisible.

Finally, when a pink-and-golden glow was all that remained in the sky, and a chill evening breeze brought goosebumps to the skin, it was time to go. Rose's fingers stuck together, her dress was stained, and even her hair was tacky with molasses. Her teeth felt slimy slick, and her tongue tasted brownish bitter as they gathered by the wagon to say good-bye.

Abe and Effie stood a little ways off, their heads bent together, talking quietly. Abe kicked up a little cloud of dust with his foot, and Effie stood with her hands clasped behind her back, staring down at the ground, giggling now and then. Mama was watching them and she looked at Papa and winked. Alva stood by her father.

"Good-bye, Alva," Rose said. "It was a wonderful day."

Alva looked away. "'Bye," she murmured.

Rose made a kissing noise and giggled. Alva looked at Rose and a shy smile quivered on her lips, but only for an instant. Her eyes stayed round and solemn.

Then everyone climbed into the wagon. Papa chirruped to the horses, and they were on their way. Rose climbed over the barrels to the back of the wagon box and waved to Alva. Alva waved once, then put her hand down, just watching. Alva's figure grew smaller and smaller as the wagon creaked and jingled along. Then the road turned a corner by a tree and Rose could see her no more.

Rose sighed heavily and slumped down against the wagon box. A wave of sadness passed through her.

Sparking

In the frosty dark morning Rose woke in her little trundle bed to the cozy clatter of pot lids and plates. She stretched her legs and arms, and her mouth opened for a big yawn when her head smacked hard against the wooden headboard.

"Ow!" she complained groggily. That was the second time in a week she'd hit her head on the bed. It was a grumpy way to wake up.

Fido came tapping into the bedroom, put his front paws up on the edge of the bed, and looked at Rose with pleading eyes and wagging tail. She gave him a sleepy scratch

47

between his ears, and he thanked her with a warm lick on her cheek and a cold nose in her ear.

"Fido, don't!" Rose complained weakly. Then he scampered back into the kitchen.

A shaft of yellow lamplight peeked around the door, beckoning to her across the floorboards. Wood crackled and hissed in the stove, and the smell of fresh coffee, sizzling salt pork, and biscuits tantalized her nose.

Mama's footsteps clumped around the kitchen, and Papa grunted as he pulled on his boots to go to the barn and feed the stock.

"Time to get up, Rose," Mama's voice sang out. "It's nearly four thirty."

Rose loved waking to the freshness of each new morning, and it had become an extra special time of day now that Abe and Swiney often came to share breakfast.

"There's no sense in a man 'baching it' with a child and trying to put a proper breakfast on the table each morning," Mama had told Abe. "You and Swiney are working with us here on the farm so much, and I have to cook anyway.

You might as well come and share the wealth," she'd added with a chuckle.

Ever since Papa had caught Swiney trying to steal eggs from Mama's henhouse last winter, the Baird brothers had become almost family. Their father and mother had died, and the eleven children had flown off in every direction like a flock of quail.

When Papa caught him, Swiney was a thin, pale, hungry boy dressed in a man's old clothes. Abe was a nearly full-grown young man trying to find work to feed them both. Abe had brought Swiney with him to Mansfield, where they lived in a tumbledown sharecropper's house close by, on Mr. Kinnebrew's farm.

They paid Mr. Kinnebrew with a share of the corn they raised, and helped him with his own crops. But the Kinnebrews didn't come from the Ozarks and they didn't like it here. They never invited Abe and Swiney in for meals.

So one night when Abe didn't come home until late, and raccoons had stolen all their food, Swiney got so hungry he sneaked over to Rocky Ridge Farm to steal some of Mama's eggs. When Mama and Papa met Abe and heard their story, Papa took Abe on as a hired hand, and Mama became like a mother to Swiney. Swiney helped out around the farm as well. He had filled out with Mama's good cooking, and she had sewed up a new pair of overalls for him.

Rose loved Abe. She liked his wonderful stories and the delightful way he told them, the way he sang and played the fiddle. Swiney, well, he was a boy and rough around the edges. A fractious little hornet, Abe called him. But it was good to have company. Rose got so lonesome sometimes, without brothers or sisters to play with.

Rose threw back her quilt, jumped out of bed into the cold, dark bedroom, and ran into the kitchen to dress by the warm stove. She wriggled shivering out of her nightgown and into her everyday blue-and-lavender gingham. She sat on a chair and Mama quickly brushed and plaited her hair into two braids. Then

Rose pulled on her stockings, heavy Brogan shoes, and coat.

She grabbed the pail of warm water Mama had put by the door, and the second pail of mash. Those were for the chickens. She went outside into the pitch-black before dawn to do her chores. She always took a moment to sit on the porch and stroke Blackfoot, her orange-and-white cat with the one black paw, who curled around her legs mewing piteously for attention.

Stars still crowded the clear morning sky in the west, shining with a steely glitter and seeming to hang just about the bare treetops. To the east, a faint glow told of the coming sun. The woods that were so noisy in warm weather with the croaking of frogs, the chattering of bird song, and the grinding of insects were silent in the predawn chill.

A lonely train whistle carried a long way through the thin air. Rose could hear the deep rumble of the cars and the rhythm of the wheels clacking and singing along the rails.

The sound of passing trains was strange

when they first moved to the farm from South Dakota. But now it was a comfort; the whistling and the rumbling and the clacking told a story of the world beyond, of life going on.

Whenever Rose heard a train go by, she'd stop whatever she was doing and listen, because it was a change from the all-the-time quiet. It always seemed mournful somehow, but an everyday mournfulness. It made her think of things she didn't know.

From the henhouse the young rooster gave out a weak, squeaky crow that was answered by the throaty cock-a-doodle-doo of his older brother. Rose carried the warm water and mash to the chickens. They crowded around her feet to be fed, and that made Rose feel like a bountiful goddess.

She collected eggs from the nests, hauled water from the spring for the horses and mules, carried in armfuls of stove wood, and helped Mama put breakfast on the table. Then Abe and Swiney rode up on Old Guts, and they all sat down to eat a big hearty meal.

"That was a fine batch of molasses we

cooked up yesterday," Papa said as he sopped up some with a piece of cornbread. "Sweet and light. That Stubbins knows a thing or two about sorghum."

"Yessir," Abe said, spearing a bit of salt pork. "And Mrs. Wilder knows a thing or two about cooking."

"She beats the nation," agreed Papa.

Mama smiled a gracious thank-you.

Swiney picked up a piece of fried potato in his fingers and started to put it in his mouth. "Use a fork, please, Swiney," Mama said patiently. "You're a big, grown-up boy, too old to be eating like a baby."

"Yes, ma'am," Swiney muttered. He picked up his fork and speared the potato, and then held the fork upside down as he put it in his mouth. Mama sighed. Swiney hated doing exactly as he was told.

"And that's a fine family Stubbins has raised up," Papa said. "That Effie's as pretty a girl as you'll find." He looked at Abe with a raised eyebrow, and Rose thought she saw a twinkle in his eyes.

53

"Mm-hmm," Abe agreed. But he looked down at his plate and the color rose up his neck.

"Why, I'd say she'd make some fella a mighty good catch," Papa went on. He glanced at Mama and winked. Mama cleared her throat and shot Papa a warning look.

Rose was confused, but she saw mirth in Papa's eyes.

"I reckon before too much longer some sharp fellow is going to start sparking with her and before you know it, she'll up and marry him," Papa said. Now Abe's cheeks flushed a bright pink.

"What's sparking?" Rose asked. She couldn't stop looking at Abe's face, shiny now and flaming brightly.

"Courting," said Papa. "When a boy and a girl keep time together."

"Oh, Manly!" Mama protested, putting her napkin down on the table. "Leave the poor boy alone, for heaven's sake." She got up and began clearing the dishes. Swiney looked at Rose and rolled his eyes.

Papa chuckled. And then Rose realized with a shock that Abe and Effie liked each other, in the special way that a father and mother like each other. She remembered them speaking to each other the day before at Mr. Stubbins's, quietly, heads bowed together as if they were sharing a secret. Rose wondered what the secret could be.

The thought of Abe and Effie sparking gave Rose a thrill, and she looked at Abe with new eyes. He was so handsome, and strong. And Effie *was* very beautiful. She had clear blue eyes and soft blond hair that she plaited into one wide, shining braid.

Now Rose felt as if she knew a secret herself. Abe had never been shy before. She had never seen him blush, and Rose almost blushed to see it. It was something to see, a grown-up acting like an awkward boy. She wanted to know more, but she knew it was not a time to ask.

Papa drained the last of the coffee from his cup and pushed himself away from the table. He craned his neck to see out the window.

The first light of dawn showed gray through the glass. "Well, I expect we may as well get to work. It's a good dry day for bringing in the corn."

Chairs scraped against the floorboards. Abe, Swiney, and Papa got their coats and hats from the pegs by the door and left for the barn, with Fido leading the way. Rose stayed to help Mama with the breakfast dishes and to sweep out the house.

"Mama, did you and Papa go sparking, before I was born?" Rose asked as she carefully dried the dishes and put them back in their place on the shelf.

"Yes, we certainly did," Mama said, scrubbing hard at a bit of crust on the fry pan in the washbasin. "But we didn't call it sparking up there in Dakota. Folks called it courting."

"What is courting?" Rose asked. The room was brightening with daylight, so she blew out the coal-oil lamp on the table.

"Courting is when a man and a woman like each other, and think perhaps they might want to be married one day. They spend time

together, to get to know each other better."
Mama scalded the fry pan with hot water
from the reservoir in the stove. Then she
handed it to Rose to dry.

"What did you and Papa do, when you were
courting?"

"Well, we didn't court at first—at least I
didn't," said Mama with a shy little smile. She
dried her hands on the roller towel and began
to wipe up the splashes around the washbasin.

"Your papa had an idea about me, I believe.
I was just a girl, not even sixteen years old,
and he was twenty-six. I was teaching in a little one-room school far from home, out on the
prairie. It was winter, and I had to live with a
family that was very unpleasant, with a baby
that cried all the time and a mother who hated
the prairie and was mean-spirited.

"I was terribly homesick for your grandpa
and grandma Ingalls and my sisters. The
weekends were dreadfully long and lonely. I
never liked to be away from home much when
I was young."

Mama fetched the broom from its place by

the door and handed it to Rose. Rose began to sweep the kitchen floor while Mama sat down to rest a minute with the last bit of warm coffee. It was always the last thing she washed, the coffeepot.

Rose hung on every word as the broom *swish-swish*ed against the floorboards. An acorn hit the roof with a *tap!* and rattled off. Outside, a flock of crows flew by cawing. The wagon passed by with jingling harness. Papa, Abe, and Swiney were going out to the corn patch.

Rose thought times like this, when she and Mama shared a chore while Mama told stories, were some of the happiest moments of her life. Mama's eyes danced like a pair of blue flames, and her clear voice rose and fell in colorful tones that rang as clear as bells. She always told a story well. Sometimes Mama could be Rose's best friend.

"One Friday, when it was bitter cold and the wind howled fiercely and the snow scoured the walls like sand, your papa just showed up at the end of school in a beautiful cutter with a team of magnificent horses. I was so surprised, I didn't know what to think. And he drove me all the way home, just so I could be with the family for the weekend."

"Was that courting?" Rose wondered.

"No," said Mama, wrapping her hands around the cup. "Maybe your father thought so, but it wasn't. We hardly said two words to each other the whole trip. And then he came and took me back to school on Sunday. But when he came to collect me the next Friday and many weekends after, I told him I was grateful for his kindness, but it didn't mean a thing at all.

"Well, it's a long story, but after some years of his being around, and coming by to take me for buggy rides, it finally became courting." Mama smiled dreamily and looked out the window for a moment, deep in thought. Rose stopped sweeping and stood there, waiting.

"Well!" Mama said with a start. "We'd best get ourselves out to the corn patch and help with the harvest."

"Mama!" Rose cried out. "You didn't finish the story!"

"I didn't?"

"I still don't know what courting is," Rose complained.

"It's rather hard to explain," said Mama. "It's spending time together and talking, about this and that. Papa and I drove everywhere in his buggy, and in his cutter in the winter. We went for lovely long drives, and he taught me how to handle the team. He had the most beautiful, graceful horses in the territory. Everyone admired them.

"We talked, about friends and family, the people in town, about crops, horses, the countryside, about our futures. And then one day I realized that I liked him very much. And after that, when he asked me to marry him, I said yes."

Rose shook her head. She still didn't understand about sparking and courting. But the way Mama's voice sparkled when she spoke of it, it sounded like great fun. And it had a happy ending.

"Mama, could I go courting someday?"

"You assuredly will, Rose," said Mama. "When you're older."

"I mean now. I want to go courting now."

"With whom?" Mama's eyebrows arched into question marks. Her eyes were the dots.

"With Abe and Effie."

Mama's mouth and eyes flew open in astonishment, and a laugh jerked from her throat, so sudden that Rose flinched. And then Mama couldn't stop laughing. Her whole body shook, and she threw her head back, her long braid trembled, and the laughter came bubbling up her throat.

Rose leaned on the broom, getting mad and madder. There wasn't anything funny about what she'd asked. Mama was making a joke of her, and Rose didn't get the joke. She began to sweep again, jerking the broom hard this way and that, scattering the dust instead of gathering it into a neat little pile.

"Oh my!" Mama finally sang out smiling when she had caught her breath. She stood up, came to Rose, and folded her arms around her. Rose wanted to pull away, she was so cross. But she didn't.

"I'm sorry, dear," Mama said softly, looking

into Rose's face with eyes that danced with warmth. The hot flush of Rose's anger began to fade. "Someday you'll see the humor in it. Little girls don't go courting, and when a boy and girl do go courting, they only go by themselves. That's the purpose of it, to be alone together.

"Now let's finish up here and get down to the corn patch. We mustn't waste the daylight."

Rose finished sweeping the kitchen, and tossed out the dirty dishwater, thinking and thinking. She thought about Abe and Effie riding across the hilly countryside in a shiny buggy with brass trimmings and brightly colored wheels. The buggy flashed down the roads, pulled by a pair of gleaming chestnut horses, feathery manes trembling and flying in the wind. She saw Abe's and Effie's heads bent together, talking quietly, laughing gently, sharing the secret that Rose could not know.

Then a new feeling Rose never had before began to fan out from her chest like a pond ripple. It was prickly hot and wicked and made her breath come in gulps. It came on so suddenly and strong, it frightened her.

Rose could do nothing to make it go away. Her insides churned like a cyclone. Her heart beat with a strange flutter. Her neck and head flared feverishly. A wave of terrible emotion stirred her up so, she just wanted to slam a door or kick over a chair.

Last of the Harvest

Mama and Rose walked through the woods to the corn patch. The last of the year's crickets and grasshoppers chirped their sad slow songs from clumps of pale yellow grass. The katydids' rasping chorus was just a memory now, and the peeping tree frogs and warty toads had tucked themselves away in the mud where they waited, sleeping, for spring to come wake them to sing again.

Rose's feet swished through the deep piles of dry leaves as she walked behind Mama.

Most of the trees were bare skeletons now. All the plants had dried to stem and seed. Every living thing seemed to be going to sleep. Soon it would be winter.

Mama carried the jug full of cold water from the spring. She had flavored it with molasses and ginger. Then she had wrapped the jug in a wet cloth so it would stay cool until they were thirsty from working.

The first rays of sun struck the peaks of the walnuts and the scaly-barked hickory trees, setting the yellow leaves flaring like giant candles. Wispy flags of mist flew just above the trees, and a coppery light spread through the forest.

But Rose barely noticed. She kicked at tree roots and stones until Mama scolded her about hurting her shoes. The whirling in Rose's heart slowly settled. In its place came a dull pain that she hugged to herself, thinking about it. She wished more than anything that she was already a grown-up girl.

Papa and Abe were toppling the shocks of cornstalks that had stood in the corn patch ever since they had cut and stacked them in rows, like sentries on guard. Swiney sat on the ground with a pile of ears he was husking and tossing into a sack. Rose and Mama sat down and husked with him.

Each time Papa and Abe toppled one of the shocks, nesting mice scattered in every direction. Fido dashed about, his tail stiff as a candle, his ears straining forward, pouncing on as many as he could. He ran around the field, his tiny forehead wrinkled with worry at the ones that were getting away. At the field's far end, hawks swooped to snatch the ones he missed. Crows stalked back and forth, hunting stragglers. Every living thing had a harvest of its own.

Rose stole glances at Abe as he worked, moving slowly down the rows with Papa, pushing down the shocks and scattering the stalks so the ears could be plucked and husked.

Little waves of hurt still lapped against her heart, but the wild animal that had reared its head inside her had slunk away. She could laugh along with Swiney and Mama at the comical way Fido stalked and leaped on the poor frightened mice.

Rose yearned more than anything to go buggy riding with Abe. She was troubled by the dark mood that swept over her in the house. Her scalp crawled just to think of it. It had come so suddenly and taken her over so completely.

Rose was too grown up for tantrums. All she knew was that she was mad she couldn't go riding with Abe. The reason was Effie, because Abe liked Effie. Rose liked Effie too. But she liked Abe more.

Rose blushed at her thoughts. Part of her felt foolish. She knew she was thinking like a child. But part of her thought like a grown-up, and that part of her realized with a thunder-clap that she was jealous.

It was too much to think about. Rose got up from husking to stretch her legs. She looked for mice. Maybe if she could catch one, she'd keep it and take it back for Blackfoot.

Under some of the shocks Rose found tiny delicate nests of newborns, pink, blind, and wriggling helplessly to escape the sudden harsh daylight. She knew the mice stole their precious corn. They needed every kernel for themselves and the livestock. But she covered the nests up with leaves when no one was looking. She hoped the mothers would come back to take care of their babies. That made her feel better, like a great kindhearted giant.

Rose, Swiney, and Mama worked their way down the rows of toppled shocks, breaking the dried ears off the stalks, tearing the husks away from the ears. They sat on the ground as they worked, tossing the naked golden ears into the sack they dragged with them.

Suddenly Mama let out a loud *"Whoop!"* and jumped up. She began slapping her dress and doing a strange little dance. Rose stared in amazement. Papa and Abe, a few shocks away, stopped what they were doing and took off their hats to see better. Fido came running, barking excitedly at the new game Mama was playing.

Then, on the toe of Mama's shoe, a little gray mouse appeared, its whiskers trembling.

"Mama, look!" Rose shouted.

The little gray mouse looked about for an instant, jumped off, and scampered away into a pile of corn shucks.

Rose and Swiney burst out laughing at the same moment. Mama glared at them. But then she blushed and patted down her skirt and apron. Papa and Abe stood staring, and then Papa slapped his knee and let out a great guffaw that echoed in the woods.

"If you men will tend to your work, I'll tend to mine," Mama said with great dignity. Then she sat down again and carefully tucked her skirt in all around her legs.

Rose was trying hard to stifle her laughter, but when Mama looked at her, they both started to giggle. Swiney blushed hard and stared into his lap, his big ears turning red and his shoulders trembling from holding the laughter inside.

Finally they calmed down and went back to work. But after that, they all kept looking about them to see if any mice were searching for a good warm place to hide.

Husking all that corn took the whole day,

almost 'til sunset, and it was some of the hardest harvest work Rose had done yet. Then Papa and Abe gathered up the bulging sacks of corn, flung them in the wagon, and drove the team to the barnyard, where they dumped all the corn into the new corncrib.

For days after they shelled part of the crop into smaller sacks. Papa would take the sacks into town to the miller, who would grind the corn into meal.

They sat on stumps in the barnyard in a circle and chatted. Mama got a jug of apple cider from Mrs. Stubbins, and they made a picnic of the work, with cookies Mama had baked. Abe brought his fiddle one day, and played and sang frolic tunes. Those were lively songs for dancing.

"Dance up to the gal with the hole in her stockin',
Her heel it kept a-rockin', heel it kept a-rockin',
Dance up to the gal with the hole in her stockin',
The prettiest gal in the room!"

Soon they were all tapping their feet to the rollicking tune.

"Step right back an' watch 'er smile,
Step right up an' swing 'er awhile,
Step right back and watch 'er grin,
Step right up and swing 'er ag'in!"

Sometimes, to break the awful boredom of shelling one ear after another, Abe told a story.

"Now this one, it's a true story," he said, a glint in his eye. "My pa told it to me, and my pa never lied once. One day this hillman he were a huntin' turkey in the woods and he heard awful a-squalling a-going on in a little hollow. Sounded like two women was a-fussing up a storm.

"He sneaked up on that noise and saw it were a cat fight a-tween two wild panthers. Big ones they was, too. Them panthers a-fought and a-scratched and was a-biting each other and nary one was a-getting tired. Them panthers got so mad they got a-chasing each other up a tall oak tree like they was a bolt o' lightning.

"And when they got to the top, that old boy

71

could hardly believe his own eyes. They just kept a-climbing, right on up into the air, a-fightin' and a-squallin', a-getting smaller and smaller in the air, 'til he couldn't see 'em no more. He waited a long time, a-figuring them cats is a-going come back down of a spell and him all set to drag home two big panthers to brag on himself."

Rose giggled.

Abe looked at Rose with a sly grin. "Now, I see by the look on your face, you cain't hardly believe it's true. And truth be told, nobody else did neither. That fellow, he walked home and told everyone he seen along the way about them panthers, and he told his neighbors and nary one, even his own wife and kids, believed a word of it. They said he went crazy from a-being out in the woods too long, or was a-drinkin' bust-head liquor and it made him senseless.

"But that night, it commenced raining cat hair. And it rained cat hair all the next day, and for two days after. Folks had to sweep off their porches to go do their chores in the morning."

Papa slapped his knee and laughed. Mama chuckled. And Rose laughed so hard she fell off her seat.

"And the womenfolk went out and gathered up them piles of panther fur and carded it and spun it to yarn and sewed their husbands up fine new suits of clothes."

Abe made the time go faster, but nothing could take the sting out of rubbing those hard kernels off the cobs. The work burned her palms, hurt her fingertips, and split her nails. All that rubbing chapped and cracked the skin of her hands. They felt like old hunks of wood. Swiney's fingers started to bleed onto the corn, so Mama sent him to tend the chickens and draw water for the animals.

Each night Mama mixed up some cornmeal with soft soap and they washed their hands with it. Then she made a salve of lard and beeswax to rub into them and heal the cracks. Each morning Rose woke up looking forward to seeing Abe but dreading another day of shelling.

One day Abe took one of Papa's water buckets, filled it from the reservoir of hot water in the stove, and set it by him. He searched through the piles of corn shuck, chose a few leaves, and pushed them down into the water. Then he went back to work husking.

"What's that for?" Rose was curious.

"Curiosity killed the cat," was all Abe would say.

After a while of shelling, Abe stopped to rest. He took a shuck out of the bucket. The leaf was limp and he wiped the dripping water off. Then he rolled it up and tied it with a bit of string he had in his pocket. Rose stopped shelling and watched. She couldn't imagine what he was doing.

Then he took from his pocket a bit of fence wire and wrapped another shuck around that. Rose was mesmerized. She stopped shelling and stood next to him, watching every move. Mama and Papa stopped shelling too, waiting and watching.

Abe's hands flew as he tore another piece of shuck and wrapped and twisted and tied. There was more folding and tying and rolling and pinching. Then he started to pull some of the shuck apart and formed a little bell in it, like a skirt.

And then Rose saw feet sticking out of the bottom of the skirt, and arms, and a head. In a few more minutes Abe had made from the dead corn leaves a whole doll! She squealed with delight. He even put a little bonnet on it. Then he handed the doll to Rose.

She just stared at it in disbelief. The delicate feet and hands, the tiny little bonnet, and the doll's blank expression with her arms outstretched as if asking someone to hug her. So Rose did.

"Well, Rose. What do you say?" Mama asked.

"Oh, thank you, Abe," and she gave him a big hug.

Abe blushed and picked up an ear of corn to shell. "Ain't nothing but a little trick I learned. Helps pass the time."

But it was no little trick to Rose. She loved that doll, all the more because Abe had made it just for her. After that she kept it in the house, in a safe corner in the trunk where it wouldn't get crushed, and took it out every few days to look at it and wonder at how it was made.

When the corn was out of the field and safely stored in the new crib or shelled into sacks, Rose helped Mama scatter dirty straw, manure, and corn husks on the garden. Then Papa hitched up the mules and plowed it all under to freshen the soil for next spring.

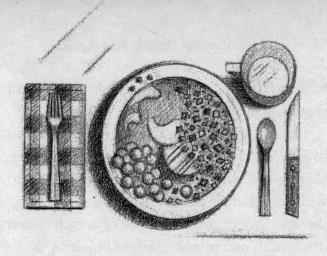

Thanksgiving

The harvest season was finally ended. Now they could enjoy their first real Thanksgiving in the Land of the Big Red Apple.

The Cooleys came to share it. They had traveled with Rose's family in covered wagons all the way from South Dakota not much more than a year before.

Mr. and Mrs. Cooley were best friends with Mama and Papa. Paul and George Cooley, their sons, were Rose's best friends from South Dakota. Paul was eleven and a half years old, a big grown-up boy who could drive a wagon all by himself. George was nine, a little bit older than Rose.

The Cooleys lived in the Mansfield Hotel in town. Mr. Cooley managed the hotel, Mrs. Cooley cooked, and George and Paul helped with the chores, cleaning the rooms, meeting the trains, carrying the bags of travelers and drummers, and refilling the coal-oil lamps.

The day before Thanksgiving, right after breakfast, Rose and Mama began cleaning the house for company.

"Paul and George will like Abe," said Rose happily as she dusted off the log walls of the bedroom. "I hope he brings his fiddle."

"Abe isn't coming," Mama said absentmindedly. She pushed the big bed away from the wall so Rose could dust behind it. Rose looked at Mama with her rag in midair. "Effie invited him and Swiney to her father's house."

"But . . . but why can't they come here?" Rose sputtered. "Abe is Papa's hired hand, and . . . and he and Swiney eat breakfast with us almost every day. Why does he have to go there?"

Rose had to fight to keep herself from whining, and a lump came into her throat.

"You mustn't pout so, Rose," Mama said. "The Stubbinses are good people. It was generous of them to offer. And besides, it's proper if a boy and girl are courting for the boy to go to the girl's house to visit."

Rose sighed heavily. She couldn't understand why Abe had chosen the Stubbinses to spend Thanksgiving with. Weren't he and Swiney practically family with Rose's family? Hadn't Abe and Swiney helped bring in their own harvest? Rose jabbed angrily at the logs with her rag, and for a long time after she made herself think unhappy, spiteful thoughts about Effie.

Rose and Mama cleaned house all day, rafters to floorboards, end to end. They carried all the furniture out into the barnyard and scrubbed the floors with sand from Fry Creek, until the planks shone bright and yellow and smelled like new wood.

Mama washed and ironed the curtains she had made out of her old red dress and hung them back up on the kitchen windows. It was Rose's favorite job to shine all the nickel parts on the new stove until she could see her reflection in them.

When the house was spotless and sparkling and smelled as fresh as clean sheets right off the line, Mama put branches of bittersweet, covered with bright orangey-red berries, on the windowsills in the kitchen and the fireplace mantel in the bedroom.

Then they cooked until late that night: apple pies, and pumpkin pies, and beaten potatoes, and four loaves of fresh white bread. Every flat place in the kitchen had a dish cooling on it. And almost everything in those dishes had grown out of their own soil, from the hard work of their own hands. All those wonderful delicious smells mixing together made Rose lightheaded with pleasure.

A cold drizzle fell most of Thanksgiving Day, and a heavy blanket of dirty clouds brushed the treetops. But inside the little house there was light, laughter, and cheer.

Mrs. Cooley brought a great fat turkey she

had cooked in the hotel kitchen. Mama roasted a wild goose Papa had shot along Fry Creek. Papa carved the meat and Rose helped Mama and Mrs. Cooley serve up the dishes. The last thing, Mama put three kernels of parched corn on the edge of each plate, to remind them of the hardships faced by the Pilgrims their first winter in Massachusetts.

Then the grown-ups sat at the little kitchen table, and Rose sat with Paul and George on the trunks that had been dragged in from the bedroom. They had to balance their plates on their laps.

"Why don't you say the grace for us, Manly?" Mama asked Papa.

"But you always say the grace," Papa protested in surprise. "Besides, I've got no notion for such things. You're the poet in this family."

"Just this one time?" Mama pleaded. "You're the man of the place, and it's a special day for us, our first true Thanksgiving in Missouri with our closest friends. And so much to be thankful for."

Mr. and Mrs. Cooley agreed that he must.

"No, no," Pa chuckled, folding his arms across his chest. "It wouldn't be Thanksgiving without your grace, Bess. You always know the right words to say. If I do it, it'll just sound common, as if I were chewing the rag with a bunch of farmers at the livery stable."

Everyone laughed, and Mama blushed.

Rose wanted Mama to say the grace, too. She loved the sound of Mama's voice. It was as clear and trilling as birdsong. But she didn't want to hurt Papa's feelings, so she kept her thoughts to herself.

"Very well," Mama sighed. The grown-ups held hands around the table. Rose put down her plate and held hands with Paul and George. Now every head bowed and the room fell silent. Mama was quiet for a long moment.

Then she began, "Dear Lord, it is the common, everyday blessings of our common everyday lives for which we are most grateful. They are the things that fill our lives with comfort and . . . and our hearts with gladness—the pure air to breathe and the strength to breathe it; the warmth and shelter and home folks; plain food to give us strength; the bright sunshine on a cold day; and a cooling breeze when the day is warm."

Mama stopped, and Rose waited for the "amen." But it didn't come. She opened her eyes a little and stole a look. Papa had put his hand on Mama's shoulder, and he was watching her with shining eyes. Mama's head was still bowed and she quickly brushed something from her cheek. Slowly, everyone's head came up to steal a look.

Rose realized with a little shock of surprise that she could hear Mama's thoughts. She knew, as surely as she knew her own mind, that Mama was remembering the home folks in South Dakota. At that very moment all those miles away, Rose's grandma and grandpa Ingalls, and her aunts Mary, Grace, and Carrie, were probably sitting down to their own Thanksgiving dinner. Mama was feeling homesick.

For a long moment the only sound in the little house was the whisper of the wind in the trees outside, the crunch of embers settling in the fireplace, and the soft, steady tick of the clock.

"My Pa used to say an old Scotch table blessing when I was a child," Mama finally murmured. "I wonder if you would mind if I repeat it?"

"Go on, Bess," Papa said softly, and Mr. and Mrs. Cooley nodded. Then everyone bowed their heads again.

"'Some hae meat wha canna' eat, And some can eat that lack it. But I hae meat and I can eat, and sae the Laird be thankit. Amen.'"

And everyone gave an answering murmur, "Amen."

The room filled with the rustle and chime of napkins opening and forks being raised from the table.

As she opened her napkin, Rose realized that she knew exactly how the Pilgrims felt. Like the Pilgrims, she and Mama and Papa—and the Cooleys, too—had left their homes and their families to settle in a new land to live among strangers.

Thanksgiving

Like the Pilgrims, Rose's family had no harvest to carry them through the first winter. They had moved to Missouri just last fall, and for Thanksgiving dinner all they had to eat was corn bread, beans, and salt pork—the same things they ate every other day.

Now Rose looked at her plate and said her own silent grace of thanks after Mama's. Then she ate every bite and went back for seconds of everything: chunks of moist goose and turkey, fried pumpkin sprinkled with brown sugar, hominy, mashed turnips with butter that Mrs. Cooley had brought, onions in cream, Mama's fresh light bread and biscuits, and for dessert, molasses cake with chunks of baked apple in syrup dripping down the sides. When she was finished, Rose's stomach was stretched tight as a drum.

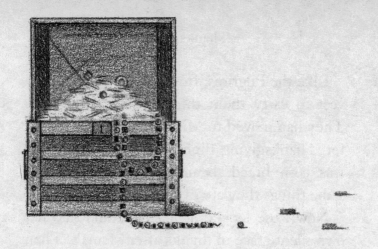

Treasure Hunt

When Papa and Mr. Cooley had lit their pipes, and the dishes had been cleared away, Mama said Rose could go outside to play with Paul and George.

Rose took them to the barn to look at the horses and mules. It was the first thing she always did when there was company. The wind blew raw and biting, but it felt good to be out in the fresh air. She let her fascinator fall to her shoulders.

"I saw the colts in town this week," Paul said, pushing back his hat. He stood in the hay, looking into Nellie's stall, his arms and chin

86

resting on the gate. Rose noticed how tall he'd grown. She and George still had to stand on a rail to see over the gate.

The three of them peered in at the mule, like birds sitting on a fence. Nellie eyed them suspiciously. The mares watched with curious eyes from their stalls across the hallway, nickering for a treat.

"Mr. Hoover had them out to a traveling man, hitched to a fine buggy with brass trim and red wheels. Those colts are the fastest team in town. Everybody says it."

Rose sighed.

Papa had traded the Morgan colts for the mules. Morgans were Papa's favorite horses. He said they were the best-tempered and most beautiful of all the workhorses. But he needed the strong mules to plow through the rocks and roots of the new ground on the farm.

Now the colts lived at Hoover's Livery in town, and they weren't colts anymore. Rose had seen them only once, through the gate of Hoover's corral, one Sunday on their way to church. The colts spent their days hired out to pull buggies for churchgoers and traveling men selling their wares, and for courting couples. A little dark cloud passed through her thoughts when she remembered Abe was at the Stubbinses'. She wished he had come, and she uttered a soft sigh.

Rose still missed the playful, soft-eyed colts that had walked all the way with them from South Dakota. She loved all the creatures of the farm. Each one, even a hen, was like a person to her, even more real than many of the real people she knew. Some were playful or bold, and some were shy. Some were gentle, and some were wicked. Some were smart, like Fido, and some were foolish, like the hens.

But she thought the stout, mossy-faced mules with their outlandish long ears and cranky manners were a poor swap for the graceful colts.

Suddenly Rose felt her head snap back. George had given both of Rose's braids a sharp, painful yank. He jerked so hard, she fell off the gate into a pile of straw, her arms and legs in the air.

"Ow!" Rose was instantly furious. She hated having her braids pulled. Hated it, hated it, *hated it*! George was always pulling braids at school. All the girls despised him for it.

Rose scrambled to her feet and looked hard into his flushed, giggling face. She quick snatched the hat off his head and flung it into Nellie's stall. The mule shied and snorted in surprise.

"Say!" George whined, his face suddenly sour. "What's the big idea?"

"And you better not go into that stall, George Cooley," Rose spat out, her hands on her hips like Mama's when she was extra cross. "Papa never allows children into the stalls. Only me. And Nellie can just eat up your old hat for all I care. She just might, too. She ate one of my shoes once." That was a lie, but the worry on George's face was worth the telling. She crossed her arms and scowled.

Rose stood back as George climbed the gate to see. Nellie bared her teeth and brayed at him. "Awww! Jiminy, Rose. Get it back, will ya? It's just about brand-new. I bought it with

my own money, from carrying bags in the hotel. She's going to step on it or something."

Rose pretended to ignore him for a moment.
Paul was giggling. Then she said, "Only if you
promise not ever, never, as long as time lasts,
to pull my braids again."

"All right, all right," George muttered with
an impatient wave. "Come on. Hurry and get
it, before she does something to it."

Rose clambered into the stall and threw his
hat over the gate. Nellie nuzzled her neck as
she climbed out.

George brushed the straw from his hat and
gave Rose a sideways glare. "Never, never,
ever again," she said, wagging her finger an
inch from George's nose. "Ever!"

"Hey, here's an old plank! I've got an idea,"
Paul shouted from the end of the hallway.
"Let's make a jump board!" They found a log
and laid the plank across. Then they took
turns standing on the ends trying to balance
and seeing how high they could make each
other jump without falling off. Paul was
biggest and he always knocked Rose and
George off. Rose bumped her nose once, but

she didn't care, she was having so much fun.

Then they played one-over, leapfrogging each other across the barnyard, scattering the chickens. Fido danced excitedly around them, yapping joyfully.

When they were finally too tired to play anymore, they sat on the porch to catch their breath.

"Hey, Rose," Paul said. "Can you guess this riddle? House full, barn full, can't get a spoonful?"

"Air!" George shouted.

"Shut up!" Paul growled. "You heard it before. I want Rose to guess. How about this one? What has eyes but can't see, a tongue but can't talk, and a soul that can't be saved?"

Rose thought hard for a moment. "A mole?"

"No."

"A bat," Rose guessed.

"Moles and bats don't have souls. It's a shoe!" Paul crowed.

Rose had to think a moment. "I get it!" she shouted and clapped her hands with delight. She loved word games.

"I don't know any riddles," she said, "but I

know where there's bats."

"Where?" Paul said excitedly.

"In the cave, in Williams Cave. I saw them all coming out one night in the summer, just before sundown. There must be millions living in there."

"Let's go look," said Paul, jumping up.

"I'm not supposed to go," Rose muttered. She glanced at the door of the house. Then she whispered, "But I do sometimes. Not very far in. I only went inside once, with Alva."

"There's treasure buried in caves," said Paul earnestly. "It's true. Some man who stayed at the hotel said Spanish explorers came here a long time ago. They brought gold to trade with the Indians, and it was so heavy they had to leave some behind. He said they buried it in caves. Let's go look."

They traipsed off down the hill, wading across Fry Creek with their shoes off. The water was icy cold, but the food and the play had warmed them up so, they didn't mind. Then partway up the hill on the way to town, Rose showed them a faint trail through the forest, off to the right.

They followed a little way through some bushes, and then by a tiny stream, to the steep side of a hill. There was a small cave mouth hidden by a tree, and then they saw the yawning mouth of the big cave.

Paul dashed ahead and inside. He disappeared around the corner where the cave curved left.

"Paul, wait!" Rose cried out. "There might be wild hogs in there. Or a panther!"

An instant later, Paul backed out, his eyes big as saucers.

"Hogs and panthers?"

Rose explained that sometimes wild hogs lived in caves, and they were mean and had a vicious bite. "Alva says a wild hog can kill a dog, if it's mad enough."

Paul tore off a branch of a cedar tree, frayed the torn end with his knife, and lit it with a match. It crackled to life, the sticky pitch hissing and bubbling on the bark.

"There, now we have a torch. No animal will fight fire." Then Rose and George followed Paul into the cave.

George jabbered all the while, "We're gonna

get in trouble and Pa's gonna give us a whipping, you'll see. Something's bound to happen. It's awful dark in here. Smells dusty. What's that noise?"

"Shut up!" Paul finally shouted. His voice echoed faintly back to them in the silence, *"Shut up . . ."*

George shut up.

"It's warm in here," said Paul. "I'm taking my shoes off so they don't get muddy." They all took off their shoes, tucked their stockings in them, and put them up on a dry ledge. Rose and George followed Paul with the flickering torch, their bare feet slithering in the mud and splashing in the strangely tepid water that flowed in a stream through the cave. Ahead of them was only darkness.

They found raccoon tracks and little piles of persimmon seeds. They saw tiny spotted frogs that sat still as statues under water as clear as glass, then darted away to hide under a rock.

They waded farther and farther back, until the damp ceiling of the cave was so low they had to bend down.

"I don't like it," said George. Now that they

were so far in the cave, the walls muffled their words and splashing sounds. "I can't hardly see where we're going. The torch is burning out. Let's go back."

"Chicken," Paul taunted. "We're explorers. Explorers don't turn back. There might be gold in here. Why don't you help look instead of complaining?"

Suddenly Paul stumbled. The torch flew from his hand and landed in the water with a hiss. Then it was dark, the pitchest, blackest dark of a moonless, starless night. They all froze.

"Uh-oh," Rose said.

"Dash it!" said Paul gruffly, his voice trembly. "My matches are all soaking wet." They stood there like that, in the cottony blackness, not knowing what to do. Rose's eyes strained to see, but there was nothing, not even a faint shine behind them in the tunnel.

Rose reached out with her hands to touch the clammy, wet walls. They were close by her head. She touched Paul's back. Little fingers of fear creeped up her legs and her scalp crinkled. Her chest tightened.

"I'm going back," George announced. There were tears in his voice. "I'm getting out of here."

Then she heard him splashing away behind her. She turned to follow and banged her head hard on something, a rock. Paul bumped into her from behind.

"I'm scared, Paul," Rose said in a wobbly voice.

"All we have to do is walk back. It can't be too far."

Carefully, holding each other's hands, they tried to find their way back, splashing and stumbling and stubbing their toes painfully on rocks. The darkness was horrible, suffocating. Rose was only her breath, and Paul and George were only their own breaths, coming faster and harder now. The rest of them had disappeared. It was as if they had been buried alive. She choked out a tiny sob.

Then, suddenly, they fell in a heap. George was crying loudly. Paul swore. All around them Rose felt rock. They had walked into a dead end!

"Shut up! Shut up!" Paul shouted at them. "Listen."

Rose held her breath. George stifled his sniffling. Far away she heard a tiny bark. Then another.

"Fido!" she gasped. Then she shouted, louder, "*Fido!* Here boy!" They all started shouting his name.

"Shhh!" Rose said.

Fido barked again, closer this time. Then suddenly she heard him panting nearby, and then his paws were in her lap and he was licking her face. Rose's eyes burned with tears. She hugged him hard.

Carefully they followed Fido, stopping to listen to his panting. Every so often he barked to show them the way. It took a long, long time, but finally, far in the distance, came the first glow of light, and then brighter, so they could see Fido's black shape, standing on a ledge, waiting for them.

Then they were out, in the chill fall air. They quick pulled on their stockings and shoes and flew home. George didn't even wait to take off his shoes to cross Fry Creek. He ran right through the water. Rose noticed with a sinking heart that she and her coat were smeared with mud.

She and Paul walked soberly up the wagon track to the house. The grown-ups were waiting on the porch, hugging themselves against the cold. George stood in front of them, his head hanging, his coat and pants and hat and face and hands covered with mud. Mr. Cooley scowled fiercely at Paul. Mrs. Cooley wrung her hands.

Rose couldn't look at Mama and Papa at first. When she did, Mama's eyes were terrible and hard, and her forehead was deeply furrowed. Papa shook his head.

"You sprouts sure got into it this time," he said sadly.

Rose's face burned with shame. She wished the ground could open up and swallow her.

Back to School

M ama scrubbed Rose's neck and ears so hard, Rose thought for certain the skin was coming off. The Cooleys had left, and Mama had made her take a bath to wash off all the mud. Mama said hardly a word. Her mouth was a thin line, and she sighed as she put Rose's coat, dress, and fascinator in a tub to soak.

Finally, when Rose was safely tucked in her trundle bed, Mama sat on the edge of the big bed and folded her hands in her lap. The hardness in her eyes had softened. "I'm not going to punish you, Rose, although I have cause to.

You could have been hurt in there, or lost. When I think, if it hadn't been for Fido . . ." Her voice broke for a moment, and then became steely hard. Her eyes narrowed.

"If *ever* I find you have been in that cave again without permission, I'll break my rule against spanking. Now, go to sleep. We won't talk about this anymore."

Mama went into the kitchen and closed the door. Rose heard the murmur of her voice talking earnestly, and Papa's low answers. The bedroom was dark, except for a thin line of light under the door. Rose closed her eyes and the horrible suffocating feeling of the cave came back. She turned her head to the wall.

She knew she would never go into Williams Cave again.

After Thanksgiving it was time for school to take up again. Rose looked forward to a change in her days, and to having time again to read. She had been so busy helping with the harvest, so tired and sleepy at the end of each day, that she had hardly read a word in two months.

But she fretted over whether Blanche Coday still meant to be "Your Friend," the words she had written in Rose's autograph book. How could Rose ever measure up to the way Blanche and the other town girls dressed? She still had only one school dress, although Mama had tatted a new lace collar and cuffs for it. Papa had patched the hole in the side of her right shoe with a sewn-on piece of leather. When Rose saw it, her spirits sank. It stuck out like an ugly scab.

The first morning Rose was so jittery, her stomach hurt, and Mama had to remind her not to peel the potatoes too thickly.

"Take your time," said Mama. "You're as jumpy this morning as a dog in high rye."

At breakfast Swiney looked at Rose in her school dress and cocked his head, "Where-at you a-goin' today?"

"Where *are* you going," Mama corrected gently from the stove where she was taking the corn bread out of the oven. "Go on now, you can say it properly."

Swiney sighed. "Where *are* you goin' at," he said. Papa chuckled into his coffee. But

Swiney didn't notice.

"To school," Rose said. "Today is the first day. You should come. It's fun, sometimes. The boys play games at recess and dinner-time."

Swiney shook his head. "Naw. I don't want to go to no school. I ain't never been and I ain't never a-goin', neither. I want to stay here and work with Abe."

"I have *never* been," Mama said.

"You ain't?" asked Swiney in surprise.

"No, I *never*," Mama said, shaking her head and chuckling. "I mean, yes, of course. I've been to school. I taught school. But the proper way to say it is, I have never been."

"Our ma and pa set no store by book learn-ing, Mrs. Wilder," said Abe. "What with the taxes and all, and there being so many little ones in the family, it was a wonder we ain't all starved. Pa always said a man don't need to know readin' and writin' to hoe corn or milk a cow."

Mama sat down, opened her napkin and served herself some potatoes. "That was true

in the past," she said. "But times are changing, Abe. Even a farmer needs to know how to
keep his accounts. And reading is a wonderful
thing for the mind. I have not been many
places in my life. But in books, I have traveled
all over the world. Just to be able to read the
newspaper and know about crop prices is reason enough."

"Yes, ma'am," Abe said as he passed the
plate of corn bread. "I reckon that's a fact,
these days. But you'uns know I ain't . . . er . . .
got no extra cash money for school taxes and
such."

They all ate in silence for a few moments.
Then Mama said, "Well, with the harvest over
now, and you helping Manly in the woodlot
this winter, I'll have a little extra time. I could,
I suppose, spend an hour or two with Swiney
each day. I have the schoolbooks, and I was a
teacher once."

Swiney looked at her with big, scared eyes,
and then he looked pleadingly at Abe.

"That's mighty kind," Abe said. "I wouldn't
put you out none for it."

"It's no trouble at all," said Mama. "I'd be pleased."

"Awww, heck!" Swiney spluttered.

"Please don't speak with your mouth full," Mama said. "And you'll mind your language. As long as your feet are under my table, you'll show a little civility."

"But . . . but, why?" he cried out. "I don't need no book learnin'."

"Now, sonny boy," Abe said. "An hour of studyin' a day won't kill you none. Seems like one of us Bairds leastways oughta be able to read a newspaper or the Bible. Like Mrs. Wilder says, it brightens your mind."

Swiney sulked through the rest of breakfast while Papa and Abe talked about the work they would do that day. Now that the harvest was past, they would cut wood again, to make fence rails and ties to sell to the railroad.

Mama packed Rose's dinner, tied her blue ribbons around her braids, tied the sash of her pinafore, helped her on with her coat, handed her the slate and pencil, and sent her off to school. Swiney stood around the kitchen, hands jammed into his pockets, scowling as Abe and Papa left for the woodlot.

At Fry Creek, Rose gave Fido a last scratch on the head, took off her shoes, and hitched her dress to wade across. The water flowed stinging cold over her feet and ankles. They still ached when she reached the front door of the schoolhouse.

But Rose forgot about her cold feet as soon as she saw Blanche, waiting in the foyer, her cheeks flushed, eyes shining, and a big smile on her face.

"Oh, hello, Rose!" she cried out. "I was afraid you might not come."

"Hello, Blanche," Rose answered. Blanche looped an arm through Rose's and tugged her into the classroom. "Come quick! Take off your coat and hang it next to mine. Put your dinner pail over here on the shelf. I saved seats for us at the front."

Rose's heart swelled with joy. As they walked into the sickly-green classroom she felt none of the shyness of her first day, although when she sat down she was careful to

tuck her feet under the bench so her patched shoe wouldn't show.

Professor Kay, sitting at his desk in the front, greeted Rose heartily. "Well, well, my star scholar returns. Hello, Miss Wilder."

Rose might not have pretty dresses and new shoes like the town girls, but she had a friend now, and everyone remembered that she had won the spelldown in September.

At the morning recess, while they watched some girls jumping rope, Blanche excitedly told Rose about the trip her father took her family on, to Chicago.

"We swam nearly every day in Lake Michigan, big as an ocean. We ate in restaurants, and saw so many people dressed as grand as can be. Father even took us for a ride in one of those new motorized cars."

"What's a motorized car?"

"It's a new machine, a horseless carriage!" Blanche said breathlessly excited. "It ran so fast, Rose. I was scared. And it made me dizzy. It was noisy, too. Oh, Chicago was such great fun!"

Rose had nothing so wonderful to tell about as a trip to Chicago. So she listened politely, and then thanked Blanche for the nice words she had written in her autograph book.

Now that cold weather had come, Blanche walked home each noon to eat her dinner. Rose sat at her desk after she ate and read *The Leatherstocking Tales*. That was a book about Natty Bumppo, a man who lived in New York State many years ago and who hunted deer in the wild forests. Professor Kay had let her borrow it from Miss Pimberton's classroom upstairs in the school.

Paul came by one day on his way back from dinner at the hotel. He said his father had given him and George a terrible switching.

"I still got the marks, but I don't care," he bragged. "Nothing can keep me from that old cave. I'm going back sometime to find the Spanish gold. I just know it's there."

Rose and Blanche sat together every day now, whispering snatches of gossip and passing notes they wrote on their slates.

"Harry Carnall is a terrible pest!" Blanche

wrote. Harry was always bringing snakes and frogs and bugs to school to scare the girls.

"School is so DULL sometimes," wrote Rose.

The first Friday Rose made head in spelling, and Blanche was second. But they didn't quarrel, and Rose made sure to compliment Blanche for spelling an extra-hard word perfectly.

It was cozy to have a friend in school, especially someone as pretty and refined as Blanche. Rose enjoyed hearing Blanche's stories about the goings-on in Mansfield.

"Dr. Padget was called in the middle of the night to deliver a baby for Mrs. Freeman. I heard Mother say it took twelve hours for it to come. And yesterday there was an awful fight in front of the saloon. The sheriff came and arrested both of the men."

Rose thought it must be wonderful to live in a town where there were so many things to see and know about, so many lives being lived. She loved the farm, and she loved the quiet, peaceful evenings after supper when Mama made popcorn and read to her and Papa while Fido curled up in front of the crackling stove. But she was curious about Blanche's life, and the people she heard about in Mansfield.

And Blanche liked Rose's stories. Rose told her stories of Mama's about living on the prairie, about Indians and blizzards. She told Abe's story about the time his father charmed a pack of wolves with fiddling. Blanche listened intently, her eyes wide, and let out a muffled shriek when Rose got to the part where the wolves chased him into the empty house.

Blanche begged for more stories, so Rose told her about Robinson Crusoe, and the *Leatherstocking Tales*, and the Baldknobbers. Blanche loved every one. She could not get enough of Rose's stories, and Rose discovered how much fun it was to tell them and watch Blanche's eyes grow big and round when she told the scary parts.

But Rose was just as bored with the lessons as she had been in the summer session. She was the best student. That meant she had to be still and listen to the other scholars reciting and ciphering lessons she knew already. Rose wanted to go on to Miss Pimberton's classroom upstairs, with the older students. But Professor Kay said she still wasn't old enough yet.

Blanche had befriended her, but Rose still felt shabby next to the town girls, and even Blanche sometimes. They made her feel poor, even though Papa had said they weren't. She knew she shouldn't, but Rose couldn't keep herself from envying Blanche's life.

Rose was torn. She liked Blanche, but she hated school. A part of her missed being home with Mama and Papa all day. And now that she was in school, she hardly ever saw Alva, which made her sad. Rose had one foot in each of two worlds. Sometimes she worried she would never belong in either of them.

Birthday

The days were much colder now, and a blustery wind blew across the high Ozark hills. On her way home from school, the bare trees made a lacy pattern against the solid, dull gray sky. The wrinkled undersides of the clouds flowed like a river across the heavens, disappearing into the horizon as if the sky was draining itself into one place.

Papa drove up from town just as Rose was crossing the creek in her bare feet. The cold water and the lifeless sky stole all the warmth from her.

Papa waited while Rose put her shoes back
on. Then she climbed up onto the wagon seat
to ride with him up the hill to the barnyard.

"Why, Rose, you're shivering," Papa said,
wrapping an arm around her shoulders. "And
your lips are blue."

"The water's cold," Rose said through chattering teeth.

"We'll get you inside and warmed up in a
jiffy," said Papa. "It's time I built a bridge over
that creek."

When they got into the house, Papa told
Mama that Rose had waded barefooted across
Fry Creek.

"Land sakes!" Mama cried out. "You'll
catch your death of cold running around in
that water. Come over here and sit by the
stove."

Mama set a chair by the kitchen stove and
wrapped Rose in a quilt.

"I'm sorry, Rose," Mama said, her eyes
mournful. "I don't know why we never
thought of it. We'll have to figure a way to get
across without wetting your feet. For now

Papa can ride you over, and meet you coming home. You can't be going to school chilled like that."

The next day was Rose's ninth birthday. Mama said she could stay home from school, and she baked a gingerbread cake for dinner. When Rose had eaten her last bite of cake, Mama gave Rose a new pair of blue mittens she had knitted with tiny yellow flowers in them. Grandma had sent a beautiful brown-and-gold fascinator. There was a card in the mail from her aunts Mary, Carrie, and Grace. Papa gave her a book, *The Wandering Jew*, that he had bought from a traveling man in town. It was written by a man with a girl's name last: Eugene Sue.

Rose flipped through the pages and saw that two of the people in that book were girls whose names were Rose and Blanche! She couldn't wait to start reading it.

After dinner Papa drove to town on an errand. Rose worked on her sewing in the afternoon, sitting pleasantly with Mama before the fireplace in the bedroom. Rose was piecing her first quilt, in nine-patch squares. It was hard work and Mama made her take out any stitches that were loose or unevenly spaced.

Mama sat knitting a new pair of socks for Papa. Fido lay curled up on one side of the hearth, his paws twitching in his sleep. For Rose's birthday Mama had let Blackfoot come in the house, and she lay on her back, her legs curled in the air, on the other side of the hearth.

When they heard the jingle of harness and the rumbling of Papa's wagon coming up the hill, Mama jumped up, put her knitting away, and went into the kitchen to start supper. She quick closed the shutter on the window that looked out on the barnyard. Rose was puzzled. Mama never closed the shutters during the day or when Papa was in the barn.

Rose started pulling on her shoes to go help Papa stable and water the team.

"Not now, Rose," Mama said. "It's your birthday, so you won't have to do the barn chores. But I want you to stir up a batch of cornmeal and then peel the potatoes."

Rose was surprised. She always helped Papa and did her other chores when he came home from town.

Papa was an extra-long time coming in. Twice Rose caught Mama peeking through the shutters. But when Rose went to look, Mama shut them with a bang and told her to pay attention to her stirring. Rose was shocked.

"I'm sorry," Mama said. "It's just that, well, there's a draft and I'm feeling a little chilled." Now Rose was mystified. The kitchen was cozy warm. She finished stirring the cornmeal. Then she sat down at the table to peel potatoes, wondering all the while at Mama's strange behavior.

Finally they heard the sound of Papa's boots clomping on the porch, and the door opened. Papa looked at Mama, and Rose thought she saw a wink.

"Hello, my little prairie Rose," Papa said heartily. His face was beaming, and little laugh

116

lines crinkled around his eyes. "Where were you? Do young ladies get a holiday from chores just because it's their birthday?"

"But Mama said . . ." Rose started to protest. She looked at Mama and saw a smile spreading across her face. *"Mama!"* Rose finally shouted. "What is it?"

"Just maybe you ought to go outside and see," Papa said with a chuckle.

Rose darted past him. She threw open the door, ran out on the porch, and looked into the long wooly face of a donkey. It was hitched to the railing, patiently munching a mouthful of hay. On its back, cinched around its low, fat belly, was a saddle, gleaming in the light of the setting sun.

"Oh, Papa!" Rose shouted. She jumped off the porch and began stroking the donkey's long neck. He turned to look at her with calm, curious eyes, his long ears pitched forward.

"Mind he doesn't step on your foot," said Mama, standing on the porch with Papa. "He doesn't know you yet, and he may be clumsy." Papa wrapped an arm around Mama's waist, and big smiles beamed on both their faces.

"For me?" Rose shouted.

"Who else do you know who needs a ride to school?" asked Mama.

"Happy birthday," Papa said.

Rose wrapped her arms around the donkey's neck and hugged it. His soft gray coat was warm and still damp from walking. She could feel the heave and whoosh of his breath and the thump of his heart. The donkey turned and snuffled in her apron for a treat.

Rose rubbed her hand over the sleek honey-colored leather of the saddle. It was too much to believe. That donkey was really hers to take care of, to currycomb, to feed handfuls of clover and bits of carrot, and to ride anytime she wished—a new friend who could go wherever she went, even to places she couldn't take Fido.

"Oh, thank you! Thank you!" Rose cried out. She gave Mama and Papa a big hug, all together.

"It's no purebred Morgan colt," said Papa, "but he seems patient and he'll get the job done."

"What's his name?"

"Don't know that he has one," Papa said. "Even if he did, he's yours now. You must think of a new one."

Rose quick untied the donkey and scrambled up into the saddle. He was so short, she could do it all by herself, right from the ground. His fat belly made her legs stick out.

Rose rode around the barnyard in a little circle, trembling with excitement and proud as a gander. She had watched Papa so many times with the horses and mules that she knew just how to hold and pull the reins to make him turn and stop. She knew the chirrup sound to get him going, and how to *whoa* him to stop. She loved being up high and seeing how different everything looked.

The donkey was patient, gentle, and obedient. Fido followed them around, barking jealously. The donkey tried to kick him when he got too close.

"It's all right, Fido. I'll still go for walks with you in the woods," Rose promised. "We can all go!"

Then Papa showed Rose where she should stable the donkey in the barn.

"You mustn't let him eat too much all at one time, or it could make him sick." Rose listened solemnly, so she would remember every word. "And when you've been riding him a spell and he's lathery hot, you must let him cool off and roll, if he wants, before giving him his water and feed. Give him water first, so he won't overeat and get colic."

Rose couldn't be still all during supper, worrying that the donkey was safe where Papa had tied him in the hallway of the barn. She kept looking out the window toward the barn, and listening.

"He's all right, Rose," Mama said. "You can check on him later. Sit down and finish your supper." Papa said he would build a new stall, on the side of the barn. It would be Rose's job to keep the stall clean and fresh.

She thought of names. As she lay in bed that night, her feet tapping restlessly against the footboard, Rose decided she didn't want her donkey to have an ordinary name, like Jack, or

Henry. She wanted him to have a name that no one had ever thought of before for a donkey, or for anyone.

She thought of names of people she had read about: Robinson Crusoe, Natty Bumppo. Then she remembered the Russians they had met along the road when they traveled to Missouri. The Russians had spoken words in a language Rose had never heard, Russian. Their throats made thick sounds that were hard to imitate.

She remembered some of those sounds, how mysterious they were, how much she yearned to know what the Russians were saying. "Spookendyke," one of the Russians had said. At least that was how it had sounded to Rose. She had always remembered it. Rose whispered it aloud to herself, to see if she liked it. "Spookendyke."

"What is it, Rose?" Mama said from the kitchen, where she and Papa were reading.

"Spookendyke," Rose called out from her bed. "That's the donkey's new name. Spookendyke."

"What sort of outlandish name is that?" Mama asked.

"I made it up," Rose said.

Mama chuckled. "Very well," she said. "Spookendyke it is. Now go to sleep."

Stubborn Spookendyke

The next morning Spookendyke stood patiently still as Rose bridled and saddled him. He breathed little clouds of steam into the chill morning air. She centered the saddle, just as Papa had showed her. She flipped one of the stirrups up over the seat, reached under, grabbed the girdle, and cinched it around his fat belly, being careful not to let him step on her feet.

She climbed up into the saddle, hooked her dinner pail over the horn, and gave a gentle little kick. The donkey had taken only two steps when the saddle slipped off to the side, dumping Rose and her pail on the hard ground. She landed with a thud, one foot tangled in the stirrup. The cinch hadn't been tight enough.

"Ow!" Rose complained loudly. It hurt so much she wanted to weep, but she was too mad. Spookendyke turned his head and peered at her with a solemn sad look on his face. Rose glared back.

She got to her feet, brushed herself off, and rubbed her sore bottom. She looked around, but there was no one to see or help. Papa and Abe were working in the timber lot. Mama was inside the house, teaching Swiney his lesson.

Rose tugged the saddle back up on top. She undid the cinch and started over. Just as she tightened it, Spookendyke took a deep breath and held it as she tightened the girdle. When she was done, he exhaled with a whoosh.

Rose climbed carefully up and settled gently into the saddle. She chirruped to him, and as soon as he began to walk, she could feel the saddle begin to slide. This time she was ready and jumped off before she tumbled.

It took Rose two more tries to get the saddle tight enough. She was exasperated. Spookendyke was patient, but he was also tricky, and stubborn. Rose had to wait until he let his breath out and quick tighten the cinch before he could inhale again.

The saddle still wasn't as tight as it should be, but Rose didn't have the heart to pull it any tighter. She had read *Black Beauty*, and she knew of the cruel things that people did to horses, and how terrible the pain and suffering those horses felt.

Spookendyke wasn't a horse, but he almost was. The saddle looked so uncomfortable, Rose's back could feel a saddle strapped to it. Her stomach could feel a cinch strap cutting her belly in two.

Finally they headed off down the hill, Fido tagging behind. But before they got to Fry Creek, Spookendyke did another devilish thing. He slumped his neck and shoulders, tucked his ears, and stopped short. Rose flew forward. Everything was upside down for an instant as she flipped right over his head.

Then she landed on the ground, with a sickening bump, on her bottom. She couldn't move. She gasped for the breath that was knocked out of her. The dinner pail rolled and tumbled down the hill. Finally it struck a rock by the creek and stopped with a hollow *clunk!*

"Spookendyke!" Rose spluttered when she could finally speak. She picked up a rock and threw it hard as she could at a tree. She wanted to swat that donkey, she was so cross. Fido's little pink tongue gave her cheek a lick, and he danced around as if it was all a game. Spookendyke's head hung and his eyes looked at Rose sorrowfully. Finally her anger melted away.

She led him down to the creek, picked up her dinner pail, and climbed back in the saddle. She said good-bye to Fido and rode Spookendyke splashing through the creek. But when they got to the other side, Rose climbed down and walked the rest of the way to school, Spookendyke mincing along behind her on his stiff legs, tugging on the reins now and then to nibble a bit of dry grass.

Every day that Rose went to school, Spook-endyke went with her. Some days he let her ride him all the way. Some days he was stubborn and made her walk. Rose never knew which kind of day it would be. But it didn't matter. She liked the company, and she liked having him to care for and spoil. If he wanted to stop and nibble some grass, Rose let him, until she got too cold and hurried him on to the warm schoolhouse.

Rose was often late for class, but she was quiet as a mouse hanging her coat, putting her dinner pail on the shelf, and sitting down. The other students stared and sniggered at her. But Professor Kay never scolded Rose. He only peered at her over his spectacles and winked. She almost wished he didn't.

It was true what Blanche had said last summer. Rose was teacher's pet. But Mama had told her not to mind the names other children sometimes called her. "You have nothing to be ashamed of," she said. "Calling names only shows how poor are the name callers." And besides, Rose knew all the lessons already. If she never went to school, she wouldn't miss a thing.

So Rose held her head high as she squirmed into the seat next to Blanche.

Each day she hitched Spookendyke in the shed next to the other children's horses and mules. But Spookendyke was the smallest of them all. They teased him, crowding and nipping at him. And he kicked back.

During recitation Rose could hear his hoarse braying, then the whickering of horses, followed by the hollow *THUMP!* of hooves striking the shed walls. All the children giggled when they heard it, and Rose's face flushed hot with embarrassment. She raised her hand.

"What is it, Miss Wilder?" Professor Kay said, poking a stick down his back to scratch.

"My donkey," Rose explained. Everyone giggled again. "May I go and speak to him? He doesn't understand about not fighting. He's very stubborn."

"Very well," Professor Kay said. "Don't be long."

"You must mind your manners," Rose

patiently explained to Spookendyke, scratching the hard, flat spot between his ears. He tossed his head and pulled at the reins. "Professor Kay will send you home if you don't. And then you'll have to stay tied in your stall in the barn. You don't want that, do you?"

Spookendyke's head hung and he looked up at her with damp, doleful eyes and nuzzled in her pinafore for a treat. Rose always forgave him, and shared a bit of raw carrot or apple from her dinner pail.

After Rose's birthday and the first days of school, the weather turned bitter cold. In the morning Rose found a little patch of ice on her quilt where her breath had frozen. She could not stop shivering when she got out of bed to dress by the stove. Even her union suit couldn't keep out the cold. The light from the lamp was dim, as if the chill and darkness were trying to put it out.

On her way to the henhouse with the warmed water and mash, the black sky arched over the earth, very large and still. Stars sparkled like bits of frost. The icy air burned the inside of her nose, and her fingers and cheeks tingled.

Ice formed around the edges of the purling spring, and around the rocks in Fry Creek. On her way to school Rose found ice growing out of the ground, here and there like flowers. The ice had spewed right from the earth, and it crackled under Spookendyke's feet. The ice flowers were made by fingers of frost that had crept up dried grass stems. They were upside-down icicles. The ground was so cold it was squeezing the water right out of it.

By the time Rose got to school, sullen clouds pressed low all across the sky. The air was still and silent, reminding Rose of being wrapped in a featherbed. The birds sat on bush branches, all bundled and fluffed up as if they were about to leave for somewhere else. And they chirped more quietly than usual.

When Rose reached the top of Patterson's Hill and she could see the schoolhouse, no children played outside waiting for the bell to ring. They rushed straight inside where the stove was, pushing and shoving, cheeks scarlet, breaths coming in puffs of steam. Rose quick tied Spookendyke in the shed and dashed inside. She wished she had a blanket to throw over him against the biting air.

The cold had frosted the windows over in clever ice designs, fan-shaped and swirly. Harry Carnall was busy melting his name in the ice with his fingertip. Some boys helped Professor Kay move all the seats close together, in a tight circle around the red-glowing stove. Others carried extra wood in and stuffed the stove full.

Rose was about to take off her coat when Professor Kay's deep voice boomed out over the noisy crowd of shouting, jostling children, "Any scholar who wishes may wear his or her coat," he said. "I see quite a few children are absent today. Must be the cold. I bet the wolves are eating the sheep just for the wool."

The room echoed with the high, light voices of laughing children, and then everyone settled noisily into the seats. Rose could not see Blanche anywhere, so she sat with Hattie Williams.

Then the students began the morning recitations.

The scorching heat from the stove made Rose's face and knees blazing hot. Her shoes were hot to the touch. But her back felt the chilling draft that sneaked in around the windows and the door. Professor Kay let them take turns standing in front of the stove.

Harry Carnall read from the reader, but Rose hardly paid attention. She thought only about her turn to stand by the stove. Then she noticed a smell she hadn't smelled before. It was strong and rank, like onions that had been fried and left to harden in the fry pan. Only stronger. Rose wrinkled her nose to get the smell out, but it wouldn't go away.

She snuck a sideways glance at Hattie. Her nose was wrinkled, too. Some of the other children around her stirred restlessly, and someone was trying to stifle a laugh.

"What smells?" Rose whispered.

"Asfettidy," Hattie whispered back.

"What's . . ." Rose was about to ask when Professor Kay's loud voice startled her.

"No talking!" he said sharply.

Rose stared down at her reader and stayed quiet the rest of the morning session. The smell wouldn't go away. It even got stronger. Rose's nose complained until she thought she might jump up and run out of that room.

As soon as Professor Kay excused them for morning recess, Rose turned to Hattie and exclaimed, "What is that awful smell?"

Hattie turned and looked at Vernice Herd, one of the other country girls in Rose's reader. Vernice's hands flew to the chest of her patched coat and she blushed hard.

"She's wearing an asfettidy bag," Hattie said.

"Roses are red, violets are blue," Elmo Gaddy, the class bully, taunted Vernice. "Asfettidy stinks, and so do you." Then he laughed roughly.

Vernice's face puckered up to cry. Then she jumped up and ran from the room.

"Elmo, you will stay at your desk for recess and dinner today," Professor Kay said in a terrible voice. Elmo scowled and sat down hard in his chair.

The children broke up into small groups for recess. No one really wanted to go outside and play a game. Finally Rose could ask Hattie, "What's asfettidy?"

"I don't know," she said. "It's something you wear, to keep away sickness in winter. But I'd rather be sick than wear any old thing like that."

Rose went to visit Spookendyke in the shed, to see if he had been behaving and was warm enough. The undersides of the clouds nearly touched the treetops, and the light shone so gray and dim, Rose couldn't tell where the sun ought to be. She shivered and pulled her fascinator tight around her head.

She found Vernice in the hitching shed, standing next to her mule. Her face was wet with tears and she hugged herself to keep warm. When she spotted Rose, she turned away.

Rose stroked Spookendyke's neck for a minute, not sure what to say, sneaking glances at Vernice's back. Vernice snuffled up her tears and leaned her head against the mule's flank. She was shivering. Rose noticed she wasn't wearing any stockings, and her union suit was tattered around the ankles.

Finally she said, "I'm sorry, Vernice. I didn't know about the asfettidy. I didn't mean to make a joke of you."

Vernice turned and scowled at Rose. "I hate Elmo!" she spat out. "He's the meanest, spite-fulest boy I ever met! And I hate school!" Her fists were clenched and her mouth was pinched in a frown. "My mama makes me wear it. If I don't, I'll get a licking. I cain't help if it stinks bad."

Rose gave Spookendyke a last scratch.

"Can I see it?"

"No," Vernice said defiantly.

"Please. I won't laugh at you. I only want to see what it is. I never saw one."

Vernice shrugged and then slowly reached inside her coat, and inside her dress. She pulled out a long string that was looped around her neck. Then came a little cloth bag, tied to the string. She fiddled with the string for a moment, and the bag came untied. She took something out of the bag and held it in her open palm.

"Give your hand here," Vernice said. She put the asfettidy in Rose's hand.

It was a little chunk of brown stuff, like tobacco, still warm from the heat of Vernice's body. It felt hard and gummy, like wax. Outside, with the cold air searing her nose, Rose could hardly smell it.

"What's it made of?" she asked.

"I don't know," Vernice said quietly. "It's a growed thing, from some faraway place. My mama says if I don't wear it, I'm a-going to come down sick. I'm a-scared not to wear it. Look at what happened to Irene Strong. She never wore none." Irene was a girl in Rose's class who had died last school session of diphtheria.

Rose was mystified. She could not imagine how a little brown chunk of a thing could keep away illness. The rest of the morning Vernice sat alone in the back, farthest away from the stove. The smell wasn't so strong then. Rose felt pity for her, teased for wearing her asfettidy bag but afraid to take it off.

Then a little seed of worry began to grow. Could asfettidy really keep away illness? If Rose didn't wear an asfettidy bag, would she get sick like poor Irene? She wanted to ask Mama about it, but she was afraid Mama would make her wear one too, and Rose would never come to school smelling like that. It was so hard to know what to do sometimes!

Just before dinner all the students were quietly busy, writing their spelling words on their slates. The only sound was the scratching of pencils and shuffling of feet. Suddenly a bright light flashed in the room, and then a clap of thunder rolled trembling and tumbling out of the sky.

Everyone looked up in shock, eyes big and mouths open, even Professor Kay.

"Now that beats all!" Professor Kay declared. "A lightning storm in this weather. Why, it's too cold for snow, let alone rain."

Everyone began talking at once, and some of the students ran to the windows to look out. More thunder rumbled up from the distance, and then little pellets of sleet began to swish against the windows. The sound of clomping feet came through from the floor above. The other classes were looking out the windows too.

"I'd say that's enough for today," Professor Kay called out above the hubbub. "Looks like we've got a bad storm brewing, and some of you have a fair piece to travel to get to your homes."

In an instant all the students grabbed dinner pails, hats, fascinators, and mittens and were jostling each other out the door. Rose quickly untied Spookendyke and climbed onto the saddle, and the donkey trotted off home, as anxious as she was to get out of the sleet and rain that lashed at their faces and eyes.

By the time Rose got Spookendyke safely in the barn, unsaddled, fed, watered, and currycombed, the sleet had piled up and the rain was freezing on everything. She fell twice just getting from the barn to the house.

Ice Storm

Rose spent the afternoon helping Mama in the kitchen. Outside, the forest was gloomy and dark, and it rained and sleeted and rained some more. The storm growled in its throat, and every so often a flash of pure white light burst through the windows, followed by the crash of a close-by thunder-clap that rattled the dishes, the lamp chimney, and the stove caps.

Papa came in from the woodlot, breaking off bits of ice that clung to his hat and the fur of his buffalo coat. Then he picked ice out of his mustache. Pieces of it fell onto the stove, hissing and steaming.

"Had to send the Baird boys home," he said, shaking off the cold like a sparrow. "The lightning's too close, and everything's so slick you can't hardly grip an axe handle. The wagon wheels froze to the ground. We had to break the ice to get it moving. I never saw a thing like it, rain in freezing weather."

Rose helped Mama make up a batch of hominy, a dish they had never eaten. Mama had gotten the recipe from Mrs. Stubbins. Mama had put some stove ashes to soak in water the week before. Now the ashes had made lye water that Rose must never touch. It was so strong it could burn the skin off your hand.

Mama put some of the lye water in an enameled pot and added two quarts of hard shelled corn. She set it on the stove to cook, and Rose stirred every few minutes with a wooden spoon to keep the kernels from sinking to the bottom and sticking to the pot. You could not use a metal spoon to make hominy. The lye was so wicked it would eat the metal.

The cooking hominy was horrible to look at, dark brown and murky, muddy as a barnyard puddle. Papa peered into the pot, looked at Rose and frowned.

"Are we really going to eat this?" Rose asked, making a face.

"Believe it or not, yes," said Mama, sitting in a chair at the table in the lamplight, darning a pair of Papa's wool socks. Her quick hands fluttered over her work like a pair of birds. "But not when it's like that. You'll see. Just keep stirring."

After she had stirred a long, long time, Mama put down her mending, fished out a kernel of the muddy corn, and tested it between her fingers. The kernel was a little bit spongy and the hull slipped off. The lye water made it do that.

"I think that's about soft enough. Now we need buckets of water to rinse off the ash. There's no sense trying to go to the spring with the ground so icy. We'll dip it up from the rain barrel."

Rose took the water bucket and followed

Mama, carrying the steaming pot of hominy out into the murky dusk to the rain barrel at the end of the porch. The edge of the porch, the steps and everything they could see was covered with frozen rain. The woods crackled with the sound of icy tree limbs rubbing against each other in the steady north wind. Rose shivered against the penetrating cold and dampness.

Fido and Blackfoot came slipping and sliding from the barn where they had been hiding from the rain and the ice. Fido ran clumsily, scrambling and slipping, catching himself from falling with his sharp nails. But when he got to the porch and leaned back on his haunches to stop, he began to slide down the slope that ran away from the house.

He sat down, but his little body just kept on sliding on the sleek ice. He turned slowly around as he slid until he was gliding backward past the porch, a comical, helpless look on his face and a little whine in his voice. Rose and Mama burst out laughing. It took him a long time to scrabble his way back up the hill, panting hard, his tail wagging furiously.

Blackfoot was more careful. She minced daintily across the icy barnyard, trying to keep one foot always off the ice. But even so, her feet slipped this way and that, her tail trembled and twitched with each step. She mewed complaints all the way, until she had climbed the porch steps and could rub and curl around Rose's legs.

"I think we could let them both in the house tonight," Mama said. "This is no weather for man or beast."

Mama had to chop the ice out of the top of the barrel. She threw the ice away and dipped up a bucket of water. She poured the brown, soupy hominy into a strainer, and then Rose poured bucket after bucket of clear water over it, to rinse away all the ash.

When the kernels looked white and clean, they brought the strainer inside and Mama poured the corn into the butter churn and added warm water from the stove reservoir. Rose dashed the corn with the butter dasher, to get all the hulls loose.

"Mama, what's asfettidy?" Rose asked as she dashed. Papa sat in the bedroom, sharpening the axe in front of the fireplace. The sound of the rasp against the blade gave Rose gooseflesh.

"I don't know," said Mama, laying thin slices of pork fat in the skillet. "Where did you hear of it?"

Rose told about the little brown plug Vernice carried in a bag around her neck.

"You mean asafoetida," Papa called out from the bedroom between scrapes of the rasp. "A-s-a-f-o-e-t-i-d-a. Mr. Reynolds sells it to the hill people. I've seen them come in and buy it when I was in his store. He says it's resin of some kind, from a plant in Asia. It's got a fierce smell to it. He has to keep it in a barrel out back so it won't ruin the rest of his stock."

"And they wear it in a sack round their necks?" Mama asked. She lifted the lid of the churn to check the hominy. "Just a few more dashes, Rose. We don't want the kernels to mush."

"The old-timers think it wards off disease," Papa said. "Especially for children. I reckon it's just some old-fashioned notion. Can't see how it could work."

"Poor Vernice. It must be terrible to go to school smelling like that," Mama said, turning the meat with a fork and holding her face back from the spatters. "Although it probably keeps people far enough away that you couldn't catch a handshake, let alone an illness."

Rose worked the dash in silence, thinking hard about Vernice, and about poor Irene. Finally, she screwed up her courage and asked, "Mama, what if I got sick sometime? What would happen then?"

Mama took the fry pan off the burner. Then she lifted the lid on the churn and looked inside. "That's done now. Whatever makes you think you might get sick? Are you feeling ill?" She held a palm to Rose's forehead.

"No."

"Well, then. Nothing to worry about." Mama dished the hominy out into a bowl.

"But what if?" Rose persisted.

"We would nurse you back to health, of course," Mama said. "Why are you fretting so about being sick?"

"I was just thinking," said Rose. She didn't know how to tell Mama that she was afraid. Rose worried about what would happen if, like Irene, she crossed to that farther shore from which no traveler returns.

What would happen to Mama and Papa if Rose was gone? The thought of them alone was too much to imagine and brought a hard lump into Rose's throat.

Before she even knew she was doing it, Rose gave Mama a big, tight hug. She buried her face in Mama's apron and breathed in the soft, warm smells of the kitchen.

"I love you, Mama," she muttered into the apron.

"Goodness, Rose!" Mama chuckled in surprise. She put down the spoon she was using to dish up the hominy, and held Rose's head tight to her. "We love you too, dearest. You're the best daughter anyone could pray for."

Mama and Rose held each other for a long

moment. Papa came to the bedroom doorway and stood with his arms folded, watching with eyes that shone in the lamplight.

"I love you, too, Papa," Rose said in a tiny, trembly voice. Then she went and hugged him as well.

"Now, don't you worry yourself about being sick, my little prairie Rose," he said in a gruff voice. "You're a big, strong, healthy girl." Then he bent down and gave her a bristly kiss on the cheek.

Rose felt better after that.

It rained and sleeted all the rest of the afternoon and evening. When Papa went out before supper to water and feed the animals, he slipped and fell on the icy porch steps.

"Durn! Tarnation!" he complained loudly when he limped back from the barn, rubbing his knee. "You can hardly walk a step out there without your feet flying out."

Night came and still the rain fell and froze. They ate a cozy supper, finished off with the hominy, which Mama had fried in the meat drippings. Each plump, flavorful kernel was coated with a crisp delicious shell and melted in Rose's mouth. Hominy was a lot of dirty work, but it was a way to make the dried corn into something fresh and filling on a bitter cold winter night.

After the supper dishes were washed, when Rose went outside to use the convenience, she found long slender icicles growing from all the eaves.

The ground was a sheet of ice, hard as a dinner plate, wet and slippery. Rose could not take a single step without falling down. So she crawled to the privy on her hands and knees, the ice prickly hot against her skin. Her palms and knees ached with deep cold when she got back inside. She stood in front of the stove a long time, warming herself up.

That night Rose got ready for bed listening to the low rumble of distant thunder, and the small liquid sounds of slow rain splashing on ice. Blackfoot curled up on top of Rose's feet. Fido lay on the rag rug in front of the hot fire Papa had built in the fireplace, his nose tucked under his paws.

But even the roaring fire couldn't fight the

cold. Slipping between her cold sheets felt like a plunge in freezing water, and she banged her head again, this time so painfully she cried out. The cold made her feel so clumsy.

Rose shivered under her covers a long time before she warmed up enough to feel sleepy. Mama had layered her bedding with old news-papers, and they rustled every time she or Blackfoot moved so much as a toe.

It was good to be safe inside and tucked into bed on such a terrible night. But it was strange to imagine the little house and the barn and the forest being covered over with ice, layer upon layer, thicker and thicker. It felt as if the sun and the warmth had been chased away and would never come back. The whole earth seemed to stop turning, to be going to sleep under a frigid, lifeless, smothering blanket.

The ice must have stopped the trains, too. Rose hadn't heard a single whistle all evening. And what, she wondered, would happen to the woods creatures and the poor wintering birds that didn't have a dry place to hide from the storm?

Branch by Branch

The dark cold morning brought more lightning, and misty rain. As she dressed by the stove, Rose tried to look out the window, but it was iced over on the outside, and a frosting of crystals covered the inside.

She pressed her palm flat against the glass to melt a spot in the shape of her hand. The instant she took her hand away, cold and wet, she could see tiny fingers of crystal begin to grow again around the edges. The cold and ice wanted to cover over everything, and nothing could stop it.

Papa sat at the table, sipping his first cup of coffee. Mama was making up the big bed. From the barn Rose could hear the mules and Spookendyke braying impatiently.

"Papa, what about the animals? They're hungry."

"We'd best wait until it's light to do the chores," he answered. "It's mighty slick out there. Trying to walk around with a lantern in my hand, I'd most probably fall and smash it. Besides, Abe and Swiney won't be by today. Nobody's going far on that ice. And school will be closed."

Rose clapped her hands with joy.

"We're going to need wood, Manly," said Mama, coming in from the bedroom, huffing from pushing Rose's trundle bed under the big one. "The box is empty. With this cold we're using it up fast. I hope this snap doesn't last too long."

"We've got enough wood to keep us going two lifetimes," Papa said. "No matter how long it lasts, Bess, it'll never hold a candle to the Hard Winter in De Smet. You remember. It was so cold, the cows were giving ice cream."

Rose giggled. "Was I born yet, in the Hard Winter?"

"Not yet," said Mama. "Your Papa and I hardly knew each other then. Sit down, so I can brush and plait your hair."

Rose sat on a chair turned sideways, and Mama sat on another chair behind her, brushing Rose's long brown hair in even strokes. The bristles tingled her scalp pleasantly and helped wake her all the way up. She felt like a colt being currycombed for a buggy ride.

Fido ate a breakfast of stale cornbread with drippings on it. Blackfoot crunched on some chicken bones Mama had saved from last Sunday's dinner.

"What was it like, the Hard Winter?"

"It was a blizzard to end all blizzards," said Mama. "It lasted from October almost to May, except for a day now and then when the sun came out. The whole town nearly starved for running out of wheat and nearly froze for lack of coal. Your papa and another fellow saved us all."

"Really? How, Papa?" Rose asked eagerly.

While Mama finished Rose's hair and cooked up breakfast and they waited for the first light, she and Papa told Rose the story of the Hard Winter in Dakota Territory, when the first settlers came to live on the treeless prairie and the trains couldn't run because of the huge snow drifts. Most of the people in that town were from back East. They never imagined anything could keep the trains from running a whole winter.

Mama told the part about Papa and Cap Garland making a dash in between blizzards to buy wheat from a settler after the people in the town had run out of food. "If it hadn't been for your father," Mama said, looking at Papa with pride, "we'd have been stewing our shoes for the leather."

Papa shrugged and got up to look out the frosted-over window.

"Is this going to be a hard winter?"

"Nobody ever knows for sure," Mama said. "Sometimes you can have a clue, from watching the animals behave. Your grandpa Ingalls used to say the thickness of a muskrat's house at harvest time tells you how bad a winter will be. But we don't have to worry. We have plenty of food and wood."

Rose tried to imagine what stewed shoe leather might taste like, but she couldn't think of a thing.

When the first light peeked through the windows, they put on their coats and mittens. Rose and Mama bundled their heads with their fascinators. Then Rose picked up the pails of water and mash for the chickens and followed Fido, Blackfoot, Mama, and Papa out on the porch.

"My land!" Mama breathed in wonderment. Rose could scarcely believe her eyes. Every blade of dried grass, every bush, every rock, every inch of ground, every tree limb, even the tiniest branches, the barn, the henhouse—everything was completely covered with a thick coat of clear ice. The whole world had turned to crystal, as if seen through a vase of cut glass.

The bitter air stung Rose's face. The rain had stopped, but dark, grimy clouds covered the whole sky. Their breaths came in thick clouds, streaming away from their mouths in the breeze. The mules, hearing the door of the house shut, began to bray even louder.

"Listen to it," said Mama. They all grew quiet. Above the braying, the forest echoed with new sounds, groanings and crackings, and tinkling and clacking, the hard mournful sounds of the forest being choked by ice. Suddenly, beyond the barn, they heard a great crackling crash followed by a roar.

"What was that?" Rose cried out. It was a terrifying, violent sound, like the footstep of a giant crushing trees as he walked through the woods.

"Probably a big limb, maybe a whole tree," said Papa. "The ice is so heavy, the trees can't bear the weight of it. If this keeps up, we're going to have a lot of ruined timber."

"Manly!" Mama suddenly remembered. "What about the orchard? The apple trees? Surely they can't stand up to all this ice."

"I'll be starched," said Papa, a frown creasing his forehead. "How could I forget? When we get the chores done, we'll take a look.

They're small and supple, but . . . jiminy, I hope they're holding up."

From every direction came the crashing, exploding sounds of ice-heavy limbs coming down. Rose noticed now that fallen limbs lay everywhere around the barnyard.

Papa went first, using a stick to lean on. He stepped gingerly down the three steps, but before he'd even reached the ground, his feet flew out in front of him.

"Manly, careful!" Mama shouted.

Papa landed hard—"*Oof!*"—on his bottom. He grunted irritably, muttering under his breath.

"Are you all right?" Mama fretted. "Are you hurt?"

Papa sat there in silence for a moment. Then he swung the stick and flung it away as hard as he could. It hit the icy ground and slid, and slid, and slid as if it never would stop. Finally it hit a tree trunk, spun crazily, and skittered over the edge of a little crest, still sliding.

Mama sighed heavily and held out her hand for Papa to grab. He clambered slowly back onto the dry porch floor, grunting little grunts and rubbing his bottom. His mouth was set in a thin line.

"There must be a way," Mama said fretfully. "We can't crawl on hands and knees all day to do our chores. The hens, the livestock. They all must be fed and watered."

Rose crouched down and ran her mittened hand over the ice that clung to the edge of the floorboards. It had been so cold when the rain fell that it froze instantly. The wood never could get wet. Through the clear ice, the boards looked as dry as a hot summer day. She noticed her mitten wasn't so slippery as her shoe. Rose had an idea.

"Mama."

"What is it?"

"We could tie rags on our shoes. Maybe they wouldn't slide then."

"Yes!" Mama said brightly. "Yes, Rose. That's a wonderful idea."

Mama dashed inside the house and brought out some scraps of old dresses and overalls. She wrapped Rose's shoes with a piece of her old work dress and made it fast with a knot at the top. Then she and Papa tied rags around their shoes.

Papa went first, holding on to a porch post. He reached the bottom and slid his feet a little at a time. "That's my smart girl, Rose," he said. "I bet it's the only way you can walk on it."

Mama went next, and then she turned around and offered her hand to Rose.

"I can do it," Rose said proudly. It felt strange, soft and soundless, like walking on clouds. She took little shuffling steps so she wouldn't fall.

Now she could see sticks and rocks here and there on the ground that looked safe to step on, dry even up close. But they weren't dry. They were encased in ice.

The branches of the cedar tree by the barn bent to the ground, glazed in a huge sheet of ice that made a tent of the branches. Rose moved a branch and it crackled. Chunks of ice fell to the ground.

She found dead leaves that had been coated with ice. She picked one up and carefully peeled away the leaf. The ice stayed in one whole piece. On the underside, the ice had made a beautiful delicate mold of the leaf, with all the imprints of the tiny leaf veins. The ice leaf made a clever little cut-glass dish.

"Bring the water and mash," Mama's voice called out from the henhouse. "Before it goes cold."

Rose picked up her pails and shuffled across the barnyard. Fido was making a game on the ice with Blackfoot. The cat sat in the middle of the barnyard, licking her paw. Fido started to scamper toward her, his tongue lolling and his breath coming in clouds of steam. At first he ran in one place, slipping with every step. But then his nails caught the ice and he started to go forward, faster and faster.

When he got close to Blackfoot, he stopped running and just slid on his feet. Blackfoot jumped to run, but her nails weren't big enough to catch. She arched her back, and her ears flattened themselves as Fido came sliding toward her and then crashed into her sideways, sending them both tumbling and skidding a long way toward the barn.

The henhouse, glazed with ice and icicles all around the roof, glistened like a crystal palace. Mama chipped the ice away from the little doorway the chickens used to come and go, and lifted it up. From inside Rose could hear the chickens fluttering down from their perches and cackling impatiently in a crowd at the door.

The first chicken, the brown-and-white one that pecked all the others, poked her head out and twisted it this way and that, looking at the ice forest with greedy, suspicious eyes. The other chickens crowded up behind, pushing and jostling, eager to be out in the chicken yard and have their breakfast after being cooped up all night.

The whole flock bunched up and pushed the first three hens out the door and down the little plank to the ground. As soon as the hens stepped on the slick plank, they skittered down it with a loud *squawk!* They skidded out onto the icy yard, flapping madly to catch their balance.

Rose and Mama burst out laughing.

The rest of the hens and the two roosters took turns peering out the door at their flopping sisters. Then they decided to stay inside in the safety of the straw-covered floor. The hens that had been pushed out scrabbled around the plank, trying to use their beaks, their feet, and their wings to pull themselves back up it. After a lot of wing-flapping and loud complaints, and a gentle push from Mama's hands, they finally made it.

Rose found six eggs in the nests, but three of them were cracked from freezing. She would give those eggs to Fido.

"I see I'm going to have to get up in the night if we're to save these eggs from the cold," said Mama. "I can't afford to be feeding them to the dog. We need every one to trade at Reynolds' Store."

When all the animals had been fed and watered, Rose walked with Mama and Papa past the barn, through the woods, to the orchard. Rose's heart sank when she saw the little trees bent over every which way under the weight of the killing ice.

Some of the smallest trees were bent all the way over, their tender limb tips frozen fast to the rough ground. She tried to loosen one, but the fragile bud at the end wouldn't budge. She gave a yank and it tore off, trapped in the ice. Rose's heart broke to see it. That was a bud that wouldn't flower in the spring.

Papa walked soberly over to one of the trees. He carefully broke the ice from the limbs. When he was done, the little tree stood up again, proud and straight. Papa sighed heavily. "We can't leave them like this," he said. "If we get any more freezing rain, the trunks'll split and they'll be ruined."

"What can we do?" Mama asked worriedly.

"The only thing we can do," Papa said. "Go through the whole orchard, branch by branch, and set them free."

The Wandering Jew

All the gray morning, in the bitter cold, they worked their way down the rows of apple trees, one by one, breaking off the clinging ice. Mama discovered they could gently hit the trunks and limbs with a stick and that would break off most of it. But they had to use their fingers and rocks to free the limbs that were stuck to the ground.

Rose's fingers quickly went numb. The bitter air burned her face, and then her cheeks turned to stone. Her lips stopped working and her words came out stupid and clumsy. Her feet ached so badly, the pain brought tears to her eyes.

She pulled her fascinator over her mouth and nose. Right away her breath froze slick and stiff on the outside of it. Papa's breath made tiny white icicles on his mustache, and Fido's nose grew tiny ice prickles.

Every little while they had to go back to the house to warm up by the stove.

"I've done just about every kind of farm work there is," said Mama as she rubbed Rose's fingers to warm them up. "But this is the hardest yet."

Papa went to the woodpile by the barn for more stove wood, but he had to come back and get the axe. The ice had frozen over the whole pile into one great chunk of thick ice. When he brought in the wood, it was coated with ice on one side and had to dry leaning against the stove before it would burn.

Saving the apple trees was miserable, bone-chilling work. Their hands became red and raw from tearing at the ice. Papa's toe tips caught frostbite. Mama rubbed them with ice as Papa sat in a chair, wincing and grunting with pain as they warmed up.

Some of the trees had been split or the limbs torn by the weight of the ice. Papa said some of those trees would probably have to be cut down in the spring.

But the ice-covered forest, with millions of little lights in all the trees, cast a spell that delighted Rose. She could hardly stop looking at everything. The woods had become a fairyland, something from a dream. Except for the hoarfrost in the fall, she had never seen anything so lovely and strange.

They worked all morning and after dinner until they finally knocked the ice off the last apple tree and it was time for evening chores.

It rained again in the night, and again the rain froze, but not enough to hurt the apple trees. In the morning when they got up, the thermometer on the porch read two degrees below zero.

When Rose and Mama went to feed and water the chickens, they found the old rooster hobbling pitifully on the icy ground outside the henhouse.

"Oh dear," Mama said. "He must have

sneaked out of the henhouse last night when I went to collect eggs."

The ice had coated all of the poor rooster's feathers. His top comb and the wattles under his chin were already pitch-black with frostbite. He was alive, but Mama said he wouldn't live for long. The frozen parts would become infected. Mama had to butcher him, and that night they had stewed rooster for supper.

Day after day, the mornings dawned cold and icy. The gray sky pressed low on the hills and the sun refused to smile.

Rose stayed inside most of the days, going out only to do her chores and get water from the spring. The rain barrel froze solid, so now they must get their water from the spring, which couldn't freeze because the water always moved. But the slope down into the gully where the spring lay was too slippery to climb.

Mama tied a rope around the bucket so Rose could throw it into the water and pull it back up. The watercress that grew by the spring still flourished and made brilliant patches of green against the silver of the ice. The bed of mint behind the spring was completely frozen over. The leaves broke off easily, and every time Rose went for water she ate a few, savoring the cool refreshing taste.

Blackfoot stayed by the barn during the day, lurking around the hallway where the bold chickadees, brilliant red cardinals, and purple finches came to hunt crumbs of corn the livestock had dropped.

Blackfoot sat on the woodpile, hunkering down and flattening her ears to blend in. She stayed perfectly still the longest time, waiting until the birds forgot she was there. When a bird wandered too near, Blackfoot pounced, going from perfect stillness to lightning speed in the blink of an eye. Around the woodpile Rose found little piles of feathers of different colors that told the story of the cat's cunning.

Rose knew Blackfoot must eat to live, but she felt sorry for the poor birds. She found two dead sparrows in the cedar tree by the barn, their tiny feet held in the ice like iron. They had starved to death. And there was nothing for the others to eat. The ice kept all the dried seeds of the grasses and bushes in beautiful prisons. No bird could peck its way through the hard ice to get them.

One morning when Rose carried the water and mash to the chickens, she spotted a little red fox watching her from behind a tree. She froze. The fox lifted its head to sniff the wind. Rose looked around desperately for Fido, but he was nowhere in sight.

Rose and the fox just stared at each other for a long, still moment. The fox was beautiful, just like a little dog. Its bright eyes looked at her warily, its breath came in quick little puffs of steam, and its thick coppery hair ended in a bushy black-and-red tail that switched nervously. Then the fox began to walk slowly toward her. Rose quick threw the pail of mash down and ran back into the house.

"What is it?" Mama said when Rose rushed in, throwing the door open with a slam.

"A fox! By the henhouse!" Rose shouted.

Mama grabbed her pistol from its hook by the front door.

"Mama, don't! *Please!*" Rose begged as she followed her back out to the henhouse. The fox was still there, lapping greedily at the mash that had spilled out of the pail onto the ground.

"Go on, *scoot!*" Mama shouted. She edged closer to the fox, but the poor starving thing wouldn't budge. Its shifting, frightened eyes looked up at Mama pitifully, but it kept on licking at the chickens' mash. The pain of its hunger had defeated its fear of people.

Mama raised the pistol and pointed it right at the fox. Rose closed her eyes and held her breath. A loud *bang!* exploded in her ears. When she opened her eyes, a puff of smoke was trailing away in the breeze. The fox was gone! Then she spotted it, loping off into the woods.

"The poor thing," Mama said sadly. "I couldn't shoot it. But we can't have a desperate fox lurking around the hens."

Papa came out of the barn where he had been grooming the horses, shuffling fast on his rag-tied shoes.

"What is it, Bess?"

"A fox," said Mama. "It was so bold, I was afraid it might be mad with rabies. But I just couldn't kill it. I frightened it off with a wild shot."

"I reckon all the woods creatures are in a rough situation," Papa said. "Nothing's stirring in this weather. I need to take a load of railroad ties into town. But I don't dare risk the horses on this ice, and the trains aren't running anyway. If this keeps up much longer, it's going to be hard on folks, especially farmers."

It had been many days without a sign of another soul, not even a train whistle. Rose was getting bored. The ice seemed to get in the way of everything. Chores were cumbersome and took twice as long to finish. It was too cold and too clumsy to play outdoors, and there was no one to play with.

The little house was quiet most of the time. Rose missed the daily chatter at mealtimes with the Baird brothers.

Mama gave Rose her lessons after breakfast and sat with a shawl over her shoulders sewing, or ironing, or kneading bread while Rose studied in her reader, or ciphered her numbers.

Only the ticking and chiming of the clock in the bedroom, the logs settling with a crunch in the stove and fireplace, and the roar of the wind in the crackling, groaning trees broke the quiet. Every so often a falling tree limb in the forest would startle them both.

Papa stayed in the house more too, oiling and fixing the harnesses, or carving a new axe handle.

But at least Rose had a new book to read, her birthday present from Papa, *The Wandering Jew*. When she was done with her lessons and chores, she sat by the warm stove with a quilt over her lap and began to read:

"The Arctic Ocean encircles with a belt of eternal ice the desert confines of Siberia and North America," she read. "The sky of a dull and leaden blue is faintly lighted by a sun without warmth." Rose looked out the window at the eternal ice and the leaden sky, and a shiver ran through her.

That book was the hardest she had ever

read, confusing at times like the Bible, and full of words Rose had to ask Mama about. Even Mama did not know the meaning of some of them. But Rose didn't care if she understood all of it. In no time she was carried away from the little house locked in ice, and on page eleven she was in a far-off place a long time ago, riding on a sleek white horse with another girl, her sister. The sisters were named Rose and Blanche. They were orphaned twins.

"Listen to this, Mama," Rose said. "'One held with her left hand the flowing reins, and with her right encircled the waist of her sleeping sister, whose head reposed on her shoulder,'" she read eagerly. " 'Each step of the horse gave a graceful swaying to these pliant'"—"To bend easily," Mama said—" 'forms, and swung their little feet, which rested on a wooden ledge in lieu of ' "—"Instead of," Mama explained—" 'a stirrup.' "

Rose had sometimes wondered what it must be like to have a twin sister. She thought it would be wonderful, like the Hibbard twins in school, to always have a best friend. Now she could read a whole book about a girl with her name, twins with a girl named Blanche, the same as Rose's friend.

Those girls, the made-up Rose and Blanche, had flowing chestnut hair and rosy, satiny cheeks. And traveling with them to keep them from harm was a handsome soldier named Dagobert with long fair curls.

Sometimes when Rose was reading, she would catch a whiff of the musty smell of her book. She put her nose down in the fold and inhaled deeply so that wonderful smell, the smell of adventure in faraway lands, would fill her up. She rubbed her hand across the pages to feel the velvety surface of the paper. When she closed her eyes, her fingertips could even feel the words that were printed there, each letter raised just a little, almost like the special language that her blind aunt Mary could read.

To Rose, a book was as real and alive as if it breathed and walked and spoke.

The Wandering Jew was a shoemaker who lived in Jerusalem the day Jesus was crucified. Jesus was carrying the terrible, heavy cross down the street when he passed by the house of the shoemaker. He asked the shoemaker if He could rest a moment on the shoemaker's doorstep. But the shoemaker wouldn't let him. "Go on! Go on!" he said. And Jesus told the shoemaker, "*Thou* shalt go on 'til the end of time."

After that, the shoemaker had to live until the end of time, wandering forever over the earth, laboring to earn his forgiveness for turning Jesus from his doorstep. In the story in Rose's book, the shoemaker had been roaming for eighteen centuries.

Rose couldn't imagine even one century. Eighteen centuries was forever, and nothing reminded her of forever. Forever could be just a minute when she was hungry and waiting for her dinner.

"I wish I could be the Wandering Jew," Rose looked up from her book and declared one afternoon.

Mama sat on the big bed, sewing a patch in Papa's overalls. She chuckled through the pins clenched in her teeth. "Whatever for?"

"I wish I could live until the end of time and wander the earth and know about all the lives of all the people. I think it would be wonderful to know and see everything."

Mama bit off a piece of thread and tied a knot. "I wonder if it would," she said. "One life is long enough to live. All the lives on earth. Gracious, Rose! Be careful what you wish for."

The next morning Rose woke up from a dream. Blanche was in the dream, riding behind Rose on a tall white horse. When Rose turned and looked at Blanche, she saw herself almost as in a mirror, with long flowing chestnut hair and rosy cheeks. When Rose laughed, Blanche laughed. When Rose frowned, so did Blanche. If either of them made a funny face, the other imitated it, and they both laughed.

They rode across great fields of ice, over green mountains, and through valleys beside rivers of pale-blue water.

And leading them all the way was a tall man with shiny, coal-black hair, riding a great bay-colored stallion. The man was dressed in a

soldier's uniform with gold fringe on the shoulders. The soldier turned and smiled back at Rose and Blanche. He had Abe's face!

The dream was so real, it went on in Rose's mind even after she woke up. It took her a long while to shake out the cobwebs and see that she was home in her bed.

All that day Rose thought about her dream, and for many nights after she tried to make it come back. She made herself think about it as she fell asleep, to will it to come back. But it never would. Ever after, whenever she read *The Wandering Jew*, or even thought of it, the first picture that came into her head was the memory of riding that white horse with Blanche.

Is There a Santa?

I t had been a week of ice and gray skies
and isolation when one morning, in the
faint light of dawn just before breakfast,
Rose heard Abe's voice outside shouting,
"Howdy!" Rose raced to the door and flung it
open. Swiney was with Abe and their shoes
made scraping sounds as they crossed the icy
yard. Swiney was limping.

Papa came from the barn, and Mama joined
Rose on the porch. It was like a reunion of old
friends.

"You fellows are a sight for sore eyes," Papa
said. "We were wondering how you boys were

getting along in this infernal weather. What's that on your shoes?"

Abe lifted a foot and showed the sole. He had tacked a little piece of tin there, with tiny holes in it.

"I took me an old molasses pail, flattened her out, and punched some holes to catch the ice," Abe explained. "It was the only way I studied to walk."

The tin soles were clever, and Abe and Swiney didn't have to shuffle when they walked.

"Swiney, what's happened to you?" Mama asked. "Why are you walking that way?"

"My feet got bit by the frost," Swiney said a bit proudly. "When I was out a-tending my traplines."

"We had ourselves a pokeful of bad luck, Mrs. Wilder," Abe said mournfully. "Old Guts went and broke his leg a-slipping on the ice. We had to put him down."

Swiney's face flushed, and Rose saw tears welling in his eyes. Abe put a hand on Swiney's shoulder.

"Swiney ain't reckoned it yet," Abe

explained. "Old Guts, he weren't much. Kinder old and ornery. But he was all we got."

"Come inside and warm yourselves up," said Mama gently. "Breakfast is nearly ready. You boys must be hungry after baching it a whole week. And I ought to take a look at Swiney's feet."

The breakfast brought a feeling of life back into the house. Abe told of the terrible hardships of the Kinnebrews. One of Mr. Kinnebrew's cows drowned in the stock pond when it walked out on the thin ice to get a drink of water and fell through. Old Guts broke his leg trying to pull it out. Some of the other cows went lame when ice froze in their hooves. Mr. Kinnebrew's oldest son, Coley, hurt his arm falling on the ice, and Mrs. Kinnebrew lost almost all her turkeys to frostbite.

"Mr. Kinnebrew, he's a-battling an uphill scrap with that place," Abe said, shaking his head. "Him and Mrs. Kinnebrew—I ain't one to tote gossip—but they's a-fightin' 'mongst theirselves most the time, and with the young'uns too. They don't like it here much. I cain't see how they's a-going to live, a-being at each other that way."

"Some folks just aren't made out for farming," said Papa. "It's always some trouble. If it isn't chickens, it's feathers. But like the old saying, There's gold in the farm, if only you'll dig it out."

Papa and Abe were draining their last cup of coffee, and Mama was dabbing coal oil on Swiney's blackened toe tips, when suddenly the kitchen brightened with a golden light. It sparkled on the nickel plate of the stove, in the coal-oil lamp, and in their faces. They all looked up in surprise. Rose ran to the window.

"The sun!" she shrieked.

They quick put on their coats and went out on the porch to look. The first rays struck the tops of the trees, sending a shower of glittering yellow light through the forest. The trees sparkled so that it hurt Rose's eyes to look at them.

The rising sun slowly crept down the tree trunks and touched the roof of the barn and the house. The first breezes of sun-warmed air stirred the branches. Little puffs of steam, like tiny breaths, showed where the warm rays melted the ice. Throughout the forest they could hear small sighs and cracklings as the earth stirred from its frozen sleep.

By dinnertime the day bloomed almost springlike. Rose could go out without her fascinator and the ice was melting everywhere, except on the shady sides of the tree trunks.

The weather stayed mild for several days until nearly every bit of ice had disappeared and the earth softened to sticky mud that froze hard as rock in the frosty nights. When Papa drove a load of railroad ties into town, he had to stop many times along the way and scrape thick red clods from the hooves of the mules and from the wagon wheels. Mama kept Rose home from school and gave her and Swiney their lessons in the kitchen.

One Saturday morning Rose woke up in the dark to the hush of the first snowfall. Blackfoot mewed loudly to be let inside by the stove. Fido shivered and shook the snow off his feet in a little dance. When the chickens came out of the henhouse for their breakfast, they stood in the snow on one leg at a time, the other tucked up in their warm feathers.

At breakfast a bright, silvery light flooded the inside of the house from all the windows. When Papa had gone to work with Abe and Swiney in the woodlot, Mama said, "Christmas is coming. Have you an idea for a gift for Papa?"

Rose made a picture of Papa in her mind's eye, and tried to think what he needed. "A muffler?" Rose finally suggested. Papa's old one was fraying at the edges.

"That's a very good idea," said Mama. "I still have yarn left from knitting winter socks. We can dye some of it brown with walnut hulls. Then you can use the plain white with the brown to knit a design."

Rose thought about that for a moment.

"But how could I work on it when Papa wouldn't see?" she asked.

"You can knit it in the evenings, after supper," said Mama. "Papa is going to be busy in the barn nearly every night until Christmas."

"Why?" Rose asked.

Mama's eyes twinkled. "He's making something. It's a secret, from you and me. We mustn't peek and spoil the surprise of it."

Now all the days were bending toward Christmas with its promise of surprises, good food, and fun. Each day Rose thought about it more and more. She and Mama sat in front of the fireplace each night, Rose knitting Papa his new muffler in brown-and-white stripes, Mama sewing up a new cloth jacket for him. In the still of the frosty night they could hear hammering and banging noises from the barn where Papa was working on the surprise.

To pass the time as they worked, Mama told stories of Christmases when she was a little girl growing up on the prairie. Rose liked best the story of the first Christmas on Plum Creek, when Santa brought Mama a fur cape and muff. But she also liked the story of the time their neighbor, Mr. Edwards, met Santa and swam a swollen, freezing river just to bring Mama and her sisters their gifts.

They knitted and sewed and chatted before the hot fire, with a kettle of boiling potatoes hung over it from a piece of an old wagon-wheel rim Papa had fastened to the chimney wall. When the flames began to die down and they felt the cold biting their ankles, they slid their chairs a little closer to the hearth. When their feet were almost in the fire and still felt the cold, Mama got up and brought in a new log from the porch to put on.

Rose watched the dying embers come to life. Mama stirred them with the poker until the fire got so hot they had to move back. She swung the kettle away from the bright, thirsty flames. The golden glow of the fire danced on Mama's smooth face, shimmered in her hair, and played along the log walls, giving cheer and comfort against the cold wind thrashing in the trees outside.

Watching the fire, Rose remembered how, at Christmases past, she worried that Santa would get burned coming down the chimney.

"Mama, how old were you when you knew there isn't any Santa Claus?"

Mama looked at Rose with an arched eyebrow and a bit of mischief in her eyes. "Who said there isn't a Santa?"

"I'm not a baby anymore," Rose declared. "Paul knows there isn't a Santa Claus. Blanche says there isn't, either. And last Christmas I saw you put the orange in my stocking."

A little smile flickered on Mama's lips.

"How do you know Santa didn't give that orange to Papa and me, to put in your stocking?"

"Did he?" Rose asked hopefully. Deep down she wanted to believe in Santa Claus, but she thought it was a childish thing to think. "Did you really see him?"

"Only children can see Santa Claus," Mama said, her hand rising and dipping with each stitch.

"Is Santa Claus like God?"

"Something like God. But not like God, too. God is with us all the time. He is a spirit of everyday life, of all living things. Even plants and birds and bugs have some of God in them.

"But Santa Claus is just once a year, and only for people. He is there when a person tries to be the most generous and unselfish as can be."

186

Is There a Santa?

Rose stared into the dancing flames and sank into her thoughts. She remembered all the Christmases Santa had come down the chimney or the stovepipe on Christmas Eve and left little gifts and candy in her stocking. One Christmas in South Dakota, Papa had even shown her footprints in the ashes in front of the stove where Santa had walked, and soot smeared on the outside of the house where he had climbed down.

It was hard sometimes to know what to believe. If only children could see Santa, why had she never seen him?

"If Santa Claus is a spirit," Rose piped up, "how does he bring the presents?"

Mama's forehead creased and she bit her lip in thought.

"Well," she began, "when you were a little girl you were too young to make gifts for Papa and me at Christmas. And you were too young to understand about the spirit of Christmas. So, Santa Claus came and filled your stocking on Christmas Eve.

"Now that you are so grown up, he doesn't

have to teach you the spirit of Christmas. He knows you understand and you will show the spirit of Christmas for him. Now, when you are generous at Christmastime, you are the spirit of Santa Claus. Do you understand that?"

"I think so," said Rose. She bent to her knitting again and saw that she had sewed a misstitch. She sighed and pulled the knots out and started again. Whether Santa was a spirit or a real person, Rose loved Christmas and she couldn't wait to see Papa's face when he saw the muffler she was making for him.

Rose was making something special for Mama, too, out of bits of cloth she had found in Mama's scrap bag. It was small and she carried it with her everywhere. She worked on it sometimes in the hayloft of the barn or at her desk during dinner hour at school.

Ozarks Christmas Eve

Rose tried to guess what Papa was building out in the barn, but she didn't have a clue. When she hauled water for the animals in the morning, she found an old sheet thrown over something in the corner of the barn hallway, with bits of shaved wood scattered about.

Every bit of her wanted to lift the corner of that sheet and have just a peek. She poked at the sheet with the toe of her shoe. It was something hard. The wood chips told her it was made of wood. Papa often made furniture for the house. He had made Mama's sewing cabinet, and the kitchen table, and the shelves.

If the thing Papa was making was for Mama, it wouldn't hurt for Rose to know about it, she thought. It would still be a surprise for Mama. And if the present was for Rose, well, she would still be happy to get it on Christmas morning, even if she did know what it would be.

Rose crouched down by a corner of the sheet and stared hard at it. She wasn't to peek, but if she just stuck her hand under, that wasn't peeking. Peeking was using your eyes. She wouldn't do that. And besides, she might not even be able to tell what it was only by touching.

She wriggled her hand under the edge of the sheet and felt around. It was wood, all right. Long narrow pieces of it, shaved smooth as silk, with holes here and there that she could fit her fingers in, and . . .

"Ahem!" Papa's voice boomed out from the other end of the hallway.

Rose's body tried to jump right out of her skin. She leaped to her feet and backed away from the sheet as if it had burned her. Papa walked slowly down the hallway toward her, his shoes crackling the straw. Rose blazed with shame. She could not bring herself to look at Papa, she felt so terrible. She stared hard at her shoe tips.

Papa just stood there for a long quiet moment. The silence roared in Rose's ears. May whickered suddenly from her stall, making Rose flinch.

"All right, Rose," Papa said gently. "Now, I know you don't want to spoil my Christmas surprise by looking."

"No, Papa," Rose said with a tiny voice. "I wasn't going to actually look. Really, Papa," she said in a pleading voice. "I was just . . . touching. Only a little."

Papa made a little choking noise that caused Rose to look up at his face. Papa was rubbing his mouth with his hand. The laugh wrinkles around his eyes twitched a little, but then Papa cleared his throat and said simply, "I see. Well, that's something, anyway."

"I won't do it again," Rose said softly. "I promise."

"That's my good girl," Papa said.

And as much as she wanted to every day before Christmas, Rose never did lift the sheet to see. She wouldn't spoil the surprise of Christmas morning for anything.

In the days just before Christmas, Mama began cooking. She baked an applesauce cake, and they popped an enormous amount of popcorn all one afternoon. They strung bowls and bowls of the snowy kernels on thread. They would take those popcorn strings to church to help decorate the Christmas tree.

Next they made popcorn balls. Mama poured molasses in an iron skillet and added a spoonful of soda to make it bubble up. She cooked it until it spun a thin thread from a spoon. When the thread broke, the molasses was ready. Then she poured it into a mixing bowl and let it cool for a few minutes.

Rose and Mama coated their hands with lard, poured some popcorn into the bowl and mixed it up. Rose couldn't resist eating some of the sweet popcorn as they worked. Then they formed the popcorn into balls with their hands and set them on a clean dish towel to harden. They made a huge pile of popcorn balls, some for themselves and some to take to church.

Finally it was Christmas Eve. They had scrubbed the house clean, top to bottom, until it shone. Rose gathered fresh branches of bittersweet berries and cedar twigs to decorate the mantel and the windows.

The house filled with the smells of fresh-baked bread and biscuits, an apple pie, and pumpkin custard. Rose had finished the muffler, and now she wrapped it carefully in store paper they had saved from Reynolds'. She wrapped her present for Mama as well. She hid them both under the straw tick of her bed.

Just before supper, Papa took down the rifle and started out the door.

"What is it, Manly?" Mama asked.

"If my aim is any good, you'll see in a minute," Papa answered with a chuckle.

Rose and Mama looked at each other with questioning eyes. A turkey? A rabbit?

A minute later they heard the bark of the

rifle in the woodlot. Then there was a second shot. Another minute and Papa came clumping back through the kitchen door.

"Wouldn't be Christmas without a little mistletoe," he said. In his hand he had a twig of leaves with white berries.

"You shot mistletoe?" Rose said, giggling.

"It was way up in a tree, growing in the crotch of two limbs. Took me two tries in the dim light, but I got it."

He tacked the mistletoe over the doorway. Then Papa swept Mama in his arms and kissed her under it. Mama gasped and blushed hard. Then Papa kissed Rose under the mistletoe. She couldn't stop giggling.

"What more could a fellow want, with his two best girls to share Christmas?" Papa said.

They ate a cold supper, took their baths, and settled in front of the fireplace. Mama read aloud to them from the Bible, the story of the birth of Jesus. She had just gotten to the part where Mary and Joseph were turned away from the inn when a loud *bang*, a gunshot, rang out next to the house.

Rose jumped straight into the air. Papa leaped up, knocking his chair over.

"Land sakes!" Mama cried out. Papa raced into the kitchen and grabbed his rifle from its rack by the door.

He was checking to see if it was loaded when many more shots rang out, all around the house. Bells began to clank wildly, and they heard crashing sounds, as if a hundred pots and pans were tumbling down a hill. Rose and Mama and Papa just stood there, frozen in surprise, looking at each other for answers.

Then laughter broke out.

"Merry Christmas, Wilder!" a man's voice cried out. "You best come on out and give us a little treat, or I cain't answer for the consequences."

More shots rang out, and more laughter.

A grin sprouted on Papa's face. "I know that rascal's voice," he said. He lit the lantern and Rose and Mama followed him out onto the porch.

A crowd of people stood in front of the house, all bundled up, their breaths puffing ghostlike in the cold air. Some had guns, some had cowbells, and some had washpans they were beating with sticks. The noise was deafening.

"Merry Christmas, Abe," Papa shouted over the clamor. "By jiminy, you got our goat that time." Swiney gave a clank to the cowbell he was carrying. Then Papa laughed his loudest, longest laugh, and everyone joined in.

"That's a new one on us," he said when he could finally speak. "So this is how you celebrate Christmas Eve in the hills, is it?"

"Yessir," Abe said. Swiney danced a crazy dance around him, jumping up and down and beating two railroad spikes together. Then Rose spied Effie standing just behind Abe, holding an old saucepan and a stick. A little wave of pain stole Rose's smile for an instant.

"And it's the rightful thing for you'uns to hand over a treat," Abe said. "Iffen you don't, I'm bound to say, it's the rightful thing for us to do a little trick on you."

Papa laughed again. "And what sort of a

trick might that be?" he asked.

"Well, we just took apart old man Kinnebrew's wagon and put her together again on his barn roof. I reckon he'll be a-walking to church tomorrow, wouldn't you say folks?" The crowd of merrymakers answered with a fresh wave of noisemaking.

"Thank goodness we made those popcorn balls," Mama said with a chuckle. Rose helped her fill a bowlful and they gave every person one, and an apple, too.

Papa invited Abe and Swiney to visit Christmas Day, and they said they would come.

Then the revelers wandered off into the night, headed for the Stubbins farm. For a long time after they left, the *bang* of gunfire, the clatter of banging pots, and the ringing of Swiney's spikes could be heard ringing through the hills.

"Whew!" Mama said when it was quiet again. "I've never been so startled in all my life."

Rose thought it was wonderful.

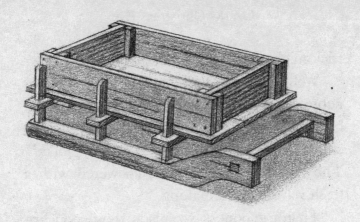

A Wonderful Gift

Rose had just drifted off to sleep when the sound of Papa's whistling woke her up. Then she heard the grinding of coffee beans in the mill. Mama yawned a big yawn from the bed, then she suddenly cried out, "Oh, Manly!"

Rose sat bolt upright in her bed, instantly all awake. It was really Christmas morning! She looked around the room. Her stocking, hung by the fireplace, was all bulgy. She squealed with delight. But something else was different in that room. At first she couldn't say what it was.

Then she shouted. Sitting in front of the

fireplace was the thing Papa had worked all those nights to make—a brand-new sled! And next to it was something else. A rocking chair, stained dark, its arms and runners gleaming faintly in the light from the kitchen lamp.

Rose and Mama bounded out of bed at the same moment. Rose knelt by the sled and just looked at it for the longest moment. She was speechless. The sled was beautiful, the wooden blades shaved feathery smooth with soft round edges. It had a box, just like a wagon box, that fitted cleverly onto pegs that stuck up from the tops of the runners.

Rose climbed into it and sat down. It fit her body perfectly. She couldn't wait to try it out. Then Rose noticed that Mama was sitting in her rocking chair. Papa stood next to her, a great grin of satisfaction on his face.

"It's . . . just so lovely, and relaxing to sit in," Mama said. Her eyes shone brightly as she ran her hands along the arms. "So much more than I expected. And so comfortable. Thank you so much, Manly."

"Thank you! Thank you, Papa!" Rose shouted, hugging his legs as hard as she could.

She never thought in all the world that Papa would make something as wonderful as a sled.

Papa was too pleased with himself to speak. He just kept on grinning and twisting an end of his mustache. Rose said a silent thanks to herself that she didn't spoil Christmas after all.

They all took turns rocking in Mama's new chair. Then Rose dug out her presents for Mama and Papa. Papa opened his first. He smiled broadly and wrapped it around his neck.

"Perfect color," he said, kissing Rose on the cheek. "Matches my mustache."

Papa opened Mama's present next and put on the new coat. It fit perfectly and he looked just grand in it.

Then Mama opened the little package that Rose had given her.

"A pincushion!" Mama exclaimed. "Made out of scraps of Aunt Grace's turkey-red dress. You little rascal. I didn't even notice the scraps were missing from my bag. The stitching is very good. What did you stuff it with?"

"Horsehair, from May's mane. Papa let me cut it."

"Well, it's just what I need. The stuffing is coming out of my old one."

Rose remembered her stocking and plunged her hand in. There was not just one orange, but two! And a little bag of lemon drops, and a tiny little wrapped gift. A shiny silver thimble! She had never had one because her fingers were too small. Now her hands had grown and she wouldn't have to jab herself sewing anymore. In the toe of her stocking she found a Brazil nut. Such a rich Christmas!

"Is that all?" Mama asked coyly. Rose held her sock upside down and shook it. She heard a clink, and then two bright, shiny pennies tumbled out and clattered on the floor.

Rose picked up the coins and looked at the clever engraving in the brilliant metal, a tiny portrait of an Indian in his headdress, and on the back the words, "one cent."

Rose turned the brilliant pennies over and over in her hand. She had never had her own money before, and now here were two whole cents, just for her!

Rose looked at Mama but she couldn't think

of what to say. Mama laughed at the expression on her face. "Now you must think of a special place to keep them."

Rose wanted to go outside and try her sled on the hill, but Mama said she must wait until after breakfast. They were just finishing up when Abe and Swiney arrived. They marched straight inside, to warm themselves by the stove.

Rose was fidgety to show Swiney her sled.

"Do you want to see what Santa brought me for Christmas?" she asked.

Swiney made a sour face as he hugged himself to warm up. "There ain't no Santa," he scowled.

"Of course there is," declared Rose. "I mean, there's the spirit of Santa. Look, I found a thimble in my stocking. And two oranges, and lemon drops."

"There ain't no Santa and there ain't no spirit neither," said Swiney. "Santa never brought me nothing. Not never in my whole life."

"Santa didn't come to your house last

night?" Rose asked in shock. She couldn't believe that Swiney hadn't even gotten an apple. "Didn't you hang your stocking?"

"Even if there was a Santa, I ain't good enough for him to come," Swiney said, his mouth pinched in a pout, his eyebrows bunched up in the middle. "Anybody knows Santa only comes to good boys and girls. Why put up a dumb old stocking if Santa ain't a-going to put nothing in it?"

The misery in Swiney's voice was like a stinging slap. Rose fell silent, thinking, while Swiney turned and turned in front of the stove to warm both his sides.

She remembered that Swiney's mother and father were dead, and all his other brothers and sisters lived far away. Swiney was practically alone in the world, except for Abe. But even Abe had given him nothing for Christmas.

It was true that Swiney had tried to steal eggs. But that was a long time ago, and Papa said it wasn't such a terrible thing for a hungry boy to do. Surely Santa could forgive that.

Like water from a leaky bucket, the Christmas spirit was draining right out of Rose.

The room suddenly seemed very quiet. Rose looked at Mama and Papa and saw that they had been listening. Mama and Papa looked at each other in the certain knowing way that told Rose they were thinking, too. Papa stroked the end of his mustache for a moment.

Then he pushed back his chair and said, "Rose, come here a minute. I want to have a word with you."

She followed Papa into the bedroom. As Papa pushed the door gently closed, she heard Mama ask Swiney to bring in some stove wood.

"Come, sit on the bed," he said. Rose ran a hand along one of the sleek runners of her sled, and then sat down next to him. She thought she might have done something wrong, but she wasn't sure what. Maybe she shouldn't have been bragging about her Christmas.

Papa spoke to her in a low voice, almost a whisper: "Do you know why Swiney got nothing for Christmas?"

"Because he was bad?"

"No," Papa said with a thin smile. "Swiney's not a bad boy. It's because Abe has no money and he's too busy working to make him a gift. Abe is poor, Rose. And he doesn't have a mother and father to remind him about the importance of Christmas for a little boy like Swiney. Abe is just an overgrown boy himself. He doesn't think the way a father would."

Papa paused while Rose thought about that for a moment.

"I think it would be a wonderful thing, in the spirit of Christmas, if we could do something for Swiney, to restore his faith," Papa said. He looked into Rose's eyes and then he looked over at Rose's new sled, then back at Rose again.

Rose was confused. She could see Papa wanted her to think of something, but she didn't know what. Her thoughts stumbled about for a moment, and then, in a flash, she understood, and gasped.

"But, Papa!" she began to cry.

Papa shushed her. "Listen to me for a

moment. Think how happy it would make Swiney to know he was not forgotten after all. A joy that's shared is a joy made double. There isn't another thing we have to give him that would be a good present for a boy. Then I'll build you another sled, right after Christmas."

Rose nearly burst into tears. It wasn't fair, what Papa wanted her to do. She stared into her lap, picking at the folds of her dress. She stole a long glance at the sled. She sighed heavily and her whole body sagged.

Not for anything in the world did she want to give up her sled. Papa had made it just for her. Another sled just wouldn't be the same. For an instant, for the first time ever in her life, Rose was angry with Papa. She felt the blood rush to her cheeks. She knew Papa was right. But she just knew she could never feel happy about it. A storm of feelings whirled through her head as she tried to think of another answer.

"Couldn't we just tell Swiney that Santa is bringing another sled and . . . and that it's coming very soon?" Rose asked in a wavery voice.

"That's not the same as Christmas," said

Papa. "And Swiney is a smart-enough boy. He'd see straight through it. That would be worse than him having nothing at all.

"It's your decision, Rose," Papa added. "I've told you what I think's the right thing to do. But it's your decision."

Rose wrestled with her thoughts. She hugged the hurt, thinking about it until she had it settled in her mind that it had to be that way.

"All right," she finally sighed.

"That's my good girl," Papa said, planting a tender kiss on her forehead. "Now, why don't you take Swiney outside to play. I'll fix everything up so he'll never know it wasn't for him all along. It'll be just our secret."

Rose and Swiney played in the snow the rest of the morning. They built snow forts and had a snowball fight. She shared one of her oranges with him, and they sat together on the porch making contented humming noises as they ate the sweet, juicy sections, and then seeing who could spit the seeds farthest.

But not for an instant did Rose think about anything except that sled, and what Swiney was about to find out. Rose wanted nothing more than to be riding it down the hill, and hard as she tried, she could not squelch the unhappy thoughts that kept popping into her head.

Then, after thinking about it a long time, a funny thing began to happen. Rose started to get excited. She began to imagine how much fun it would be to see what Swiney did and said when he found out. Having a secret made her a little giddy.

By the time Mama called them in for Christmas dinner, Rose was nearly breathless from holding in the secret. She quick looked around the kitchen and spotted a bundle in the corner, covered with a sheet. She almost giggled, but Mama gave her a stern look, with a sly wink.

Over the scraping of chairs as they all sat down to eat, Papa's voice rang out heartily, "You know, Swiney, a strange event seems to have happened around the place last night."

Swiney looked at Papa with narrowed, suspicious eyes.

"I ain't done nothin', Mr. Wilder. Honest," he protested.

"Yes," Papa said. "It was a very strange event, indeed. When I went out to the barn after breakfast to pitch some hay down for the horses, I put my fork in and struck something hard. I dug it out. It was the most unusual thing to find in a hayloft, and I was standing there scratching my head when I noticed a note stuck to it that explained everything."

Papa reached into his jacket pocket and carefully pulled out a piece of folded paper. He opened it slowly, and began to read.

"This is what it says. 'Dear Wilder, One of my reindeer threw a shoe and went lame on me last night.'"

Swiney's eyebrows flew up. Rose couldn't stifle a small chuckle.

"'I was running mighty late when I got to your spread. I just didn't have time to make it over to the Baird place.'"

Swiney's jaw dropped.

"'I wonder if you would be so kind as to see that Swiney Baird gets this. He's a good boy, all in all, and I'd hate it for him to think I forgot him. Tell Swiney I'm real sorry about the mix-up. Merry Christmas to all.'"

Papa looked up and gazed calmly at Swiney, who was staring back, still as a mouse.

"And it's signed, 'Santa Claus.'"

At those last words, Swiney's eyes flew wide open, big as dinner plates. His mouth moved like a fish gasping for air; no words came out. Rose felt a jolt of excitement along all her nerves.

"Well, if that ain't something," Abe said softly. He looked at Papa reverently, and shook his head in wonderment.

"The thing this note was stuck to is over there, under that sheet," Papa said pointing. "Why don't you have a little look-see?"

Swiney knocked his chair down pouncing on the sheet. He tore it off. There sat the sled, gleaming and shiny smooth and smelling of new wood and wax. Swiney sank to his knees just staring at it, almost as if he were going to pray. He ran his hands all along the sideboards, and felt the smooth, sanded runners. He tilted it up to look at the bottom.

Finally he turned and peered up at everyone sitting at the table. His face beamed with joy, and a single tear coursed down his cheek.

"God bless dear old Santy's heart," he croaked. "God bless his old heart."

Everyone's eyes shone fiercely now. A hard lump stuck in Rose's throat. Mama handed Abe a neatly wrapped package that he opened without a word. It was a pair of new wool socks that Rose recognized. Mama had knitted them for Papa. Abe tried to speak. His lips moved and his Adam's apple bobbed up and down. But nothing came out.

They all just looked at each other and smiled sweetly. No one dared try to speak. But Rose knew without anyone saying so that this was the best Christmas any of them had ever had. No gift could ever be as wonderful as the glowing, happy look on Swiney's face.

A Terrible Lie

All the rest of Christmas day Rose and Swiney took turns sledding down the hill toward Fry Creek, shrieking with delicious terror as they hurtled and bounced over the snow. The sled was very sturdy, and the smooth, polished runners made it very fast.

Rose forgot all her dark thoughts, and her heart glowed with warmth to see the broad grin on Swiney's face and to hear the pure laughter in his voice.

When they tired of sledding, they hunted animal tracks. The snow could keep no secrets. All through the forest, no woods creature had stirred without leaving the story of its passing. They found the dainty prints of a fox and holes in the crust where it had dug down looking for a mouse. They found large furry paw marks of a bobcat. And everywhere birds had left their scratchy claw marks, and little hollow places where they had taken snow baths.

It had been a wonderful Christmas, Rose thought as she tucked her pennies into her autograph book that night and changed into her nightgown. In Swiney's joyous face, she had finally seen Santa Claus. And now she truly understood about the spirit of Christmas.

A warm spell after New Year's melted the snow. By the time Papa finished making Rose's sled, only small patches hid themselves on the shady sides of trees and in the hollows where the sun couldn't reach. Her sled stood propped up on the porch, leaning against the wall, waiting. This time, Papa had carved her name in the sideboards. No one could own that sled but Rose.

For weeks Rose watched the sky for snow

clouds and sniffed the air for the scent of it. She jumped hopefully out of bed each morning and ran to the front door to look out. But each morning all she found was the dark bare earth, hard as iron, filmed by frost. When the sun rose it sent no warmth, but by midmorning even the delicate whiteness was gone, and the farm looked desolate and gray.

The new meadows, with dead tree stumps sticking up here and there, were a sullen brown. The plowed land lay rough and unkempt, and the slanting winter light showed every ridge and clod. The manure heaps by the barn steamed in the cold air, and then froze into odd shapes.

But evenings were cozy in the cabin. A good fire of hickory logs crackled in the fireplace while Papa worked oil into the harness straps between his oily black hands, and Mama sat by the table, knitting needles flashing. Sometimes she read aloud from a book propped under the purring coal-oil lamp. She liked to read poems from her book by Alfred, Lord Tennyson. And she read books borrowed from school: Prescott's *Conquest of Mexico* and *The Green Mountain Boys*.

Each day at school, Rose and Blanche always sat together in Professor Kay's third reader. Rose enjoyed seeing Blanche, and hearing about the comings and goings of the people in town. But the lessons still bored her. And she never felt she fit in with the other girls.

As the winter session wore on, she begged Mama more and more to let her stay home. And more and more, Mama did, so long as Rose kept up all her lessons and helped Swiney with his as well.

Helping Swiney made Rose feel like a big sister. Sometimes they sat in front of the fireplace and she read aloud from Mama's poetry books. At first Swiney fidgeted and made faces. But in no time he settled down and sat very still with his elbows on his knees, his freckled face cradled in his hands, his brow a little bit pinched in thought, listening to the words. When he did that, Rose felt very grown-up.

Winter was a time of timbering on the farm. Papa and Abe worked in the timber lot, with Swiney helping after his lessons, felling trees and making railroad cross-ties and fence rails. On days when she went to school, Rose walked with Spookendyke through the woods and over Patterson's Hill, the thuds of Papa's axe sounding fainter as she went. Coming home, with the sky flaming a dark red behind her, she could hear the *whirr-whirr* sound of the crosscut saw growing sharper in the frosty air.

Papa traded some of the fence rails he made with Mr. Stubbins for milk. Once a week he drove a load over and brought back a big creamy pailful. One day Mama said she would make a lemon cake for the church social. But she had no milk and Papa was away delivering a load of railroad ties in town. So Mama sent Rose to fetch a small pailful.

"You may visit awhile, and play with Alva. But you must tell Mrs. Stubbins she's to send you home before dark," Mama said as she tucked Rose's fascinator into her heavy coat.

Rose ran most of the way, to stay warm and

to have more time to play with Alva. The sky was a deep cloudless blue, and the frosty air bit her nose as she flew through the woods. The empty pail clattered loudly against her legs.

At the Stubbinses' house, Alva's mother took the pail and set it by the stove to warm. When Rose was almost ready to go home, Effie would milk the cow into the warm pail. That way the milk would keep from freezing in the cold air until Rose got home.

Then Rose played with Alva on the iced-over stock pond. They ran and slid, fell on their bottoms, and laughed.

Since the sorghum harvest, they had visited together only two other times. They never talked about Rose's autograph book, and Rose was careful not to mention school or Blanche.

When they were all out of breath, they sat on a log to rest.

"My sister Effie's gone all goosey on Abe," Alva declared, grinning. "My ma says them two is thick as thieves. She says they're a-going to marry one of these days."

Rose was too stunned to speak at first. Quick as a pulse beat, a gust of confusion blew up in her heart. Not since the sorghum harvest and Thanksgiving had she thought very much about Abe and Effie. She knew Abe sometimes went to the Stubbinses' house for Sunday dinner, but it was too cold for buggy rides. They couldn't be sparking, so how could they be getting married?

Rose remembered the picture her mind made of Abe and Effie courting in a beautiful buggy, their heads leaning close together, smiling over the shared secret. But in Rose's *Wandering Jew* dream, there was no Effie.

"That's a lie!"

Rose blurted the words out before she even knew she had thought them, and then blushed so hard at her freshness that she felt prickly hot all over, even in the frosty cold.

Alva's eyebrows arched and she looked at Rose with stealthy eyes, like a cat with a twitchy tail. "It ain't no lie when Abe comes to visit Effie near every week," she said in a taunting voice. "Ain't no lie when Effie's a-playing the fool around him. You don't need no eyes in your head to see they're a-gettin' sweet on each other."

The wicked, door-slamming feeling Rose had in the fall came back. Her thoughts skittered about like so many field mice looking for places to hide.

"It can't be!" she said desperately.

"Oh yeah?" said Alva. "Why cain't it?"

"Because . . ." Rose fumbled for words. "Because . . . Abe likes somebody else."

Rose heard the words from far away, as if they had come from someone else's mouth. She had told a terrible, bold-faced lie without knowing why. But now that she had told it, she couldn't stop herself. More words tumbled out.

"He's sparking with another girl," she rushed on, her breath coming in shallow gulps. "Nobody knows about it but me. And he likes her better, and . . . and someday they're going to be married."

Alva gasped. Her mouth made a big O.

"Golly!" Alva finally breathed. "Golly! And poor Effie, a-thinking he's a-going to marry

219

her. Golly! Ain't that something awful."

The look on Alva's face made Rose's stomach flipflop; to think she could tell such a horrible fib. Part of her wanted to shout out that it was all just a joke. But another part of her enjoyed causing the shock on Alva's face. Rose sat there, spellbound by her own wickedness, and too proud to take back her words.

Suddenly Alva's pale-blue eyes narrowed and bored into Rose's. "Well, who is she, then?"

Rose looked away. "Who's who?" she said, kicking at a piece of ice and trying to sound bored.

"You know. Who's the other girl? The one Abe's a-sparking with?"

"I . . . I don't know. Not for sure, anyway," Rose mumbled.

"How'd you know, then?" Alva demanded. "How come you're the only one to know?"

Rose's mind scrabbled about, looking for an answer. "She's . . . I saw them in a buggy once. Driving in town. She's a town girl, I think."

"A *town* girl!" Alva spat the word out as if it

made a bitter taste on her tongue.

Just then Mrs. Stubbins came out on the porch and called them inside. Rose and Alva walked soberly into the house. Alva's mouth was clamped tight and her forehead was pinched in thought. Rose's spirits sank lower and lower as she began to imagine the trouble she had stirred up.

But before she could build up her courage to think how to undo it, they were inside the house and Mrs. Stubbins was handing Rose and Alva cups of hot cider to drink. Rose mumbled her thank-you and couldn't bear to look Mrs. Stubbins in the face, she was so miserable.

"You feelin' a mite puny, Rose?" Mrs. Stubbins asked kindly. "Maybe the cold's gone and wore you out, a-playing so hard."

"No'm," muttered Rose. "I'm fine, thank you."

Mrs. Stubbins went out the door to go to the other side of the house, across the dogtrot. A moment later Effie came in, pulling on her coat. Her face was rosy from bending over the hot stove, and her golden hair hung loose and shimmered in the lamplight. She smiled at Rose as she tied her fascinator around her head.

"You young'uns go warm yourselves by the stove whilst I get Mrs. Wilder's milk," she said gaily. She grabbed the pail from its place by the stove and blew out the door. Alva took her cider and slumped down into a chair by the stove. Her head hung so low, her chin nearly touched her chest.

Rose sat at the table nearby, frozen in her shame, warming her hands around the cup and staring into the cider. There was no other noise, and Alva and Rose kept their thoughts to themselves.

The spicy steam of the cider smelled delicious, but Rose took only a little sip. Her whole body wanted to jump up and run away, as fast and as far as she could. The silence in the house was terrible as they waited for Effie to come back with the milk. As soon as she did, Rose set down her undrunk cider, threw on her coat and fascinator, muttered a thank-you, and dashed out the door.

As she left, she heard Effie's voice, "Say, Alva, what's a-bothering Rose?"

The sun was already below the horizon, the air had turned crackling cold, and the woods were murky dark. Night was clamping down. The dark path was narrow, crooked, and rough. Rose had to walk carefully so as not to spill any of the milk.

Every step of the way she scolded herself for lying, and for leaving so late. Every step of the way she became more and more worried. How would she ever explain herself? Now Alva would never be her friend again, and Abe! He would be so angry. A sob burst from her throat.

Rose had never walked home in the dark from Alva's, and every little sound gave her a terrible start. Somewhere nearby a tree cracked in the stillness. Then she heard a rustling noise ahead of her. A ghostlike shape seemed to move among the darker shapes of the trees. Rose stopped, her heart pounding in her ears. Tingling fear crept up her legs.

Then she heard a soft lowing sound. It was only one of Mr. Stubbins's cows! It must have gotten out of his pasture. Rose let out a quivering sigh of relief. The cow lumbered off and Rose went on, picking her way home through the dark forest.

New House

Why Rose, you're pale. And shivering like a leaf," Mama said as soon as Rose walked in the door. "Are you ill?"

"No, Mama. Something scared me. In the woods coming home."

"Well, I shouldn't wonder," said Mama, taking the pail of milk and laying a cloth over it. "If you'd left a little earlier, it wouldn't have been so dark out for the walk home. Let that be a lesson."

Rose quietly and soberly did her chores. At supper she just picked at her food, even though Mama had made dumplings to go with the leftovers of her good chicken pie. Rose prayed to herself that Alva would just forget her poisonous words. Maybe everything could go on just as it had before. Rose promised herself she would never tell another lie as long as she lived.

Mama scolded her for eating so slowly, but then Papa said something that made Mama forget Rose's strange behavior and even made Rose forget her misery.

"The weather's going to break soon," he said calmly, chasing the last bit of gravy on his plate with a piece of corn bread. "I'd say it's about time we raised a proper house on the place." Papa looked at Mama with a gleam in his eye.

"A house?" Rose asked.

"Oh, Manly, do you mean it?" Mama cried out. She put down her fork, leaned forward and looked at Papa with eager eyes. Then quickly she added, "But how could we pay for it? Surely there must be some expense."

"Well, I've been setting aside some good

timber for a while now. Enough for the amount of house I had in mind, anyway." He put down his napkin and took out his pipe to fill it. "Wouldn't cost us but a barrel of nails, a few rolls of tarpaper, some glass windows, and a few more aches and pains.

"The wood's all seasoned out and cut," he went on. "Abe and I have got ourselves a bit ahead on the timbering. And I've shaved enough shingles in my spare time to cover the roof. I'd say we have enough time to build the place before plowing starts. What do you say, Bess?" Then Papa sat back with a look of great shining satisfaction on his face and lit the pipe.

"It's . . . it's just wonderful!" said Mama, her face suddenly glowing with pleasure. "I can scarcely believe it. A new house, and so soon!"

"A new house?" Rose said. "But why, Papa?"

"I've been listening to you bang your head on that little trundle bed of yours," Papa said. "Now why do you suppose you've become so clumsy all of a sudden?"

Without thinking, Rose touched the place where she was always bumping her head and shrugged.

"I'd say you're getting a little big for that bed."

Papa was right! Rose remembered that if she stretched, her feet touched the footboard, and her head just rubbed the headboard. She was growing right out of her bed!

Papa chuckled. "I reckon it's time I built you a bigger bed. But there's no room in this little house for two regular beds, and before long you'll be sprouting like corn in July. So, I might as well build us a whole new house."

Mama and Rose started chattering at the same time.

"But . . . where would we put it?" Mama began talking very fast. "Oh, I know just the place. Next to the big oak. It gives wonderful shade. And a porch. I must have a porch. And . . ."

"Where will I sleep?" Rose butted in.

"Now slow down, girls," Papa shushed them both. "Let's not get too far down the road just yet."

He got up and went into the bedroom, leaving Rose and Mama staring after him with open mouths. They heard him rummaging around in one of the trunks. Then he brought back his account book and a pencil. Mama and Rose got up and stood behind him, looking over his shoulder, breathless as Papa sketched out on a blank page an idea of a new house.

First he drew the floor plan. It was a big rectangle, divided almost in half. The bigger half would be the kitchen and the smaller half would be Mama and Papa's bedroom, and the parlor when they had company. Papa drew a small rectangle where the bed would go.

"But, Papa. That's the same shape as this house. What about my bed?" Rose wondered impatiently.

"First of all, this house will be a bit bigger," Papa said. "And it'll be made all of boards cut from our own trees. We'll use this same kitchen, and add to it. No more plain log houses for us. And a room for Rose."

"My own room?" Rose shrieked. It was too much to imagine. How could the pencil scratches on that piece of paper become a whole house? Papa was so clever, and thoughtful, too. She threw her arms around his neck and gave him a big kiss on the cheek.

The next morning was Sunday. Abe and Swiney didn't come to breakfast on Sundays. The day dawned mild with bright sun. The frozen ground turned spongy, and there was a whisper of spring in the air. Rose was so excited about the new house, and her own room, she did not think much about her lie, except in church when Reverend Ritchey spoke about the sinners mending their ways. Every time he said the word "sinner," Rose felt a little shiver run up her back.

After church, and after they'd eaten their dinner, Mama left Rose to finish drying the dishes while she and Papa looked for a good spot to build. Rose hurried her chores and then sat watching on the porch, with Fido and Blackfoot wrestling next to her.

In their Sunday clothes they went walking slowly over the land. They stood and talked under the big white-oak tree not far away,

Mama in her brown-sprigged white lawn dress, her long braid hanging down her back, Papa in the new coat Mama had sewed him for Christmas. They talked a long while. Finally Papa went to check the livestock in the barn and Mama called Rose to see.

"Right here," she said proudly. She traced in the air with her finger a big rectangle at the edge of the hill behind the spring, just next to the oak. In that place the ground sloped more gently down into the ravine.

"It will be a white house," she said excitedly, her violet eyes wide and dancing. "All built from our farm. Almost everything we need is on our land: good oak beams and boards, stones for the foundation and the fireplace.

"It will have large windows looking west to catch the sunsets, and a nice big porch to the north, where it will be cool on hot summer afternoons. And mosquito netting on the windows, and bookcases in the parlor, and a dining room, and good cabinets in the kitchen. Oh, and a pump for water. No more hauling water from the spring."

"All of that?" Rose asked in astonishment.

"Well, not right away," Mama said quickly. "First we'll build a little house, just as Papa explained last night. But in a few years, when the apples come in and we can pay off the mortgage, we'll build the rest of it."

All that week the weather stayed warm, and all they did, besides the regular chores, was work on the house. Mama said Rose could stay home from school and there were no lessons for Swiney. If they were to build the house before plowing, they must work fast.

Rose and Swiney helped by loading stones into the wagon. The stones were from the pile they had taken out of the fields and garden. Then Papa drove the wagon over by the house site and dumped them. They would use those stones for the foundation and the chimney. Papa showed Mama how to lay the stones, and she began to make the outline of the walls on the ground. The house would have no cellar because the ground was too rocky to dig one.

Abe and Papa hitched the mules and snaked

the logs up from the timber lot. Then Abe squared them off and Papa split them into boards, using a heavy iron wedge that he hit, ringing every time, with the flat edge of the axe. He fought the logs all the way down, until a fresh board fell on the ground. Then he started at the beginning again.

Rose and Swiney brought Mama stones to pick from. Each stone must fit perfectly against the others to make a good solid footing for the house to stand on. The little stone wall was short and only as big as one room. Mama said the foundation for the kitchen would be rebuilt underneath it, after they had moved it over from the log house.

"Move it?" Rose asked. "How can we do that?"

"You'll see," Mama said.

Rose could sit for hours and watch Abe swing the big, shining broadax again and again, shaving the sides of each log perfectly square, without ever drawing a line, or breaking his pace, or growing tired. Papa said he had the best eye of any woodsman he'd ever seen.

Soon the house site was adrift in shavings. Rose loved to run her hands through the piles and to walk on them and feel the lovely cushion they made under her feet.

The air filled with the new smell of fresh-cut logs, of resin and tannin, a forest odor. It seemed to Rose a kind of miracle that those trees could be cut and shaped into a house for people to live in. When Abe and Papa had made a big pile of lumber, and Papa had helped Mama finish off the foundation, they built the fireplace chimney. Abe hauled clay to chink it with from a special place in Fry Creek. It was Rose and Swiney's job to keep the clay wet by throwing water on it now and then. All in an afternoon, Papa helped Abe build a sturdy, stout chimney that could never burn or fall down. It would last until the end of time.

Now they were ready to build.

Chasing Thistledown

The next afternoon, after church and dinner, Mama, Papa, and Rose stood inside the low foundation wall, admiring the new chimney and the great fireplace with its yawning mouth.

"It's just beautiful," Mama said, running her hands over the thick oak mantel Papa had built into it. "I like a big fireplace, one that will burn a stick of wood as large as a man can carry. A good fireplace is protection from disease. The fresh air it gives is better than a doctor's medicine."

Just then they heard the jingle of harness in the valley. Fido ran barking to see who the visitor might be.

A few moments later a buggy pulled by two beautiful Morgan colts crested the rise and drove into the barnyard. Rose didn't recognize the driver at first. Then she gasped. It was Abe!

He was dressed all in a beautiful dark brown suit, with a clean new hat, and a starched white collar with one of the wings sticking out. His tie was on crooked. Rose had never seen Abe dressed like that; she always saw him in overalls and muddy shoes. He cut such a dashing figure at the reins of the sleek, fast-looking buggy and the perfectly matched team.

Then Rose squealed with delight. "Papa, Mama, look! It's Little Pet and Prince."

"Well, I'll be starched," said Papa. Those were the colts Papa had traded to Mr. Hoover at the livery stable for the mules, almost a year ago. Abe had rented the buggy in town, and Mr. Hoover had given him the proud dark Morgans to pull it.

Rose raced over to the horses to stroke their foreheads and rub their silky ears, just the way she used to when they were little and lived on the farm. Prince snuffled her neck and Little Pet nudged her elbow jealously, just the way they used to. Rose marveled at how tall they had become.

But Abe wasn't grinning the way he always did, as if he were about to crack a joke. His mouth made a straight thin line. Without waving hello, he climbed wearily off the buggy and tied the team to a tree. Rose's hand froze where it had been stroking Pet's velvety neck. Her insides became very still.

"What brings you by today?" Mama said pleasantly. "And where's Effie? I thought you two were going driving."

"We was," Abe said mournfully. His hands balled themselves into fists. He took off his hat and kneaded the brim. He stared at his feet. "But Effie, she's . . . well, she's got her feathers all a-ruffled about something. We went round and round on it some, and, well . . . I just left. I studied on it and reckoned leastways you folks could take the buggy for a spin. It's all paid for and I got no use for it now."

Mama quickly took Abe by the arm and

steered him toward the house. "Come inside and have some coffee and a piece of pie." Papa followed her. Over her shoulder she called out, "Rose, run and fetch some water and a handful of corn for the horses."

Rose walked slowly to the barn to fetch the cedar water bucket, a fist closing on her stomach.

In the barn hallway she dawdled with the bucket in her hand, standing just out of sight inside the hallway, peering around the corner. But no one came back out of the house, so she went down to the spring and dipped a bucketful of water for the horses and went back for the corn.

Then she walked quietly up to the house and stepped softly onto the porch. The deep murmur of Abe's voice came through the door. She tiptoed over by the front door and tilted her head to hear better. Her heart pounded in her chest.

"Mrs. Wilder, it just ain't so," Abe was saying in a pleading voice. "There ain't nobody but Effie. I been a-studying on it, but I cain't think how she got the idea I was a-sparking with another gal. It just ain't so."

"There, there," Mama said soothingly. "I'm sure there's an innocent explanation."

Rose's heart sank. She leaned against the wall and sighed heavily. She knew what she must do, but it took her a minute to draw up her courage. Then, with trembling small steps, she let herself in the door.

Mama, Papa, and Abe, sitting at the table, turned all at the same time to look at her.

"You can play outside, Rose," said Mama.

"But Mama," Rose mumbled. "It's all my fault."

"Whatever do you mean?" asked Mama. "What's happened? What's your fault?"

Rose felt her eyes begin to burn. She opened her mouth to confess, but the words wouldn't come out and she started to cry. And the crying made her feel worse. She was too old to cry.

"Land sakes, Rose. Speak up," Mama said, standing up. "What's wrong?"

Through her sobs Rose blurted out the story

of her wicked lie. "It's all . . . my . . . fault. I told Alva . . . that Abe was sparking . . . with another girl. I . . . made it . . . up. I . . . I was afraid. I didn't . . . want Abe . . . to be married . . . and go away. I'm . . . I'm sorry."

And then she cried hard; deep, bone-rattling sobs. She couldn't catch her breath and nothing could stop the tears and the shaking. Rose had never felt so miserable and ashamed.

All the grown-ups sat still as statues, staring in astonishment. Then Mama shook her head slowly. "Oh, Rose," she sighed. "How could you be so mean?"

Suddenly a laugh jerked from Abe's throat. He threw his head back and laughed uproariously. That startled Rose out of her sobs, and she stood there all wet from crying and shaking, wondering what was so funny.

"Well, ain't that something?" he said, a big smile in his eyes. He got up, came to Rose, and gave her a big hug. Then he squatted down on his heels to look her in the eye, and took Rose's hands in one of his big rough palms. He took out a clean white handkerchief and brushed the tears from her cheeks.

"I'm sorry," Rose blurted out again, a fresh wave of misery heaving up in her chest.

"Now, now, little girl," Abe said in a comforting voice. "Don't you trouble yourself. You just made me the happiest fella alive. Here I'm a-thinking I lost me the prettiest gal in these here mountains. Ain't no harm done, so don't you be a-fretting so. It's all fixed up and forgot about now."

Rose looked at Abe gratefully, and she could see in the kindness of his eyes, and the glow of his face, that he really meant it.

He stood and tucked his handkerchief back in his pocket. "Ma'am, if you and Mr. Wilder will excuse me, I reckon I'll be a-heading back over by the Stubbins place and make things square with Effie. Ain't no harm done. Just a little misunderstanding is all."

Rose felt a small wave of relief flow through her body. The fist gripping her stomach began to let go a little.

"And you, little girl," he said to Rose. "Don't be a-worrying yourself about old

Abe a-flying off. Your folks have been kin same as my own. I aim to stay right put, and I'll nary be a-setting foot outside these hills, not 'til I'm a-laid to my final rest. All right, now?"

"Yes, Abe," Rose said in a tiny, stuffy voice.

Then Abe took his hat from the table and said his good-byes, and Papa went with him to help with the team.

Rose stood there, staring at her shoes in the silence, snuffling up her last tears, waiting for Mama to scold her.

"Come here." Mama said it so gently Rose looked up in surprise. Mama's eyes looked at her tenderly. "Come here and sit on my lap."

Mama put her arms around Rose and rocked her a little.

"It's a terrible thing, lying like that," she said gently, brushing a stray hair from Rose's face. "I see you know it and have been punishing yourself enough. You see now that a lie does the most harm to the one who tells it."

"Yes, Mama."

"There is an old story your grandma Ingalls

242

told me about lying. Once, a long, long time ago, there was a woman who confessed to her preacher that she had told a mischievous lie on her neighbor. The preacher told her that, for her punishment, she must pick a ripe thistle head and scatter its seeds on the wind. Then she was to come back and see him again."

"Why?" Rose asked.

"Well, she was just as surprised as you, and wondered why. But she did as she was told. She went into a field, picked a thistle and broke it open, scattering the fluffy seeds on the wind. There were hundreds of them, and the seeds floated far and wide.

"She thought to herself, 'That was simple.' But her punishment was just beginning. Because when she went back to tell the preacher she had done as he asked, the preacher told her, 'Now the thistledown is scattered the same as your lie. Go and gather up the thistledown.'"

"You never could do that," Rose said quietly.

"That's right," said Mama. "A lie can travel around the world before the truth can lace up its boots. Now, do you know what you must do?"

"What?" Rose said, a feeling of dread rising in her chest.

"You must gather your thistledown. You must write a letter to Effie and tell her you are sorry and ask her forgiveness. It's the right thing to do, and the Stubbinses have been good neighbors. We don't want anything to poison our friendship with them."

Rose's heart sank. She would have been happier to just forget about the lie. But she saw that she could not.

Mama went into the bedroom and fetched from the trunk her writing desk, the clever hinged box that Papa had made for her, with the beautiful green felt writing surface. She opened it, lifted the inside lid, and fished out a piece of paper and one of her pencils.

"You may use my desk," said Mama. Rose looked at her in surprise. She hardly ever let Rose use the desk, and right away Rose's mood began to brighten, like the first light of rain-washed sun peeking through fleeing storm clouds.

Rose felt better knowing she didn't have to carry her secret around inside her, and that she didn't have to apologize to Effie to her face. Rose just knew she'd cry if she had to do that, and she hated anyone except Mama to see her crying.

Rose took a long time writing that letter. It wasn't very long, but she wanted it to say exactly the right thing, and she was careful to make each letter perfectly, just as she'd been taught. When she was done, she showed it to Mama.

"'Dear Effie,'" Mama read aloud. "'I am very sorry that I told a lie about Abe. It wasn't true that I saw him driving with another girl. It was a foolish thing to do and I apologize to you for it. I hope you can forgive me. Yours truly, Rose Wilder.'

"That's my good girl," Mama said, smiling. "We'll give it to Papa to drop off next time he's going that way. I'm sure everything will go back to normal after this.

"Now, what do you say we go for a little walk in the woods? It's a pleasant day, and maybe we can find some watercress to munch on."

Rose's New Room

Everything did go back to normal. At breakfast the next morning, Abe was his cheerful self and Rose knew that everything was all right with Effie. He never said another word about Rose's lie.

That day the morning breeze blew fresh and damp with the first scent of spring. The peeper frogs in the marshy place by Fry Creek began to sing. And the house began to rise.

First Papa and Abe laid the heavy wooden joists on top of the good foundation Mama had built. Then up went the skeleton made of boards Papa called studs. Then they nailed on the rafters for the roof.

Next they nailed down the wooden floor-boards that Papa had polished smooth so no splinters could hurt their bare feet. In no time at all the walls went up, first the inside walls, then tarpaper, then another wall on the out-side. The tarpaper would keep the house dry and keep out the bitter winter winds.

In the holes they left for the windows, Papa put in brand-new bought windows on shiny brass hinges.

Rose and Swiney stood on a ladder and handed the shingles up to Papa and Abe so they could nail them in place to make the roof. The woods rang with happy, busy sounds of banging hammers and clattering planks.

Then the bedroom was done, shining golden, fresh and clean in the sun.

"Now what?" Rose wondered as she stood in the new room looking out the window at the old house.

Papa and Abe began snaking more logs up from the timber lot. They laid them out in parallel rows, alongside the kitchen, spaced equally apart.

"What's that for, Papa?"

"You'll see," he teased.

The next morning Rose woke early to the clattering of a pot lid near her ear. Mama was putting the spider-legged pan in the fireplace to heat the beans and ham for breakfast. Rose stumbled out of bed and walked sleepily into the kitchen, where she always dressed by the warm stove. But this morning no heat came from it.

"We won't use it today," Mama called out. "It's moving day. Hurry and dress, now."

As soon as the dishes had been washed and put away in their box, Swiney helped Rose and Mama move the table and chairs into the log part of the house, where they had been sleeping ever since they moved to Missouri. The kitchen was made of boards, like the new bedroom.

Then they took the pots and pans, the dish box, the washstand that Papa had made, the sacks of flour and cornmeal; every single thing in the kitchen had to be moved out and piled up in the other room. Papa and Abe even took down the stovepipe and hauled the stove outside into the barnyard. It was too big to fit in the log room.

Then, when the kitchen was completely bare, Papa and Abe climbed up on the roof with long iron bars and began prying the rafters away from where they had been nailed to the log house. After that, they pried the walls away. Next they knocked stones out of the foundation. Before long they had taken out almost all of the stones except the ones at the corners. The house still stood up off the ground.

Rose and Swiney carried the stones over to the new house, and Mama told them exactly where to set them so every stone would be in its right place to rebuild the foundation.

One by one, Papa and Abe hauled the logs and slid them under the kitchen, parallel to the way they had been sitting on the ground. The logs stuck out a little way on each side. The final thing they did was knock the last of the foundation out from under, and the whole kitchen settled onto the row of logs.

Then they did the most extraordinary thing. They hitched the mules to the kitchen porch with heavy ropes and pulled the entire kitchen away from the log house. The kitchen rolled on top of the logs as if it were on wheels!

The mules dragged the kitchen all the way to the new house. Each time a log rolled out from under the back of the kitchen, Papa and Abe stopped and dragged it around to the porch. Always there had to be logs under the whole kitchen or it would fall to the ground and wouldn't move.

Rose kept running this way and that to see how it was going. Looking in the open end, the one that had been up against the log house, it was something to imagine, the place where they had eaten all those meals, shared laughter and tears and holidays, where Rose had studied her lessons, where just a few days ago she had confessed the worst thing she'd ever done—a whole roomful of life creeping away from its old home to a new one, like a giant clumsy turtle picking its way across a field.

The little log house sat forlorn and lonely

and shabby to look at, just the way it had greeted them when they first moved in all that time ago.

"While Papa and Abe are moving the kitchen, we can start moving things from the log house," Mama said. Rose carried armfuls of bedding, her straw-tick mattress, the hanging clothes—bit by bit until all the bedroom things had been moved into the new house. By the time they took down the big bed and moved the rails and the headboard and footboard, Papa and Abe had finished moving the kitchen into place, up against the new bedroom.

"Now it's starting to look like a real house," Mama said, brushing dust from her hands.

After dinner Papa and Abe took the logs out from under the kitchen, jacked the kitchen up high, and rebuilt the foundation underneath. They let it down onto the foundation and nailed the roof and walls to the new bedroom. They put the stove and stovepipe in place, and then that part of the house was done.

That night they all ate dinner together in

the new house, as a celebration. Then Abe and Swiney took the mule Roy to ride wearily home in the dark. Papa gave Abe his extra lantern to light the way.

They slept in the brand-new bedroom for the first time. Nothing was put away properly, and Mama had to look a long time to find the bedclothes. Then they climbed into bed and fell into a deep, weary sleep.

The next morning Rose woke up confused. Nothing was in its right place. The new fireplace was on the opposite wall from the old fireplace, and the room was brighter, all new wood instead of the old dark logs. And there were two windows now, one more than in the log house.

Right after breakfast Papa and Abe tore the shingles off the kitchen roof and took down the rafters. Rose and Mama did the house chores with sunlight pouring down into the kitchen through the bare branches of the towering oak tree. A curious chickadee came and sat on the open wall to peer in.

That afternoon Papa and Abe laid joists

across the ceiling and nailed boards over them. The kitchen would have a real ceiling!

Then they raised the walls higher, put back the rafters, and finally nailed the roof on. The kitchen had grown to two stories, and there was a window in the second floor, under the peak, overlooking the porch.

They all stood outside and admired the new house.

"Rome wasn't built in a day, but this is as close as we'll get," Papa said proudly, wiping his face with his kerchief. "A coat of whitewash and it's as good as any house we've ever lived in."

"But Papa," Rose asked. "You said I would have my own room. Where is it?"

"Up there," Papa said, pointing to the second-story window.

Rose chortled, "I can't climb in there every night."

"You can when I've put the stairs in."

And that was the last thing he did. Inside the kitchen, next to the door into the bedroom parlor, he built a narrow little stairway

up to a hole in the ceiling.

When it was done, Rose raced up the stairs to look. A patch of light from the window lay on the floor. From the window she could see the barnyard, and the barn, and beyond it the new meadows near the orchard. The roof sloped down on both sides from the peak. Rose couldn't walk all the way around the edge of that room because the roof came down too low, but it was very cozy. And it was all hers. She couldn't wait to sleep in it.

Now their life could really begin in the new house. Mama and Rose carried her trundle bed upstairs and Rose made it up neatly, being careful to tuck in all the corners of her quilt. The little bed looked so small in that big empty room. Papa said he would make a new bed for Rose, and a little night table, after the first plowing.

After they had put all the furniture in place, they swept up all the sawdust and leaves and bits of wood. Mama rehung the curtains in the kitchen, and the new curtains she had sewed up out of an old sheet for the bedroom windows, and for Rose's room. On the mantel of the new fireplace in the bedroom Mama set the clock. The last thing, next to it she placed the glass bread plate that read "GIVE US THIS DAY OUR DAILY BREAD."

"There," Mama said, smoothing her apron and sighing with satisfaction. "I never feel moved in until the bread plate is in its rightful place. It reminds me of your grandma Ingalls's china shepherdess. It was always the last thing she set out when we moved into a new house. That's when we knew we were really home."

After supper, while Rose dried the dishes and Papa sat reading in the bedroom, Mama paced around the house, a thoughtful look on her face. She moved the table and chairs in the kitchen. She slid the rag rugs to new places, then stood back and looked at them, her chin in her hand. Then she moved them back. She fluffed the curtains on the windows. She changed the order of the pots hanging from their nails by the stove.

"What is it, Bess?" Papa finally asked. "You're as restless as a cat tonight."

"I can't think what it is," Mama said, standing in the middle of the room with her hands on her hips. "The house is just beautiful, but it seems bare and empty. Something's lacking."

Papa got up from his chair and came into the kitchen. He looked around, stroking an end of his mustache. "It could use a few shelves and a flour cabinet in here," he said. "I'll get to it in time. But I'd say it just needs a little living. Give it time."

"Yes," said Mama, chuckling. "It's true. I hadn't thought of it. All the place needs is a few memories, for us to live in it and furnish it with everyday thoughts of friendship and cheerfulness and hospitality. Well, it's time we turned in anyway. Rose, run upstairs now and change into your bedclothes."

Rose realized with a start that she might never change in the kitchen again. When she climbed the stairs with the kitchen lamp, she felt as if she were going away somewhere to a different house.

In the wavering lamplight she pulled off her

dress, slipped it on its hanger, and hung it carefully on the rope Mama had strung between two rafters. Next to it hung her school dress, her pinafore, and her extra union suit. She set her shoes underneath, with the toes perfectly lined up.

When she had wriggled into her gown, she came back downstairs to say good night. Mama and Papa were all changed, and Rose gave each of them a kiss. Mama said, as she always did, "Sleep tight and don't let the bedbugs bite." Then Rose just stood there.

"What is it?" Mama asked.

Rose looked at her feet a moment, and then said softly, "Could you come and tuck me in?"

Mama smiled. "Of course. You get into bed. I'll be there in a moment."

Rose snuggled down in her covers in the dark room. She heard Mama's bare feet padding on the little staircase, and then she was beside Rose, patting the covers in place and tucking the corners in snug.

"Do you like your new room?" asked Mama.

"Yes, very much," Rose said, and she meant it. "But I never slept alone before. Could Fido sleep with me tonight?"

"You'll get used to it in time," Mama said. "Fido needs to be out in the barn, to protect the livestock. Papa and I are right downstairs. Now get some sleep."

Mama kissed Rose again, and then Rose was alone. She was anything but sleepy. She lay wide awake in the new room, watching the moonbeams playing upon the windowsill and listening to the wind whispering in the oak tree outside the window. *My* window, Rose thought.

Little creaking and cracking sounds of the new wood startled her. The murmuring of Mama's and Papa's voices drifted up the stairway. She strained to catch what they were saying, but all she could hear were Papa's short deep rumble, and Mama's long light answer. Then it was very quiet and still.

Across the hills the bellowing and howling of a lone hound broke the hushed silence. The music of the hound died away for a little while, and her eyes grew heavy and languid as she listened to the trickling and splashing of the spring below the house. Then more hounds joined, their voices varied in tones like the church bells in town.

Milk and Honey

The March winds dried the fields and roads and finally Papa could hitch up the mules to plow the meadows, around the orchard trees, and the garden. Rose and Mama had already planted the peas, and soon the potatoes would go in. School was out again for planting time. Rose put her shoes away, to wear them only to church.

Already there was a feeling of hope in the air. Suddenly, one morning, the sullen meadows were tinged with green. A faint haze of color came on the leafless trees.

A scraggling bush in the corner of the

barnyard burst into a blaze of purple redbud blossoms. Papa came from the woodlot one morning, bringing Mama the first violets and a bouquet of sweet-smelling phlox.

Now the doors and windows of the new house were thrown wide open all day long. The horses, mules, and Spookendyke went out to pasture.

They had eaten up nearly all of last year's harvest, the sweet potatoes, pumpkins, onions, cabbage, all gone. The last of the carrots had long ago turned woody, and they had fed them to the animals. The few apples still in the ground tasted mealy and flat, not even good for cooking.

The corncrib was nearly empty. They had eaten all the hams, ribs, and chops from butchering. Only white meat remained, soaking in a barrel of brine in the smokehouse. But soon there would be fresh greens to eat.

And then, one day, when Rose was hunting for a nest that one of the chickens had hidden, Papa came driving into the barnyard from a trip to the Stubbinses'. He had a broad smile on his face and waved his hat to Rose.

"Mama! Come look," Rose cried out.

Tethered to the end gate of the wagon was a cow! She was beautiful, the color of creamed coffee with a dark breast and belly. Tagging behind her, bawling piteously, was a fawn-colored calf with dark, soft eyes. Rose squealed with delight. When she scratched its forehead, the calf butted Rose's hand and tried to suck her fingers.

Pride beamed in Papa's face, and Mama was all smiles. Finally they would have their own milk, and cream and butter to trade at Reynolds'. That cow brought such a rich feeling to Rocky Ridge.

Papa put them out to pasture right away. Then he tore up the floorboards in the old log house to make a stable for them.

Rose helped bring straw down from the hayloft to make a soft bed for the calf to lie in. Then Papa led them inside. The calf sniffed the walls and pranced playfully around the room. It was funny to see a cow and calf living where people used to sleep.

"I'd say this is the only cow in the country

that has a fireplace in her stall," Papa joked.

"What are their names?" Rose wanted to know.

"I don't know," said Papa. "Why don't you and Mama think on it?"

Mama said she liked the name Bunting for the cow. Rose picked Spark for the calf, because it was just a spark of a thing, stiff-legged and curious.

"Best milk in the world comes from a Jersey," Papa said as he hammered a railing on the milking stall, a look of satisfaction in his eyes. "If she doesn't give pretty near her weight in milk in a month I miss my guess."

Then Papa recited a ditty he remembered from when he was a boy growing up on Grandpa Wilder's farm in New York State.

> "She's a thing of beauty and a source of wealth,
> She's a sure guarantee of riches and health,
> To the one who lives by the sweat of his brow,
> God's greatest gift is the Jersey cow."

"Yessir, a darn good cow!" Papa said, slapping her flank. Bunting turned her large eyes upon them and licked her nose as if to say thank you.

That night at chore time, Papa taught Rose how to milk. Mama came from the house to watch. He brought a small block of wood for her to sit on and set the pail between her legs.

"Now you must lean your head against her flank, always on the left side, so she can't get her foot up and kick your head. Jerseys are feisty and unpredictable."

It took Rose a few tries to get it right. Bunting did kick and knocked over the bucket, and once knocked Rose off her seat. At first she couldn't even get a squirt. Bunting's swishing tail slapped her in the face, and Rose had to mind her feet that the cow didn't step on them.

She grabbed hold of Bunting's teats and squeezed and pulled, but her hands were not very strong, and she was afraid of hurting the cow's bag.

"Put some muscle to it," Mama said. "A

cow likes to be milked." She showed Rose how to massage the bag to get the milk to come down.

Finally the milk came out, a thin stream of pearly liquid steaming in the cool evening air. The stream sang in the bottom of the pail, foaming up, creamy and sweet-smelling. On the other side, Papa held Spark while he sucked his dinner from one of Bunting's other teats. Blackfoot curled around Rose's leg and licked at the milk that had spilled on her feet, tickling her unbearably.

When Rose had squeezed out all the milk she could, and Spark had drunk his fill, Papa stripped the last of the milk that Rose couldn't get. Then Mama took the bucket, covered it with cloth, and set it in the spring to cool, so the cream would float to the top.

"Now that we have the cow, we'll have a treat for Sunday supper," said Mama. "French toast with molasses."

Rose clapped her hands in delight. Their own milk, anytime they wanted it! It was almost too good to be true.

Then, one night at supper that next week, Papa had another surprise.

"Kinnebrew is quitting his place, putting it out for sale," he said quietly. Mama's fork stopped in midair. Papa didn't look up from chasing the last beans with a piece of corn bread.

Papa finished his supper in silence, as though he had been discussing nothing more than the weather, or complimenting Mama's cooking. But Rose knew better. Papa was always calm when he had something exciting to tell.

"Well," Mama finally said, setting down her fork. "Kinnebrew is selling out, is he?"

"Yep," said Papa. "His wife pushed him to it. Never did fancy these hills much. Said she couldn't bear another summer of heat and pests. Going back to Illinois." Then he looked at Mama and wiped away the last crumbs from his mustache.

"It's a fine chance for us to pick up a few more acres, Bess," he said, his voice turning earnest. "We couldn't handle all sixty acres.

But Kinnebrew is offering us a twenty-acre piece that shares a border with our land. Got enough in pasture to feed the horses, mules, and the donkey. We wouldn't need to buy so much hay this spring. It's got two good fields for corn and oats, too."

"I don't know," Mama said fretfully. "It's a long step for us. How much?"

"Five dollars an acre, half what we paid for Rocky Ridge. He'll take it on a mortgage. Best part is, Abe's cabin is on the land, and Abe could stay and farm it on shares. He and Effie . . . well, if they do hitch up, it be a smart place for them to settle. I figure the extra acreage ought to pay for itself in four years or so."

Rose smothered a joyful little cry. Abe and Effie, living right on their own land!

Mama sat back and folded her arms, her forehead knitted in thought. "I don't know," she said slowly. "If only it wasn't so soon after paying for the cow, and it being spring and having to run up our account at Reynolds' for seed and supplies. And crop prices so beaten down. It's a terrible chance."

Papa pushed away his plate and filled his pipe from his leather tobacco pouch. "Kinnebrew won't get more for it from anyone else," he said. "Opportunity never nibbles twice at the same hook. And a farmer always takes chances. All he can do is plant and water the seed. It's up to Providence to give any increase."

He lit a match and touched it to the tobacco. Then he blew out a big cloud of smoke. "We can make it, Bess," he said. "You'll see. By guess or by golly, we'll make it."

That night, as Rose drifted off to sleep, Mama and Papa sat on the porch, below her window, talking in low, sober voices. Rose didn't know what to think about Mr. Kinnebrew's land. But if buying it meant Abe would stay and help, she hoped Mama and Papa would do it.

In the morning Mama said it was all settled. They would buy the land. She whistled while she cooked breakfast, and outside the birds sang their spring songs. Rose couldn't help skipping as she did her chores. The future never seemed so bright.

Gentle rains in April softened the earth. The garden plants pushed up their tender green shoots. Then the hickory trees on the hill put out young green leaves, the oak trees unfurled their tender pink sprouts, and all the flinty ground beneath it lay a blue-purple mat of dog's-tooth violets.

Along Fry Creek the sarvice trees bloomed misty white. In the morning Rose looked out her window as she dressed and watched the young squirrels whisking in and out of their nests in the hollow branches of the old oak.

The apple orchard burst into bloom, a soft cloud of cottony white drowsing in the bright sunshine and gentle breezes. Only here and there was a tree without blossoms that the winter ice storm had hurt. All the rest had survived and seemed to be rejoicing in their new life. The small branches reached out with delicate new shoots as if the entire orchard stood on tiptoe, stretching with all its might to reach the sky.

One day, after they had whitewashed the new house until it gleamed, Papa said it was as good a time as any to whitewash the apple trees. They each carried a pail of the soupy mixture and carefully painted the trunk of each tree with a hunk of rag dipped in the whitewash. They painted from the ground up as high as the first branch. The whitewash would protect the bark from the burning heat of the hot summer sun.

The orchard hummed with the work of hundreds of bees. The sound of all those bees singing was almost a roaring in Rose's ears, and she stopped from time to time to watch a single bee butting in this blossom, then flying quickly to that one, and another, scrambling hurriedly over the petals until it pushed its nose into the center. Finally, its furry legs dusty yellow with pollen, it buzzed away. The bees went about their business at a frantic pace. You never saw one just resting on a log. Rose thought no creature on the earth worked so hard as a bee.

They took a rest at midmorning and sat in a

circle in the middle of the orchard, taking turns drinking from a jug of switchell Mama had made up. Switchell was spring water flavored with vinegar and molasses, and it was very refreshing to drink after hard work on a warm day.

The whitewash spattered them all, especially Swiney, who had it in his hair and all down his front and over his feet. But it was fun painting the trees, and it made the orchard rows as pretty as painted fences.

Rose watched a bee sniffing around the rim of the jug. It walked around, and flew off.

"Where do the bees go?" she asked.

"They live in a hive somewhere," said Mama. "But I've never seen one."

"These bees here, they ought to be a-hiving up not so far off," Abe said, craning his neck to scan the sky for a moment. "I reckon they's hived up yonder, on the far side of that ridge. Bees are the most curious thing you ever fooled with. They got more sense than people reckon. They got special bees in the hive that only carries water. They got bees that makes the honey. They got another bunch that guards the hive and the queen. And they got bees that stands in the hive just a-flapping their wings to put a breeze on and cool the honey of a hot day."

Rose wanted more than anything to see a bee hive. She remembered last summer when she and Alva tried to course some bees carrying water, but they never could find the nest.

"Well, little girl, they mostly lives in trees, in a hollow place," Abe said. Rose always liked it when Abe called her little girl. It was a nickname he had made up for her. "I was a-thinking, now's the time to get us a mess of honey, and maybe catch you a swarm you could put up in a bee gum here in the orchard."

"That would be swell," Papa said eagerly. "I was reading that some orchard men think a hive in an orchard makes a better crop."

"And it would be wonderful to have honey," Mama said, putting the stopper rag back in the jug. "It's been such a long time since we've seen any, and what's left of the molasses has started to turn."

"Let's course 'em, Abe!" Swiney shouted out. "Abe's the grandest bee courser you ever seen."

"The best you ever *saw*," Mama corrected.

"That's right," said Swiney, excitedly.

"Tell you what," Abe said, getting to his feet and picking up his whitewash pail to go back to work. "You'uns come with me tomorrow, and I'll find that nest or I ain't no proper hillman."

The Bee Tree

The next morning after breakfast, they all went out to finish whitewashing the apple trunks and see if Abe really could course the nest. Rose and Swiney skipped ahead, to study the bees and see if they could tell which direction they were flying.

In the middle of the orchard, Abe squatted down and pulled out a little wooden box. Everyone crowded around to look. All the sides of that box were wood except one, which was a little piece of glass that slid in and out on grooves.

"This here's my bee box," Abe explained. "My pa gave it to me afore he passed on. He's the one learned me to course and rob a bee tree."

In that box was a dribble of molasses. Abe slid the glass window out of its groove and set the box on the ground.

"Now we'll work for a spell and wait for them bees to come find the 'lasses."

Rose and Swiney wanted to wait and see if any bees came, so Mama said they could. They squatted down by the box and watched and watched.

Swiney got out his pocketknife and tested it on the little hairs of his arm, to see if it was sharp.

"I guess Abe's a-going to marry Effie," Swiney said quietly. "He's a-saying there ain't . . . er . . . isn't any other girl for him."

"Yes," said Rose, rubbing a bite on her foot. "And you and Abe are going to stay and live on the land my papa's buying from Mr. Kinnebrew. I'm glad you're staying."

"Really?" Swiney said, looking at Rose with raised eyebrows.

"Of course," Rose said. "You and Abe are just like family now. It wouldn't be right for you to live anyplace else."

"I wouldn't want it neither," said Swiney. "I like it here. I like it a lot. Except I miss my kin sometimes." A mournful look came over his face and he looked away.

That surprised Rose. It was the first time Swiney had ever talked about his family. He was a tough little boy. No one could ever see him sob.

"But your mama, she's real good. I mean, she's kinder strict. But she's nice," Swiney said. He rested his chin on his knee and stared at the bee box. "And your papa, he's real smart, and he treats me near like a growed man. And . . . and you too, Rose," he added shyly. "For a girl, you ain't so bad."

Rose felt a glow coming in her chest. It was hard to believe that Swiney was the same shabby boy Papa caught stealing Mama's eggs. His ears still stuck out too far, and his table manners were still a boy's. But now Mama kept his hair cut neatly, she made sure he had a bath every Saturday, and she even sewed up new overalls when he needed them.

Swiney was learning to speak better, too. And sometimes, when they read poetry or stories together, Rose saw a little fire of imagination in his eyes. Swiney was like a wild animal that they had all tamed. It was a wonderful thing to see the good coming out in a person.

Now they watched the bee box in silence. A crow cawed three times from the woods, and an answering crow flew past overhead.

Finally a bee buzzed and wobbled around and around the box and then landed on the edge. Rose and Swiney sat up alert at the same moment. The bee walked around the box once and then climbed down to taste the sweet molasses.

"Here's one!" Rose sang out. Just then two more bees arrived and began to eat. They wriggled their bottoms happily.

Abe ran over, with Mama and Papa behind him. He fished a little fold of cloth out of the pocket of his spattered overalls. He quickly opened it. It held a small bit of flour. He took a pinch of that flour and dusted the bees. The bees were so greedy to eat the molasses, they didn't even notice that their backs had turned white with flour.

"Why?" Rose wondered.

"These here are my coursin' bees," Abe said. "They's a-going to tell us where the honey is."

Rose giggled. How could a bee tell a person anything?

In a moment the bees had eaten their fill. The first one climbed up on the rim of the box and took off. It was so heavy with molasses, it had to fly around and around in circles, higher and higher, until finally it was so high above the orchard that it had become just a speck against the blue sky.

Then that bee took off in a beeline, toward the ridge behind the orchard.

Rose ran after it, but Abe called her back. "Not yet, little girl. Just you wait a spell 'til he comes back."

Soon other bees came to the box. Abe said

the flour-dusted bees had told them about the molasses and they'd come to get some, too. Rose was simply amazed. She never knew bees were so smart.

Abe told Rose and Swiney to keep watch on the box and tell him when the floured bees came back. Then he went back to whitewashing. In a few minutes more, one of the bees in the box was a floured one. Then, a moment later, the second and third floured bees lighted in the box.

Now Abe quick slid the glass lid into its groove. The bees were trapped.

"Let's take us for a walk," Abe said. They all left their whitewash pails covered with the rags, and walked through the orchard toward the ridge. Abe kept looking in the box. He showed it to Rose. The bees were too busy eating to notice they were going for a walk, too.

When they got to the top of the ridge, Abe set the box on the ground and pulled out the glass lid. The bees were eager to leave. They had eaten their fill and wanted to take it home. They flew right out of the box. But they flew about a little confused at first, before they found the beeline and flew off.

Everyone shielded their eyes from the sun and followed the flight of those bees as long as they could. The bees swooped down the hill.

"Looks like they's a-headed for that grove of trees in the hollow," said Abe.

Now they waited some more. Soon the floured bees were back, with even more bees. Again Abe slid the glass lid on and they all walked down the hill until they stood at the edge of the tree clump. Abe opened the box and the eager bees flew around and around and up. This time they flew a little off to the left, behind a pine tree, not so high.

" 'Less I miss my guess, them bees is a-holed up right over there." They all plunged into the thicket of trees, looking up and up. They fanned out so every tree could be seen, from every side.

Suddenly Rose spied a blur high up on the trunk of a big dead chestnut. It took her eyes a moment to understand, and then she heard the high frenzied whining—*mmmmmmmmmm*—of many wings beating.

"I found it!" she cried out. "There's a whole bunch of bees going in and out of a hole! Up there!"

Everyone came crashing through the under-growth and looked up where Rose proudly pointed.

"Right as rain," Papa said. "Looks like a big one, too. Good eyes, Rose."

"How are we going to get the honey down from way up there?" Rose asked.

"Cut the tree down and rob the hive," said Abe. "But not now. We'll do it tonight, when the bees are all a-sleepin'. It's hard robbin' bees when they're a-working. Ain't it, Swiney?"

Swiney blushed and looked away with a lit-tle crook in his mouth.

Abe laughed. "He got all stung up once, a-trying to rob a hive by hisself. He looked like an old pincushion."

Rose knew it was true. Once a bee was fly-ing a beeline and stung her on the arm just from running into her by mistake. A bee that was being robbed would be twice as mad.

"But Abe," Papa said, looking around. "This tree isn't on our land. If I'm right, this grove is on Stubbins' land. That makes it his tree."

"Yessir," said Abe. "It's his tree by all that's right, and we ain't a-going to help ourselves to a thing what ain't our'n. This here honey belongs to the folks what finds it. Mr. Stubbins, he'll be a mite sorrowful he ain't coursed it hisself. But he knows that's law in these hills. What man finds the hive, it's rightfully his'n. Don't matter whose land the bees are a-living on.

"I seen a bad fight once over some fellow jumping a bee tree coursed by his neighbor. Honey gets a high price this time of year, when it's clean and yellow. This hive looks real good. I'd say maybe twenty gallons. Now Swiney boy, hand over your knife." Abe put out his hand.

"I know how to do it," Swiney said. He went to the tree and slashed at the trunk until the knife had made a big X showing bright through the dead bark.

"Now, that there X is the mark of the fellow that coursed the hive," Abe explained. "It tells anybody that the hive is spoke for. Any man who'd steal out the hive of another'd be no more than a common thief."

"By jiminy," Papa chuckled, taking off his hat and mopping his neck with his kerchief. "That's one up on me. But I reckon you could say those bees robbed the nectar from our apple blossoms. We ought to get something for it."

All the rest of that day while she whitewashed the last of the apple trees and while she did her chores, all Rose could think about was that bee tree and how clever Abe was to find it. She wondered who could ever have thought up such a way to make the bees tell them where they hid their honey.

She thought about how wonderful it would be to have honey on her pancakes and over her corn bread. Honey tasted even better than sugar, and Mama hardly ever got white sugar from Reynolds'. That was long sweetening, and long sweetening was too much to pay for. Molasses was short sweetening. You could get it on shares, as Rose's family had, or buy it for less money. But it left a dark taste in your mouth, and it took more of it to sweeten a pie well. Short sweetening was short on taste. Long sweetening went a long way.

That night, after supper and chores, when the sky showed only the last light of day, Abe set off with Papa, Swiney, and Rose. Mama stayed to watch the house and catch up on her mending.

"You children be careful," Mama said from the porch, hugging herself against the night chill. "Don't get mixed up with those bees, and stay out of the way."

In the wagon box with Rose and Swiney were Mama's good washtub, two axes, the big crosscut saw, three lanterns, and a section of a hollowed-out log with some boards nailed on each end. There was a little notched hole in the side of it, at the bottom. That hollow log was the bee gum.

The grove of trees was very dark and

spooky in the wavering light of the lanterns. Rose held one and Swiney held the other, on each side of the tree. The chips flew fast and furious, and in no time Papa and Abe had cut through the tree and it came down with a roaring crash. The horses snorted in surprise. The rotted trunk had burst open.

"A good fall," Abe said, peering in. "The hive came right side up."

Rose edged closer to look. Something was moving in there. She held the lantern closer. At first it looked like trickling water glistening in the light. But then she saw it was a river of bees, all crowded together, milling confusedly around the hive! The sight of all those bees sent a shiver up her spine. She hated to be stung.

Abe quick put his hand in the opening.

"Be careful!" Rose cried out.

"Don't you fret, little girl," Abe said. "Them bees is too sleepy and cold to bother with me."

He pulled out a small chunk of comb, dripping with syrupy honey. He licked his fingers and held the comb out so everyone could put their finger in and take a lick. Some bees walked on Abe's hand, but they didn't sting and he just brushed them off. The honey was delicious, with a delicate flowery taste in it.

Abe moved quickly now. Papa brought the hollow log and the tub. Abe set the hollow piece so it sat up like a table, with the notched hole at the bottom, right next to the hive. He pried the top off and set it aside. Then he showed Papa how to pick out the combs with the honey and put them in the tin wash-tub.

"You kids bring them lanterns up real close," Abe said. "I'm a-lookin' for the queen. She's fat and she's got real small wings."

"Is that it?" asked Papa.

Abe reached in and plucked out one very big bee, bigger than any bee Rose had ever seen. That was the queen. He put the queen in the hollow log, put in some of the combs, and pounded the lid back on with the side of the axe.

Right away the river of bees started to flow

out of the shattered log across the ground and into their new home where the queen was. How did the bees know? Abe took a stick and dipped it into the hive, picking up bunches of bees, hanging on like grapes, and brushed them off in front of the hole. Right away they began to wriggle their way inside.

Then Abe and Papa robbed the rest of the honey. Summer was just coming, and the bees would have time to make more honey, enough for the bees to eat all next winter.

They set the filled tub and the bee gum in the wagon and drove slowly through the dark woods into the orchard. They lowered the hive gently down, right in the middle of it. Then they drove to the house. Papa and Abe lugged the heavy tub into the warm, cozy kitchen and set it down. The tub brimmed with honey-soaked combs. The yellow syrup shone like melted gold.

"Oh, my!" Mama gasped when she saw it. "I've never seen so much honey at any one time."

All the next morning Rose helped Mama

squeeze all the honey out of the combs and strain it through a cloth to get out the drowned bees and bits of tree bark and wood. They put the combs in the empty molasses barrels that Mama had scalded clean and poured the honey back over them. When it was all done, they had robbed almost thirty gallons from that hive.

Papa insisted that Abe take half.

"By rights you folks ought to have the most of it," Abe protested. "It just a-being me and Swiney, and there a-being three of you'uns."

"Won't hear of it," said Papa. "There wouldn't be a drop of honey if you hadn't found the hive. Besides, you can sell some of it. You'll need a little cash money for when you're married."

And so it was settled. They were rich in honey, and Rose could have it on her bread almost anytime she wanted.

For a long time after, every chance Rose could, she sneaked away from her chores to walk to the orchard to look at the bee gum.

The Bee Tree

The bees had moved right in. On hot days the gum buzzed with the singing of thousands of tiny wings. She could sit for hours just staring at the little door, watching the bees come and go, wondering at the magic that was going on inside.

Sprout-Cutting Time

Now the days turned sultry hot, the air lay on the hills as heavy and damp as wet hay. The sun rose early and beat down on the earth with all its might. Howling thunderstorms blew up in the afternoons, thrashing the trees and crops, sending everyone rushing about catching livestock, closing windows, and slamming doors.

One day a funnel poked down out of the churning dark clouds. Rose watched it from the garden where she was hoeing the potatoes. She stood in frozen terror as its evil tongue flicked like a snake's at the trembling earth.

But then the clouds sucked it back up and the skies cleared and the sun came back out to beat down on the valley.

They were busy all day, every day, with planting, plowing, hoeing, taking care of the livestock, milking, and, worst of all, cutting sprouts. All the stumps left in the new ground of the meadows and around all the apple trees had sent crowns of sturdy new shoots as high as Rose's chest. The hardy, stubborn stumps were trying to make new trees. Now each and every sprout had to be chopped or knocked off. Otherwise the tree would grow back.

One day Papa came back from an errand in town with two bright new hatchets with red handles. He gave one to Rose and one to Swiney.

"This is yours to keep, son," Papa told him. "Mind you care for it, and don't be nicking the blade up on the rocks."

"Golly, ain't . . . isn't that something!" Swiney cried out with pleasure. "I'm a-going to carve my name in it, right now." When he showed it to Rose, she didn't have the heart to tell him he had left out the *e*.

Then Papa gave Rose a stern lesson on how to chop safely.

"I like my prairie Rose with all her fingers and toes on," he said. Swiney already knew. He had cut sprouts before, for Mr. Kinnebrew. Now it was Rose and Swiney's job to cut all those sprouts, everywhere on the farm, even on the new land they'd bought from Mr. Kinnebrew.

That was a lot of sprouts.

It was stifling hot and prickly working in the sun. Each stump had a ring of new shoots around the edge. Rose had to bend each one down and give it a good whack to break it off.

Her arm ached, and the chiggers bit up her legs. The chiggers were too small to see, but you always knew when they had bit you. They left deep itching welts that got so raw from scratching that Mama had to dab them with coal oil at night.

Sometimes Rose's leg would brush against a clump of seed ticks clinging to a weed leaf.

Then dozens of the tiny ticks would quick spread out, walking all over her body. She had to go back to the house and take off her dress so Mama could help find them all and pick them off. Rose hated having those bugs all over her.

She came close to rattlesnakes sunning themselves on stump tops, giving her a horrible start with the shattering buzz of their warning rattles. Then she called Papa or Abe to shoot them.

After long days working until dark, Rose fell into bed too tired and achy sometimes even to change out of her dress. And her cozy room with the sloped ceiling had become an oven on the hot days. All the heat of the house went up the stairs and waited for her to come to bed. Then her prickly skin and the itchy chigger bites and the racket of the night songs of insects and tree frogs made her sleep restless and filled with unpleasant dreams.

But everywhere the farm showed the fruits of their labors. The corn came up strong and green. Papa plowed it a second time when it was waist high, and then that work could be laid by until harvest time.

The first cutting of hay was safe and dry in the hayloft, and the second crop had sprouted thick and green in the meadows. The furry heads of the oats rustled in the wind and dipped in waves like a little ocean surrounding the apple trees. The garden had been hoed clean and fluffy as a comforter between the rows.

Then it was almost the Fourth of July.

"We've earned a day of entertainment," Papa said wearily. "I say this year we do it up in brown rags."

"I'll pack a nice picnic," agreed Mama. "We could all use a diversion."

Rose woke that morning to a distant boom echoing in the hills. At first she thought it was thunder. But then she remembered, it was Independence Day! The people in town were firing off an anvil, putting gunpowder under it and lighting it like a cannon, like the cannons that declared America free more than a hundred years before. In towns all across America people were celebrating their freedom by firing anvils.

Then she heard all the church bells in town ringing. Like the song said, Rose thought, let freedom ring! She bounded out of bed.

When Rose was dressed and came down to breakfast, Mama was packing up the last of the fried chicken and corn bread in a basket. Rose quick did her chores, and they ate a small, cold breakfast with Abe and Swiney.

Abe was all dressed up in his good suit, but this time Mama made sure his tie was straight and starched collar wings tucked in. Abe blushed crimson as Mama fussed over him until she was satisfied. Then they all admired how handsome he looked. Swiney had on a fresh pair of overalls and a clean blue shirt. He scowled a little as Mama combed his hair neatly with a dab of Papa's bay rum.

Then Papa put on his good suit and gray felt hat. Rose and Mama wriggled into their dresses, Mama in a beautiful white lawn that would be cool on a hot day, and Rose in her best calico. They tied on their good bonnets and Rose began to walk out the door.

"Where are you going?" Mama asked. "You forgot your shoes."

"Oh, Mama, please. Must I?" Rose pleaded.

"You certainly must. No daughter of mine is going into town in her bare feet. And you, too, Swiney," Mama called out to him on the porch.

Rose exchanged a grumbling look with Swiney as she sat on the porch to put on her stockings and pull on the heavy black shoes that Mama had greased and shined the night before. How she hated wearing shoes in summer. Her feet swelled from going bare, and the shoes pinched terribly.

Then they all walked to town, leaving Fido to mind the farm. The horses and mules would stay to pasture that day. There was no sense tying the horses up to a dusty hitching post just to stand in the hot sun.

The fresh morning smiled down on the farm and the valley, with Fry Creek a sparkling ribbon running through it. A startled heron flapped off as they walked across the log Papa had felled across the creek. He had nailed a simple railing on the trunk, for something to hold.

The sun shimmered on the open road with just a few puffy clouds in the sky. Rose and Swiney raced each other ahead of the grown-ups, feeling clumsy in their heavy brogans. Even before they reached the hill leading down into town, they were damp from the heat and running and excitement. But Rose didn't care. She couldn't wait to see the Fourth of July picnic.

Then they started down into town. Right away, far down the street, they could see the hubub of activity. Many wagons and buggies, and even a surrey or two with trembling fringe, were arriving from every direction. The people in those wagons and buggies were all dressed in their best clothes. Everyone looked just grand.

Red, white, and blue bunting hung across the street from the telegraph wires. Every house had an American flag hanging from the porch or on a pole by the front door. Some had many small ones planted in the yards. The sound of all those people murmuring and horses whickering and firecrackers crackling grew until finally they came to the square.

The whole town was changed by the picnic. Rose couldn't stop looking at everything. From every lamppost, from the bandstand, from the building fronts and even the trees hung more bunting and more flags. From Reynolds' Store hung a big sign, painted on a sheet, that said, WELCOME TO THE UNION. UTAH, 45TH STATE. JULY 4, 1896. Another sign hung from the Boston Racket Store building. It said, FREE SILVER! SQUASH THE GOLD-BUGS!

Rose wanted to ask what a goldbug was, but she was too busy looking. All around the square were stands, little houses with canvas walls and ceilings, and counters along the front. They were hung with more bunting, and the air was full of the smell of cooking smoke and roasting meats and sweets.

Somewhere in that great crowd someone was playing a lively fiddle. A group of older men proudly stepped past. Several leaned on canes. One had a long white mane of hair and a great white mustache. They were all dressed in uniforms of soldiers. Some were tattered, but most were clean and had polished brass buttons. Some wore blue and some wore gray. One had a long sword hanging from his belt. They were the veterans of the Great War Between the States, celebrating the peace between North and South.

Rose nearly jumped out of her skin when some boys exploded a string of firecrackers behind the livery stable. All the horses snorted and pulled at their reins. One of the teams nearly upset its wagon.

All that noise and all those people and horses and smells made Rose giddy with excitement.

"Looks like the whole country turned out," said Papa.

"We'd better find us a good spot before they are all taken," Mama said.

"Think I'll take me a turn round the square," said Abe. "See if Effie's come yet."

Papa, Mama, Swiney, and Rose made their way past stall after stall, looking for a place to walk between them to the lawn in the middle of the town square.

"Ice-cold lemonade, made in the shade, stirred with a spade," an old man with a big bumpy nose called out. He stood over a tin washtub full of floating lemon rinds and pink lemonade. A big chunk of ice floated in the middle. Rose had never seen ice in the summer. Her mouth watered just looking at it.

"Right this way. Three throws for a nickel," a young boy in a soldier's cap cried in a hoarse voice, his bumpy Adam's apple bobbing. Behind him was a great rack of beautiful dolls, all dressed in brightly colored clothing. "Step up, fellows, knock 'em down and win a pretty doll for your best gal."

On a table behind him there were three grinning wooden cats, one balanced on top of the other. The boy juggled some balls in his hand. Then he threw one at the wooden cats, knocking off just the top one.

Finally they made their way into the square,

onto the lawn near the bandstand. Mama pulled an old sheet and an old comforter out from the picnic basket. Then she picked a place under a tree where they could sit in the shade. She and Rose spread them neatly next to each other on the soft grass. Then they started unpacking the picnic.

"I'm a-going to look around," Swiney said, his face flush and his eyes gleaming.

"All right," said Papa. "You can both take a look around. But first"—and then he dug into his pants pockets and pulled out some coins— "it wouldn't be right to go to a Fourth of July picnic without a little pocket change. Here's two nickels. And here's two for you, Rose. Now you kids stay out of mischief. And keep clear of that saloon on the corner by the depot. That's a rough crowd of men in there."

"Golly, thanks, Mr. Wilder!" Swiney shouted. He slipped them in his pocket and gave the pocket a little jingle. Then he was gone in a flash, disappearing into the crowd. But Rose just stood there, staring in awe at the two shiny nickels in her palm. Ten cents! It was so much money, as much as Mama got for a whole dozen eggs, five times as much as Rose found in her Christmas stocking. She was so stunned, she forgot to thank Papa.

Rose felt helpless. She looked at Mama. "What should I do with them?"

"Whatever you like," Mama said.

Rose knew right away. She wanted a drink of lemonade. But she decided she would wait until she was good and thirsty. She gave one of her nickels to Mama to keep until she was ready.

Fourth of July

The whole square swarmed like a flight of bees looking for a place to land, and Rose was right in the middle of it all. Everywhere she looked she saw people of every size and shape—tall, lean men and short, squatty ones, tall and short women with children of all ages hanging on to them, babies crying in their arms.

Some of the girls were fluffed up like little birds in delicate white dresses with puffed sleeves, and beautiful hats. Those were town girls. And the girls in patched calico dresses,

305

plain bonnets and bare feet, they were farm children like Rose. Rose thought she could be content to spend the whole Fourth of July just watching the people.

The rough, hurried voices of the hawkers crying their games mingled with the hum of the crowd.

"Over here! Say, little girl! Over here!" Rose noticed one of the hawkers was shouting at her. He was a tall, lanky man wearing a red-and-white striped vest over a red silk shirt, and a red hat. Even his face was flushed and blotchy red. He was smiling broadly at her. She didn't move at first. But then he called out again, waving her over with his hat, "Come on over, don't be shy! Come on, then."

Rose walked slowly over to the stall. The man's hand rested on the edge of a great wheel, painted in bright colors, with numbers written all around the edge. All behind the red man hung prizes of every type: toy whips with green handles, cut-glass vases, dolls, feather dusters, pocketknives, little statues of dogs made out of plaster of Paris. There were more wonderful things in that stall than Rose had ever seen before.

"What's your name, little girl?" he asked, leaning over the counter and grinning at her with teeth that were stained brown.

"Rose," she said shyly. She didn't like that man, but she must be polite to strangers.

"Well, Rose. I'll bet your papa just gave you a couple nickels to rub together, now didn't he?"

"How did you know?" Rose asked in astonishment.

"I have a knack for knowing such things," he said, crossing his arms. "For example, I happen to know that the number twelve is bound to come up pretty soon. Folks have been spinning and spinning this old wheel, and the number twelve hasn't come up in a long time. Bound to, just about anytime now. Probably the next spin it'll be twelve. Now I'm telling you this as a favor, you understand. Just between you and me. I see you're a good little girl, and you deserve a little break."

"I do?"

"Sure you do!" he said heartily. Then he leaned over and said, "And if you put your nickel on old number twelve, and I spin this wheel and this little piece of leather up here lands on twelve, which is sure as shootin' just about to come up, why you could pick out any of these fine items of the highest quality that you see behind me. You'd like to win a nice flower vase for your mama, now wouldn't you?"

"Yes," said Rose, and she meant it with all her heart. It would be a wonderful thing to surprise Mama with a beautiful vase for the flowers Papa brought her from the fields each day.

Rose chewed her thumb in thought. "I don't know," she said. "I only have one nickel. I saved the other for lemonade."

"Only takes a spin to win, and you can't win until you spin," he said, rubbing his hands together. "You could spend that nickel on a bag of popcorn and that'd be gone in the wink of an eye. But a glass vase. Now, that's something to last a lifetime."

Suddenly Rose wanted that vase more than anything in the world. She wanted to make

Mama happy, and to see the look of surprise on her face when Rose brought it to her. And number twelve was just about to come up. The man had said so.

"All right," Rose said. She put the nickel on the counter. Then she noticed there were the same numbers painted on the counter as on the wheel, all in a row.

"That's a smart girl," the red man said. "Now you're thinking." He quickly slid the shining nickel over until it rested on top of the number twelve. "Number twelve!" he cried out. "Lucky number twelve. Anybody else?" he called out, hawking to the crowd. "One last chance. You there, young fellow. Your girl wants you to win her a little present. What you say? No? All right," and then he spun the wheel.

"Round and round and round she goes," the hawker cried out to the crowd. "Where she stops, nobody knows." Some curious people walking by stopped to watch.

The painted numbers became a blur of colors, and the wheel made a furious clicking noise. Then the wheel began to slow and slow and slow and the clicks came slower too. Rose had one eye on her nickel and the other on the wheel. She could hardly breathe, knowing she was going to win that vase. In a moment it would be hers.

Just then a hand reached out and palmed Rose's nickel right off the counter.

"Say, what's the idea!" the hawker shouted.

Rose whirled angrily to see who it was.

"She isn't playing," Blanche said tartly, then to Rose with a smile, "Hello, Rose."

"That's my nickel!" Rose spluttered. "I was going to win a vase for my mama. How could you!"

Blanche handed the nickel to Rose. "You weren't going to win a thing," she said loudly, and glared at the hawker. The wheel had almost stopped. "This game's fixed. You can't win anything from that wheel."

"Now just a minute, you," the hawker snarled at Blanche. Rose was stupefied. What was going on?

"See," said Blanche, "your number didn't

come up. It's twenty-three."

It was true. Rose breathed a quivery sigh of relief. She almost wasted a whole nickel, for nothing.

"Say, I ought to get the sheriff on you," the red man said, his face getting redder. "That's same as stealing."

"Go ahead," Blanche said defiantly. "He won't do a thing. He plays cards with my father."

The red man snorted and turned away.

"How did you know?" Rose wondered.

Blanche's face went smug. "My papa told me. He knows all these games are fixed. You have to spend more nickels to win a prize than the prizes cost in a store."

Rose looked at her saved nickel and just stared at Blanche in amazement and gratitude.

"If you kids aren't playing, get away from my stall," the red man growled at them. He turned with a look of disgust on his face and shouted to the hawker in the next stall, "No good bunch of kids. Never spend a penny, just stand around gaping."

"Don't pay him any mind," Blanche said. She slipped an arm through Rose's and walked her around the square, waving to people she knew and chattering away as if such a thing happened every day.

"Now, you must get your lemonade early," Blanche was saying. "Later the ice melts and it gets warm. Then they add water and it's hardly even lemonade anymore. Say, let's get some now. I had one drink already, but this heat makes me thirsty."

"I'm saving my other nickel to have lemonade later," Rose said. "I only have two." But Blanche was already flouncing off toward the lemonade stall, pulling Rose along by the hand.

"I'll treat," she said. "Look, my papa gave me a whole dollar of nickels." She poured a whole fistful of nickels out of a little blue velvet purse she carried on a strap around her wrist. The purse matched her dress, and she had a big blue bow in her curly black hair.

Rose had never seen so many nickels before. She wasn't sure if it was all right to

let Blanche pay for lemonade. Mama always said never to be beholden to anyone.

"Don't be foolish, Rose," Blanche told her. "I'd just waste them on myself. It's fun to treat."

So they each got a dipperful of the delicious lemonade. It was icy and sweet and tart, and Rose's mouth felt all refreshed. Rose thanked Blanche politely. Then they walked all around the square, looking at everything.

There was a merry-go-round with wooden horses on a spinning wooden platform that was pulled by a mule. A man stood in the middle, turning round and round, playing the fiddle. Blanche treated Rose for a ride, and they shrieked with delight at the wind blowing in their hair and the blur of faces whipping past them.

Rose had to stand still for a moment after, to get her balance.

"See that ball toss there, the one with the cats?" Blanche said. "That's crooked, too. He's got lead in the bottom of the cats. My brother told me. You couldn't knock them over with a baseball bat."

They shared a bag of buttery-fresh popcorn, and then a bag of peanuts. Best of all was the candy stand where a man threw ropes of taffy over hooks and pulled the candy, over and over again until it reached just the right brittleness to break into small piece.

Blanche bought a sack of taffy, still warm and fragrant with vanilla. The pieces melted in their mouths.

They went by a stall where George and Paul Cooley were serving up lemonade and dough-nuts. A big sign on the top said, MANSFIELD HOTEL, MOST REASONABLE ROOMS IN THE COUNTY.

"Howdy, Rose," Paul called out as he dipped up a dipperful of lemonade for a cus-tomer. Paul gave them each a free drink.

"I'd give you a doughnut," he said. "But my papa counted 'em and I got to have the money or the doughnuts." So Rose spent her first nickel to treat Blanche to a fried doughnut with snowy sugar sprinkled on top. Blanche broke it in half and gave half to Rose. It was delicious and she took small bites to make her portion last. Blanche ate hers in three big bites.

Finally Blanche said she had to go and help her mother. "The parade's starting soon, and after that it's dinnertime. I'll look for you after," she cried out as she dashed away.

Rose was in heaven.

She flew back to the picnic spot under the tree.

"Well, how did you spend your nickel?" Mama asked as she laid out the plates.

"Oh, Mama, I had a wonderful time. I had lemonade and popcorn and peanuts and taffy, and I rode on the merry-go-round."

Mama's eyebrows flew up. "All for one nickel?"

Rose told Mama about Blanche saving her nickel and then treating her to everything.

"That was very nice of Blanche, and it was the right thing to do, sharing your nickel in return," Mama said. "But I don't approve of such extravagance. Throwing money away as though it grew on trees."

Rose knew Mama was right, but she had had such a wonderful time with Blanche. Today she didn't care about right or wrong.

Suddenly they heard the sounds of drums beating and horns playing. They all went to the street to see better. The parade was coming! All the people crowded up to the hitching posts. Fathers held babies high on their shoulders. Rose wriggled her way through the crowd of legs and skirts until she found a good spot at the railing.

First came the sheriff, riding a gleaming black horse that tossed its head nervously and sidestepped. Then came the band, so many people dressed in high hats and shiny buckles and playing "Yankee Doodle" with all their might. The music echoed against all the buildings around the square. A whole row of drummers came by, and a whole row of cornet players, and even a man playing a great golden tuba with a deep, deep voice.

Then came a crowd of little girls, all dressed in long skirts of red-and-white bunting with white blouses and scarves of blue. Draped across each shoulder was a piece of red-and-white bunting. Each one had the name of a different state on it. Rose counted forty-five in all, one for each state of the Union.

Then came the fire department's team of white horses pulling the water wagon, and the firemen dressed up in uniforms with round hats. After that came a float, a platform built on a wagon, draped in more red, white, and blue bunting. On top of the float was a tall green statue of a lady with a crown, carrying a book and holding a torch high over her head.

"What is that?" Rose asked Mama.

"It's the Statue of Liberty," said Mama. "It was given to America by the people of France to put in the harbor in New York. She lights the way for the new Americans."

"Is that the real statue?" Rose marveled.

"No," Mama laughed. "It's just a model, made out of papier-mâché. The real one is very tall and made of metal. You couldn't move it."

Finally the parade had ended and they ate their picnic lunch. Rose was so excited, and she'd eaten so much before with Blanche, she hardly had an appetite. So she gave her chicken leg to Swiney. He had lost both his nickels on the pitching game.

All around them other families ate their dinner, too. Children chased each other between the picnic blankets, and families visited with one another.

Abe came by with Effie for a little visit, and brought a delicious iced watermelon they all shared. Rose was bashful at first. She had not seen Effie since she had lied about Abe. But Effie's face was radiant as she hung on Abe's arm, and she was very pleasant to everyone, even Rose.

The past was all forgotten, and Rose could see that Effie loved Abe and he loved her back. Now the idea of them marrying gave Rose a secret thrill. They would live on Papa's farm, and Rose's family would get bigger and happier. And maybe there would even be little babies to spoil!

Just when all the families had begun to put away their dishes, the band assembled in front of the bandstand and began to play "The Star

Spangled Banner."

Every man, woman, and child stood and a hush fell over the square, except for a squalling baby and a last rattling plate. They stood like a sober forest of people at attention, their hands over their hearts. The stall hawkers all around the square stopped crying their games. The merry-go-round fiddler put away his fiddle.

There was a small pause after the last note, and then the band struck up a lively beat to the tune of "Dixie." The crowd went wild, shouting and applauding.

"Look away, look away, look away, Dixie Land," everyone sang the chorus together. But Mama and Papa did not sing. They stood closed-mouthed. All of Rose's grandparents had been Unionists in the Great War of the Rebellion. "Dixie" was a song of the rebels who wanted to split the Union.

Finally the band finished the last chorus, and a man stood up on the platform and began to recite the Declaration of Independence. But before the man could get to the list of the sins of the king of England that made Americans declare their freedom, a high, shrieking train whistle filled the square. The man stopped reading and looked up in surprise. All the heads of all the people craned to see, wondering what was going on.

And then a great black steaming locomotive slid into the depot, covered with bunting and two large American flags flying from its nose. Two beautiful shiny-new passenger cars came into view, also hung with bunting, and the train screeched to a halt. At the back of the last one was a little platform. Some old men, soldiers in uniform, waved to the crowd. Everyone forgot the Declaration and surged toward the depot.

Swiney dashed off to look. Rose got up to follow. "Stay here," Mama said sternly. "You'll get yourself trampled in that crowd."

"It's McKinley's people," one man cried out. "The nerve of them goldbugs. Breakin' up our celebration."

The band struck up "Dixie" again, and people applauded wildly.

"Send 'em on!" another man shouted. "Tell 'em this is free silver country. Send the yellow dogs on!"

Papa chuckled. "What is it?" Rose demanded impatiently. "What's going on?"

"Those men on the train are campaigning for William McKinley to be elected the next president, in the fall," he explained. "I reckon they're going to all the towns along the railroad, trying to drum up support for their candidate."

"But why are the people yelling at them?"

"It's hard to explain," Papa said. "People say McKinley is for the rich and the privileged. Folks around here are mostly poor. They don't like McKinley."

Rose could hardly see from where she stood, but heard a great commotion around the back of the train, and then she gasped. People were throwing something at the old soldiers, who were ducking and shaking their fists. Watermelon rinds!

A moment later, the locomotive blew its shrill whistle and the train began to chuff out of the depot, slowly at first, then faster until finally it disappeared behind the corner of the square. A great cry rose up from the crowd and the people began to drift back.

"Terrible," said Mama. "I've never seen such a rude display, and on the very day we celebrate our freedoms. One can disagree and still be polite about it."

But Papa only laughed. "They sure gave those McKinley boys a run for their money. It's politics, Bess. A man sticks his chin out, he has to know somebody's going to take a poke at it. Folks are just wound up with all the fun, is all."

After the man finished reading the Declaration, there was a baseball game on the other side of the railroad tracks, and on the main street two men had a slow-mule race. It was one of the funniest things Rose had ever seen. The men bet five dollars on who had the slowest mule. The mules danced and stepped sideways and backed up. Neither one could get even close to the finish line. Finally the men gave up, laughing so hard they fell down when they got off their mules.

The sun began to dip toward the west, and one by one the families gathered up their picnic baskets and folded up their comforters and blankets and sheets.

Rose helped Mama clean up. Papa went and found Swiney. When they got back, Swiney's nose was bloody, and his shirt sleeve was torn.

"Had to pull the little feist out of a fight," Papa said.

"I was a-licking that boy some good," Swiney grumbled. "He called me a name. I was a-licking him good if you hadn't of stopped me."

Mama clucked in disapproval. Now she would have to mend his shirt. But Papa just chuckled and tousled Swiney's hair. "That boy's friends were getting set to jump you," he said. "Then they would have cooked your goose. You ought to thank me for coming along when I did. Quit when you're ahead, I always say. Those boys'll remember how tough you were."

Swiney let a little grin creep onto his lips. "By golly, I guess so," he said, his face lighting up with pleasure.

Then they all walked home, dusty, their hands sticky from food, hot and sweaty. Swiney and Rose fell in together behind Mama and Papa, each picking a wheel track in the road to walk on.

"That was a swell time. Best I ever saw," he said.

"Yes," said Rose, and she really felt it. "It was the best time I ever saw, too. I wish every day could be like the Fourth of July."

"Just you wait 'til next year," Swiney said. "I'll be bigger then and nobody's a-going to get away with a-calling me a country jake."

Then Rose remembered her other nickel. She'd never spent it!

"You can put it with your pennies," Mama said, fishing it out of her bag and handing it to Rose. "It's yours to do with as you please."

The Wedding

July and August drifted by, like a leaf slowly floating down the summer-shrunk pools of Fry Creek. Rose went back to school for a time, but then in August, Mama kept her home to help with the second cutting of hay, the oat harvest, and all the endless other work that needed doing on the growing farm.

Abe and Effie came by one Sunday in a rented buggy, all smiles and shining faces, to tell Mama and Papa they were really going to be married. The wedding would be at the

Stubbinses' house, and everyone was invited. After that, all the days leaned toward the wedding day.

Abe and Papa worked in the evenings in the barn, hammering, sawing, sanding, and building furniture for Abe and Effie. Then Papa spent two days at Abe and Swiney's little log house, fixing the windows and the doors and putting on a new, tight roof to keep out the rain and wind.

One day Rose and Mama went there and cleaned the whole house, top to bottom, scrubbing the floors with sand and painting the walls of the little kitchen with whitewash.

"It's a modest little house," said Mama, wiping a bit of whitewash from her cheek. "But a sight better than some of the homestead shacks I grew up in on the prairie. They'll be nice and snug here."

It was terribly exciting for Rose to be helping Abe and Effie start their new life. Now Swiney would have a proper home, and someone to cook a good meal when he was hungry.

Rose realized with a little squeeze of sadness in her chest that soon Abe and Swiney wouldn't be coming to breakfast anymore. But they lived just a short ride away, and Abe would still come to work, with Swiney, too. And they would continue their lessons together.

When the little house was all fixed up, Rose and Mama got out their needles and thread and sat late into the evenings by the lamp finishing up a wedding quilt. Then they began baking pies, lemon and apple, and one of Mama's wonderful gingerbread cakes.

Finally it was the day of the wedding. Abe came by in the morning so Mama could give him a haircut. He sat on the porch, a sheet draped around his neck, while Mama combed and snipped and combed and snipped. A butterfly landed on Abe's shoulder for a moment, then flew off into the woods.

"You nervous, son?" Papa asked him from the steps, putting a foot on the porch and leaning on his knee. "It's the big day. You can still change your mind."

"Oh, Manly!" Mama scolded, but she saw he was joking and smiled.

"No sir," Abe said, scratching his neck where a bit of hair had fallen. "I ain't looked back once. I just know we're a-going to get along like a couple of hogs in a mud puddle.

"The thing I ain't reckoned yet is how I'm ever a-going to thank you back for all you done for me and Swiney. I cain't think where we'd of ended up iffen it wasn't for your kindness."

"Don't you even mention it," said Papa.

"'He who sows kindness harvests joy,'" Mama recited the old saying.

When Abe was all spruced up, he and Swiney went back to their house to get ready.

Rose and Mama and Papa all took their baths, dressed up in their Sunday best, and drove off through the cool afternoon to the Stubbinses'. Their yard was already littered with buggies and wagons and teams, parked at every angle like jackstraws. People, mostly strangers, friends of the Stubbinses and of Abe, milled around outside the house.

Alva came out of the crowd to greet Rose. It was the first time Rose had ever seen Alva dressed up. She had on a beautiful yellowsprigged red dress and had a red hair ribbon in her red hair. She even had on a pair of shiny new shoes.

"You look very nice," Rose said.

Alva's face broke into a wide grin, showing the gap where she had lost a tooth. Rose had made up with Alva about her lie one day that summer when the two families went fishing together. Now everything seemed right in the world.

A minister Rose had never seen before came out of the dogtrot between the houses and called everyone together in the yard. A bell made of folded paper hung from the second floor, with white bunting draped on either side. The men got together and brought home-made benches from the side of the house and set them up in rows, as in church. Then everyone sat down politely.

Rose went to sit with Mama and Papa in the back, but Abe stopped them.

"I saved a place of honor for you'uns," he said. Then he took Mama's arm and guided her to a bench in the front. Then they all sat down.

The Wedding

When everyone was settled, Effie came out of the house. Everyone smiled and murmured, and she smiled and giggled shyly. She was wearing a light green taffeta dress, with three ruffles all around the bottom, and mutton sleeves, and a wide satin collar with lace trim. Her face glowed orangey-pink in the golden light just before sunset.

"Isn't she lovely?" Mama whispered. She was, and she and Abe made a handsome pair together as he slipped an arm through Effie's and walked her up to stand in front of the minister to give their vows. A cool evening breeze rippled Effie's skirt.

There was a quietness on the hills, as if the whole valley had hushed itself to hear the wedding vows. Gold and purple and scarlet faded slowly from the sky. Bats fluttered soundlessly high in the air, darting to catch bugs. The clouds turned gray and silver, and the great spaces between them were clear as spring water.

The minister opened his mouth to speak. But Mr. Stubbins's geese in the stock pond began honking loudly. Everyone laughed nervously. Finally the geese stopped honking, and the minister began.

"We are gathered here today . . ."

And it was all over in a few moments. Effie said, "I do." Then Abe said it back to her, they kissed, and everyone applauded loudly.

Rose was disappointed. This was her first wedding, and it was all over in a flash.

"All right, friends and kin!" Mr. Stubbins hollered above the hubub of people crowding around Abe and Effie and giving their congratulations. "Let the eatin' and the frolickin' begin. Ever'body step over to the barn."

The crowd broke up slowly and drifted in little knots over to Mr. Stubbins's threshing barn.

"Come on, Rose!" Alva said, grabbing her hand. "We got a feast a-going in the barn. And after that, dancin'!"

The barn had been cleared out and boards laid down on the floor as in a house. Mrs. Stubbins and Alva's sisters were busy lighting lamps that hung from every corner and the rafters. Then Rose saw table after table, groaning with hams and a roasted goose and bowls full of steaming mashed potatoes and corn. And one table was piled with every kind of cake and pie. And a big tub of lemonade, made with cold spring water.

The men moved the benches inside, and everyone filled plates at the tables and sat down to eat. Everything was delicious, and Rose went back for seconds and even thirds. Abe and Effie moved around the room, talking to friends and neighbors and relations. They never could find time to eat their dinner. Effie blushed often and giggled shyly.

Then, when the last of the plates was put back on the tables, the men moved the tables out of the barn and pushed all the benches back against the walls, and everyone sat back down. There was a pause, and feet shuffled all around the room in uncertainty. Everyone looked at everyone else, waiting and watching.

Finally Mr. Stubbins walked out into the middle of the room.

"Folks, this is a mighty happy day for us all," he said, and everyone murmured and nodded their heads in agreement. "A-watchin' my little girl all growed up and hitched to a fine young fellow like Abe Baird. Why, there ain't another thing in this world I'd lift a finger to take. Now, that's enough speechifyin'. Gents, take your partners!"

And with that, a tall lanky young man in the corner stood, raised a fiddle, tucked the brown curve to its place against his neck, and began to play and sing, tapping his feet to keep the time.

"Lips a-like a cherry,
Cheeks a-like a rose,
How I love that little gal,
God a'mighty knows!

"Get along home, Cindy, Cindy,
Get along home, Cindy, Cindy,
Get along home, Cindy, Cindy,
I'll marry you sometime."

But no one was brave enough to be the first

to dance. Everyone stirred restlessly, but no one stood. Papa leaned over to Mama, "Will you do me the honor of this dance?"

Mama giggled and twisted her handkerchief in her hands. "Shush," she whispered, looking around slyly. "Not yet."

So Mr. Stubbins strode across the room and pulled Abe and Effie off their benches, shouting, "Come on, now. It's a frolic, ain't it? Show us some steps."

Now Abe wasn't shy at all. He began to swing Effie around. Rose's feet began to tap to the beat of the music, and she felt a rush of blood to her head, and a fluttering in her chest. Then other couples began to join, and soon the floor was thud-thudding with the sound of many feet beating, and the air rang with laughter.

The fiddler changed the tune, and the beat came faster.

"Circle eight, circle eight, circulate, circulate," he called out above the music. Now Papa grabbed Mama's hand and pulled her out onto the floor.

"Swing 'er by the right and swing 'er by the left and two-hand swing."

Papa's hand missed Mama's and she almost stumbled and fell. But Papa got her by the other wrist and swung her through. Mama's blue eyes flashed gaily and she even threw her head back and laughed.

"And sashay up and down the hall!

"Oh, you Buffalo gals,
Ain't you comin' out tonight,
Ain't you comin' out tonight,
Ain't you comin' out tonight?
Oh, you Buffalo gals,
Ain't you comin' out tonight,
To dance by the light of the moon?"

Rose grew lightheaded watching all those skirts swirling, and all those bodies twirling round and round, braids flying, smiling faces flashing past, eyes glowing bright, faster and faster.

"First gent break and make a figure eight!"

All around in circles the dancers whirled,

feet clomp-clomping on the floor.

"Do si, ladies, do-si-do! Come down, honey, on your heel an' toe." And the fiddle sang its heart out and Rose was clapping her hands to the music as loud as she could.

"Come on, Rose!" Alva shrieked, her face an inch from Rose's. She grabbed Rose's hands and pulled her out onto the floor. Rose began to laugh uncontrollably as she and Alva tried to imitate the grown-ups' dancing. They couldn't, but it didn't matter. Just whirling and circling and stomping was good enough. Alva grabbed Rose's hands, and they whirled each other in a great circle, faster and faster until Rose thought that if she let go she'd fly through the air.

In the blur of skirts and coattails, the rosy faces glistening with sweat, she caught glimpses of of Mama and Papa, and Mr. and Mrs. Stubbins, and Abe and Effie, and even Swiney, who was doing a funny little dance by himself in the corner.

Every face smiled, and Rose's heart filled with an unspeakable joy. She let her head fall back and closed her eyes as she whirled. She felt herself being lifted up by the trembling, soaring voice of the fiddle and the throbbing of the whole barn—up and up, into the clear autumn air and out into the perfect moon-kissed night.

8/13 LUNES NOCHE — paíg. 14 - 15 - 1 - 2 - 3 - ✓

8/14 MARTES — 2 - ✓ - 4 - 5 - 8 -

8/15 MIERCOLES — 122 ✓

8/16 JUEVAS - Pag 9 y 24 y 31

8-18 paginas 26 - 29 - 37

8/20 " 45 - 46 - 48 - 155 - 156 - 158 -

8/21 paginas 63 - 64 - 65 - 66

8/22 pag 33 - 72 - 73 - 74 - 75 - 77 - 84 - 86
1/2 paginas   1/2 pagina

y 90, 56 - 57 - 58 - 59 -

8/23 pag. 61 - 141 - 39

8/24 pag 123 - 124 - 125

8/25 pag 109 - 113 - 114 y 115

8-28 pag. 126 - 128 - 129 - 130 - 134 y 135

8/29 pag 132 - 137 - 138 - 140 - 136 ✓

8/30 pag. 99 - 100 - 101 - 102 - 103 -

8-31

GRADED EXERCISES

IN

SPANISH

BY

JULIO I. ANDÚJAR
AND
ROBERT J. DIXSON

PRENTICE HALL REGENTS, Englewood Cliffs, NJ 07632

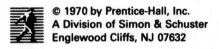 © 1970 by Prentice-Hall, Inc.
A Division of Simon & Schuster
Englewood Cliffs, NJ 07632

Printed in the United States of America

10 9 8 7 6 5 4 3 2

ISBN 0-13-361973-7 01

Prentice-Hall International (UK) Limited, *London*
Prentice-Hall of Australia Pty. Limited, *Sydney*
Prentice-Hall Canada Inc., *Toronto*
Prentice-Hall Hispanoamericana, S.A., *Mexico*
Prentice-Hall of India Private Limited, *New Delhi*
Prentice-Hall of Japan, Inc., *Tokyo*
Simon & Schuster Asia Pte. Ltd., *Singapore*
Editora Prentice-Hall do Brasil, Ltda., *Rio de Janeiro*

PREFACE

The prime intent of this book is to provide a teaching-learning source of supplementary drill material in basic Spanish, at any level of instruction.

It offers a systematic, graded presentation of basic elementary-to-advanced principles, correlated with a similar grading in vocabulary and sentence structure.

The page-by-page unit design lends itself particularly to a variety of uses, both in and out of the classroom: as a workbook, as a basis for written and homework assignments, in oral practice and in lesson planning.

It is especially recommended as a review for intermediate and advanced students of Spanish.

A complete answer book to all the exercises is available to teachers upon request.

TABLE OF CONTENTS

GENDER OF NOUNS — *The Indefinite Articles*

All nouns in Spanish are either masculine or feminine. There are no neuter nouns.
Nouns which end in *o* are generally masculine. (Examples: *libro, maestro*).
Nouns which end in *a* are generally feminine. (Examples: *mesa, hermana*).
The indefinite articles in Spanish are *un* and *una*. With masculine nouns *un* is used. (Examples: *un libro, un* maestro). With feminine nouns *una* is used. (Examples: *una* mesa, *una* hermana).

o = un , a = una

Put the correct indefinite article (*un* or *una*) before these nouns.

1. *una* casa
2. *un* niño
3. *un* perro
4. *un* hermano
5. *un* amigo
6. *un* piano
7. *una* hija
8. *un* cielo
9. *un* libro
10. *un* zapato
11. *una* corbata
12. *una* ventana
13. *una* carta
14. *un* curso
15. *una* mesa
16. *una* playa
17. *un* primo
18. *un* camino
19. *un* cigarrillo
20. *una* cartera

21. *una* pluma
22. *un* carro
23. *un* paseo
24. *una* pelota
25. *una* pizarra
26. *una* iglesia
27. *un* negocio
28. *un* regalo
29. *una* guitarra
30. *una* música
31. *una* escuela
32. *un* cuarto
33. *una* silla
34. *un* plato
35. *un* vaso
36. *un* abogado
37. *un* periódico
38. *un* ingeniero
39. *una* puerta
40. *una* manzana

1

THE DEFINITE ARTICLES, Singular Form

The definite articles, singular form, in Spanish are *el* and *la*. *El* is the definite article used before singular masculine nouns. (Examples: *el* libro, *el* cuchillo). *La* is the definite article used before singular feminine nouns (Examples: *la* mesa, *la* casa).

a = la   o = el

Fill in the blanks with the necessary definite article.

1. *la* silla
2. *el* piano
3. *el* cielo
4. *el* libro
5. *la* manzana
6. *el* negocio
7. *la* bomba
8. *el* año
9. *la* semana
10. *el* teléfono
11. *el* plato
12. *la* iglesia
13. *el* regalo
14. *el* carro
15. *la* playa
16. *el* zapato   shoe
17. *la* guitarra
18. *el* vaso
19. *el* camino
20. *la* carta

21. *el* cigarrillo
22. *la* rosa
23. *el* cuadro
24. *la* regla
25. *el* apetito
26. *el* ojo
27. *la* planta
28. *el* mosquito
29. *la* mosca
30. *el* asiento
31. *el* resultado
32. *la* pera
33. *el* capítulo
34. *la* cosa
35. *el* suelo   floor
36. *la* sala   parlor
37. *el* patio
38. *el* colegio
39. *la* milla
40. *la* lluvia

2

GENDER OF NOUNS — *Continued*

We learned earlier that nouns in Spanish ending in *o* are generally masculine; nouns ending in *a* are generally feminine. There are some nouns, however, which do not fall under either of these rules. Study the following:

1) Irrespective of ending, nouns denoting male beings are always masculine; those denoting female beings are always feminine. (Examples: *un* hombre, *una* mujer; *un* rey, *una* reina).

2) Nouns of Greek origin ending in *ma* are generally masculine. (Examples: *el* cli*ma*, *el* siste*ma*). Days of the week are also masculine. (Examples: *el* martes, *el* jueves).

3) Nouns ending in *ión* and in *d* are generally feminine. (Examples: *la* edición, *la* conversación, *la* lección, *la* ciudad, *la* bondad, *la* curiosidad).

4) There remain many nouns of common usage whose gender follows no rule. In the exercises below, these nouns are marked (m) for masculine and (f) for feminine.

A) Put the correct indefinite article (*un* or *una*) before these nouns.

B) Repeat exercise, this time putting the correct definite article (*el* or *la*) before each noun.

1. (una, la) ciudad	16. *una, la* exhibición	31. *una, la* nube *claus* (f)
2. (un, el) color (m)	17. *un, el* hospital (m)	32. *un, el* mes (m)
3. *una, la* mujer	18. *un, el* jabón (m)	33. *una, la* tarde (f)
4. *una, la* calle (f)	19. *un, el* diente *tooth* (m)	34. *un, el* guante *glove* (m)
5. *un, el* lápiz (m)	20. *una, la* flor (f)	35. *una, la* edad *age*
6. *un, el* problema	21. *un, el* árbol *tree* (m)	36. *un, el* sistema
7. *un, el* hombre	22. *un, el* automóvil	37. *un, el* martes
8. *una, la* clase (f)	23. *una, la* noche (f)	38. *un, el* traje *clothes* (m)
9. *una, la* pared	24. *un, el* tren (m)	39. *un, el* cine (m)
10. *una, la* lección	25. *un, el* sol (m)	40. *una, la* nariz *nose* (f)
11. *un, el* papel (m)	26. *un, el* pie (m)	41. *una, la* verdad *truth*
12. *un, el* reloj (m)	27. *una, la* razón (f)	42. *una, la* madre
13. *un, el* héroe (m)	28. *un, el* lente (m)	43. *una, la* vez (f) *pl-times*
14. *un, el* clima	29. *una, la* estación *season*	44. *una, la* edición
15. *una, la* curiosidad	30. *un, el* baile *dance* (m)	45. *una, la* voz *voices* (f)

3

PLURAL FORM OF NOUNS

Nouns which terminate in a vowel form their plural by adding *s*.

Singular	Plural
libro	libros
mesa	mesas
calle	calles

Nouns which terminate in a consonant form their plural by adding *es*.

Singular	Plural
papel	papeles
color	colores

Supply the plural form of the following nouns.

1.	piso	*pisos*	21.	noticia	*noticias*
2.	lámpara	*lámparas*	22.	rey	*reyes*
3.	cuaderno	*cuadernos*	23.	campo	*campos*
4.	nube	*nubes*	24.	reloj	*relojes*
5.	automóvil	*automóviles*	25.	minuto	*minutos*
6.	dolor	*dolores*	26.	papel	*papeles*
7.	señor	*señores*	27.	atención	*atenciónes*
8.	café	*cafés*	28.	pozo	*pozos*
9.	lección	*lecciónes*	29.	alemán	*alemánes*
10.	cara	*caras*	30.	revista	*revistas*
11.	asunto	*asuntos*	31.	dólar	*dólares*
12.	mujer	*mujeres*	32.	profesor	*profesoras*
13.	nación	*naciones*	33.	cuchillo	*cuchillos*
14.	hospital	*hospitales*	34.	corbata	*corbatas*
15.	gato	*gatos*	35.	nación	*naciones*
16.	hora	*horas*	36.	color	*colores*
17.	balcón	*balcónes*	37.	burro	*burros*
18.	clase	*clases*	38.	metal	*metales*
19.	violín	*violines*	39.	favor	*favores*
20.	francés	*francéses*	40.	león	*leónes*

4

THE DEFINITE ARTICLES — *Continued*

As we have already learned (page 2), the definite articles in Spanish, singular form are *el* and *la*. The plural form of *el* is *los*. *Los* is thus the definite article used before plural masculine nouns. (Examples: *los* libros, *los* maestros). The plural form of *la* is *las*. *Las* is thus the definite article used before plural feminine nouns. (Examples: *las* mesas, *las* muchachas).

	Singular	Plural
(Masculine)	el	los
(Feminine)	la	las

Provide the necessary definite article.

1. *el* ruido
2. *las* muchachas
3. *los* lápices   m
4. *la* persona
5. *la* nube
6. *la* corbata
7. *las* noches
8. *el* zapato
9. *las* lecciones
10. *el* rey
11. *las* señoras
12. *los* colores
13. *las* calles
14. *la* razón
15. *las* flores
16. *el* cielo
17. *las* horas
18. *la* prima
19. *los* dólares
20. *el* camino

21. *las* playas
22. *el* regalo
23. *los* hombres
24. *los* relojes
25. *el* plato
26. *la* cocina
27. *las* salas
28. *las* luces
29. *los* diente
30. *el* ejercicio
31. *la* hora
32. *la* tarea
33. *las* veces
34. *la* oficina
35. *las* ciudades
36. *los* padres
37. *el* jabón
38. *la* pregunta
39. *los* minutos
40. *las* mujeres

ADJECTIVES

Adjectives in Spanish generally follow the nouns which they modify. (Examples: un libro *nuevo,* una mesa *redonda*).

Most adjectives in Spanish terminate in *o,* which is the masculine form. Such adjectives change the *o* to *a* to form the feminine. In the plural, *s* is added.

(Masculine) Singular	(Feminine) Plural
rojo	rojos
roja	rojas

In Spanish, all adjectives always agree in gender and number with the nouns which they modify. Thus the four forms of the adjective listed above are used in the following manner:

el libro *rojo*	los libros *rojos*
la mesa *roja*	las mesas *rojas*

Supply the correct form of the adjectives given in parentheses.

1. una niña (bueno)................
2. tres lecciones (largo)................
3. un libro (rojo)................
4. una casa (viejo)................
5. una silla (cómodo)................
6. los ojos (negro)................
7. unas frutas (fresco)................
8. una lección (corto)................
9. los hombres (grueso)................
10. la cara (ancho)................
11. una camisa (blanco)................
12. las mujeres (alto)................
13. un hombre (viejo)................
14. unos zapatos (negro)................
15. las muchachas (bonito)............
16. una cosa (famoso)................
17. unos ejercicios (fácil)................
18. dos revistas (viejo)................
19. una puerta (abierto)................
20. unas joyas (caro)................

21. un plato (roto)................
22. unas calles (estrecho)................
23. unas manzanas (rojo)................
24. una lámpara (moderna)............
25. dos automóviles (elegante)........
26. las flores (amarillo)................
27. unos papeles (blanco)..............
28. una nariz (largo)................
29. unos asientos (incómodo) ....
30. dos corbatas (rojo)................
31. un piano (pesado)................
32. dos maletas (pesado)................
33. la mesa (redondo)................
34. dos cajas (redondo)................
35. una iglesia (nuevo)................
36. un regalo (bonito)................
37. unos cigarrillos (largo)..............
38. el ingeniero (americano)..........
39. los colegios (privado)................
40. un paseo (largo)................

In the last exercise, we learned that adjectives which terminate in *o* have four differents forms (Examples: *rojo, roja, rojos, rojas*). All other adjectives — that is, those which do not terminate in *o* — have only two forms, one form for the singular and one for the plural (Examples: un libro *grande,* dos libros *grandes;* una mesa *grande,* dos mesas *grandes*).

If the adjective terminates in a consonant (*fácil, popular, joven*), it forms its plural in the same way as nouns which terminate in a consonant, namely, by adding *es* (Examples: el ejercicio *fácil,* los ejercicios fáciles).

Change each of the following phrases to plural form.

1. El muchacho simpático.

   (Example: Los muchachos simpáticos.)
2. La lección fácil.
3. El estudiante joven.
4. El libro caro.
5. El hombre inglés.
6. La pluma dorada.
7. El pantalón gris.
8. La tarde tranquila.
9. La vacación corta.
10. El error grave.
11. La estación central.
12. El baile regional.
13. La razón principal.
14. La fruta madura.
15. El hombre rico.
16. El mes pasado.
17. El avión supersónico.
18. El jefe militar.
19. El tren expreso.
20. La nube gris.
21. El reloj suizo.
22. La mujer francesa.*
23. La comida española.
24. El día caluroso.
25. El alumno inteligente.
26. La ciudad grande.
27. El examen difícil.

---

* Adjectives of nationality ending in consonant add *a* to the masculine to form the feminine. Thus, inglés, inglesa; español, española.

The verb SER

The verb SER is conjugated in the present tense as follows:

yo   *soy* (I am)

tú*   *eres* (you are)

usted**

él, ella } *es* (you, he, she is)

nosotros   *somos* (we are)

(vosotros   *sois*) (you are)

ustedes

ellos } *son* (you, they are)

Supply the correct form of the present tense of SER.

1. El......*es*......estudiante. ***
2. Nosotros...*somos*...amigos.
3. Ellos.....*son*.....estudiantes de inglés.
4. El señor García......*es*......profesor de español.
5. Juan y tú......*son*...primos.
6. El señor López.....*es*......comerciante.
7. Tú....*eres*.....buen estudiante. (   )
8. María...*es*.........amiga de Juan.
9. El cielo.....*es*.......azul.
10. Dos y dos.....*son*.....cuatro.
11. Nosotros...*somos*...americanos.
12. La capital de Bolivia......*es*......La Paz.
13. Los hijos de los Hernández....*son*......muy estudiosos.
14. Hoy.....*es*......martes.
15. Juan.....*es*......rubio.
16. Juan y Luis.....*son*......altos.
17. Ustedes......*son*....estudiantes de español.
18. Juan......*es*......de Costa Rica.
19. Juan y Mario.....*son*......viejos amigos.
20. Usted.....*es*.........muy amable.
21. El profesor......*es*......mejicano.
22. El perro de Juan......*es*......blanco.

---

* The familiar form with *tú* (Ex. Tú eres) is generally used only with peers, or members of one's family. *Usted* is used in all other cases.

** In Spanish, *usted* (pl. *ustedes*) is a contraction of *vuestra merced* (your grace); therefore it is considered third person and, accordingly, always requires the third person form of the verb.

*** Note that the indefinite article is not used in Spanish before predicate nouns, especially those indicating nationality or profession. (Examples: El es médico. Ella es enfermera.) See later exercises, page 10.

SUBJECT PRONOUNS

In Spanish the subject pronouns are often dropped from the sentence. For example, we say "Somos amigos". Here we omit the subject pronoun *nosotros* because the form and ending of the verb clearly indicate that the subject is first person plural. Many students learning Spanish, however, find it easier at first to include all subject pronouns. There is naturally no rule against such usage. There are even cases where, for reasons of clarity, the pronouns must be included (Example: *Ella* es buena pero *él* no).

In the blanks, insert the necessary subject pronoun. In sentences where a choice is possible, include all possibilities.

1. ....*Yo*....soy amigo de Juan.
2. *Ustedes, ellos*..son soldados.
3. *Nosotros*.somos miembros del club.
4. *Ud., él*.....es jugador de béisbol.
5. *Uds., ellas*.son altos.
6. ..*Tú*....eres aplicado.
7. *Ud., él, ella*.es gentil.
8. *Nosotros*.somos amigos.
9. *Uds., ellas, ellos*.son corteses.
10. ...*Yo*....soy ciudadano americano.
11. *Nostros*...somos americanos.
12. *Uds., Ellos*.son hijos de la señora Pérez.
13. *Ud., Ella*.es profesora de francés.
14. *Ud., él, ella*.es muy amable.
15. *Nosotros*.somos viejos amigos.
16. *Uds., ellas*.son compatriotas.
17. ..*Yo*.....soy maestro de español.
18. *Nosotros*.somos estudiantes de español.
19. *Ud., él*...es rubio.
20. *Uds., ellos*.son primos.
21. *Ud., ellas*.es enfermera.
22. ..*Tú*....eres muy alto.

9

INDEFINITE ARTICLE — With Predicate Nouns

We learned previously (see footnote, page 8) that the indefinite article is not used in Spanish before a predicate noun, especially one indicating nationality or profession. (Example: El es médico. Ella es cubana.) However, if the predicate noun modified by an adjective, an indefinite article is used. (Example: El es *un* médico famoso. Ella es *una* cubana muy simpática).

Read these sentences and supply the correct indefinite article (*un* or *una*) where required.

1. El señor García es....................profesor.

2. El es....................profesor cubano.

3. María es....................colombiana.

4. El * doctor González es....................médico muy bueno.

5. La * señorita García es....................secretaria muy eficaz.

6. Tú eres....................ingeniero.

7. La señora García es....................ama de casa excelente.

8. Juan es....................estudiante de inglés.

9. El es....................muchacho fuerte.

10. Ernesto es....................abogado.

11. El es....................abogado famoso.

12. El es....................americano.

13. Roberto es....................vendedor de automóviles.

14. Usted es....................estudiante aplicado.

15. El Tiempo es....................periódico importante.

16. Tú eres....................joven.

17. Ella es....................muchacha joven.

18. Usted es....................una persona muy amable.

19. Miguel es....................comerciante.

20. El es....................comerciante astuto.

21. El señor Hernández es....................agente de seguros.

22. Elena es....................enfermera muy capaz.

---

*Notice that except in direct speech, where one speaks directly in conversation to a person, the definite article is used before all titles in Spanish.

VERBS OF THE FIRST CONJUGATION — -AR ending verbs

There are three differents conjugations in Spanish. Verbs of the first conjugation terminate in *ar*. (Examples: *hablar, explicar, estudiar.*) The conjugation of the typical first conjugation verb *hablar* in the present tense follows:

yo hablo	nosotros hablamos
tú hablas	(vosotros habláis)
usted } él, ella } habla	ustedes } ellos } hablan

The present tense in Spanish is used in the same way as the simple present tense in English, namely, to describe an action which goes on everyday or in general. (Example: El maestro siempre *habla* español en la clase. Ellos *estudian* en la misma clase).

Supply the correct form of the verbs given in parentheses.

1. Nosotros....*estudiamos*(estudiar) español.

(Example: Nosotros *estudiamos* español.)

2. La señora García....*compra*......(comprar) mucha * ropa.
3. Ustedes.....*viajan*.....(viajar) a Europa con frecuencia.
4. Ellos.......*toman*.....(tomar) mucho café.
5. Elena....*habla*.........(hablar) varios idiomas.
6. Usted...*fuma*....(fumar) demasiado.
7. Los García..*cambian*.(cambiar) de automóvil todos los años.
8. El maestro...*enseña*......(enseñar) muy bien.
9. Ellos....*tratan*......(tratar) de aprender mucho.
10. Juan y Carlos...*trabajan*...(trabajar) en la misma fábrica.
11. Yo...*tomo*....(tomar) poca agua en las comidas.
12. Ellos...*gastan*......(gastar) mucho dinero en diversiones. *[NO ES VERDAD]*
13. Tú.*descansas*.(descansar) mucho y..*trabajas*.(trabajar) poco. *[NO ES VERDAD]*
14. Ernesto...*maneja*......(manejar) un autobús.
15. Nosotros...*pasamos*...(pasar) las vacaciones en las montañas.
16. Enrique siempre..*contesta*....(contestar) bien todas las preguntas.
17. Yo....*miro*.........(mirar) televisión por las noches.
18. Tú...*tomas*......(tomar) demasiado vino.
19. El autobús....*para*.........(parar) en cada esquina.
20. Nosotros........*necesitamos*........(necesitar) mucha práctica de conversación.

---

* Note that the so-called limiting adjectives (mucho, poco, mismo, etc.) precede the nouns they modify; note also that their endings must agree in number and gender with the nouns they modify (mucho dinero, muchos días, etc.) See exercise, page 6.

For further practice with verbs of the first conjugation, change the subject of each of the sentences below, substituting in its place the six different subjects given. Make corresponding change in form of verb where necessary.

1. *El* habla español bien.

  1. Nosotros ....
     (Example: Nosotros *hablamos* español bien).
  2. Ella ....   4. Usted ....   6. Ustedes ....
  3. Yo ....   5. Juan y Enrique ......   7. Ellos ....

2. *Ellos* estudian mucho.

  1. Ustedes ....   3. Juan y usted ....   5. María y yo ....
  2. María ....   4. Yo ....   6. Tú ....

3. *Yo* viajo en avión.

  1. Ustedes ....   3. Elena y yo ....   5. Ellos ....
  2. Enrique ....   4. Nosotros ....   6. Juan y usted ....

4. *Uste*d toma agua fría.

  1. Nosotros ....   3. Usted y yo ....   5. Yo ....
  2. Ellos ....   4. Ellas ....   6. Enrique y yo ....

5. *Juan* trabaja ocho horas.

  1. Yo ....   3. María ....   5. Ellos ....
  2. Ustedes ....   4. Usted ....   6. María y yo ....

6. *Yo* gasto mucho dinero.

  1. Ellas ....   3. Tú ....   5. Usted y yo ....
  2. El ....   4. El y Alberto ....   6. Ustedes ....

7. *Nosotros* compramos ropa nueva.

  1. Usted ....   3. Eduardo ....   5. Ustedes ....
  2. Ella ....   4. María y Eduardo ....   6. Usted y yo ....

8. *Yo* descanso los domingos.

  1. Tú ....   3. Usted y yo ....   5. Ella ....
  2. Usted ....   4. Ustedes ....   6. Ellos ....

NEGATIVE FORM

Negative form in Spanish is obtained by placing *no* before the verb.

Ella *no* habla inglés bien.
No compramos muchos libros.
Carlos *no* es un muchacho fuerte.

Change the following sentences to negative form.

1. El profesor enseña inglés.

    (Example: El profesor *no* enseña inglés.)

2. Yo tomo mucha agua en las comidas.

3. Nosotros trabajamos todo el día.

4. Ustedes estudian mucho.

5. Tú gastas mucho dinero en cigarrillos.

6. La muchacha fuma demasiado.

7. Juan es amigo de Miguel.

8. Elena toca el piano muy bien.

9. Alberto compra corbatas elegantes.

10. El cuchillo nuevo corta bien.

11. Son estudiantes de medicina.

12. Nosotros tomamos mucho café.

13. Los ojos de María son negros.

14. El clima de Caracas es fresco.

15. Los Pérez pasean en carro los domingos.

16. Los estudiantes prestan atención.

17. Los asientos son cómodos.

18. Tú y yo somos amigos.

19. Nosotros usamos ropa ligera en verano.

20. Ustedes estudian mucho.

21. Juan trata de contestar bien todas las preguntas.

22. Nosotros practicamos el español con el profesor.

INTERROGATIVE FORM

Question (interrogative) form is obtained in Spanish by placing the verb before the subject. (Note that an inverted question mark always precedes any question in Spanish.)

> *¿Habla ella inglés bien?*
> *¿Es la lección de hoy fácil o difícil?*

(Note: It should be mentioned that question form is much less rigid in Spanish than in English and that it is common practice in Spanish to indicate a question, not by placing the verb before the subject, but simply by altering the intonation or the voice.)

Change these sentences to question form.

1. Usted trabaja los sábados.

   (Example: ¿Trabaja usted los sábados?)

2. El autobús para en la esquina.

3. La exhibición es interesante.

4. María y Elena son hermanas.

5. Tú llegas a las ocho.

6. Ustedes pagan demasiado.

7. El ejercicio es complicado.

8. Yo necesito más dinero.

9. Usted necesita más práctica de conversación.

10. Ellos estudian juntos.

11. Usted toma mucho té.

12. Enrique pasa por aquí todos los días.

13. Nosotros compramos en el supermercado.

14. María toca bien el violín.

15. Tú hablas alemán.

16. El es cortés con las damas.

17. El entra al trabajo a las ocho.

18. Paseamos por el parque por las tardes.

19. Juan fuma mucho.

20. Ustedes bajan las escaleras.

14

As we learned previously (See exercise, page 4) nouns which end in a vowel form their plural by adding *s*; those which end in a consonant form their plural by adding *es*. Other special group of nouns form their plural as follows:

a) Nouns which end in the letter *z* change this *z* to *c* in the plural (Examples: *lápiz, lápices; vez, veces,* etc.).

b) Nouns which end in *es* or *is,* without an accent, retain the same form in the plural as in the singular (Examples: *el lunes, los lunes; la crisis, las crisis*).

c) Nouns ending in *ión* lose their accent in the plural (Examples: *lección, lecciones; nación, naciones*).

Change the following phrases to plural form.

1. La voz femenina.

    (Example: Las voces femeninas).

2. El martes.
3. El jefe militar.
4. La lección final.
5. La edición nueva.
6. El color azul.
7. La mujer feliz.
8. El vendedor eficaz.
9. El balcón alto.
10. La dirección útil.
11. El error común.
12. La muchacha gentil.
13. El pantalón azul.
14. El compositor francés.
15. El guante gris.
16. El dolor fuerte.
17. La lección fácil.
18. El metal útil.
19. La región central.
20. La canción popular.
21. La exhibición industrial.
22. El pez dorado.
23. El dólar americano.
24. El escritor alemán.
25. El lápiz gris.
26. El hospital principal.
27. El profesor capaz.

VERBS OF THE SECOND CONJUGATION — -ER ending verbs

Verbs of the second conjugation terminate in *er* (*vender, comer, aprender*). The endings of verbs of the second conjugation, present tense, follow:

yo	vend*o*	nosotros	vend*emos*
tú	vend*es*	(vosotros	vend*éis*)
usted } él, ella }	vend*e*	ustedes } ellos }	vend*en*

Note that endings of verbs of the second conjugation correspond with those of the first conjugation (See exercise, page 11) except that wherever *a* occurs in the endings of first conjugation verbs, *e* is substituted in second conjugation verbs.

In the blanks at the right, supply the correct form of the verbs given in parentheses.

1. Yo (leer) el periódico todos los días.

   (Example: Yo leo el periódico todos los días).

2. El....*vende*........(vender) relojes finos.

3. Ustedes...*corren*......(correr) muy rápido.

4. Nosotros...*bebemos*...(beber) agua mineral.

5. Tú...*aprendes*..(aprender) idiomas con facilidad.

6. Ellos...*deben*........(deber) miles de dólares al banco.

7. ¿Qué...*cree*.....(creer) usted del asunto?

8. Nosotros...*aprendemos*..(aprender) algo nuevo en cada clase.

9. Alberto no...*come*..........(comer) mucho.

10. María...*rompe*..........(romper) muchos platos.

11. Los estudiantes no...*comprenden*..(comprender) la regla.

12. Yo....*como*.......(comer) mucha carne.

13. Los niños...*corren*.......(correr) mucho.

14. Tú....*crees*......(creer) que Juan no fuma.

15. ¿Ustedes....*leen*..........(leer) el periódico?

16. El señor Pérez....*vende*.......(vender) automóviles.

17. Nosotros..*bebemos*...(beber) agua antes de la clase.

18. Yo....*leo*............(leer) un poco todas las noches.

19. Ellos..*responden*..(responder) bien a todas las preguntas.

20. Tú....*vendes*......(vender) automóviles usados.

16

VERBS OF THE THIRD CONJUGATION — -IR ending verbs

Verbs of the third conjugation terminate in *ir* (*vivir, subir, escribir*). The endings of verbs of the third conjugation, present tense, follow:

yo vivo	nosotros vivimos
tú vives	(vosotros vivís)
usted } vive	ustedes } viven
él, ella }	ellos }

(Note that endings of verbs of the third conjugation are exactly the same as those of verbs of the second conjugation (see previous exercise, page 16) with this one exception: In the first person plural, verbs of the third conjugation end in -*imos* while verbs of the second conjugation end -*emos*).

In the blanks at the right, supply the correct form of the verbs given in parentheses.

1. Elena......*vive*......(vivir) en un apartamento.

(Example: Elena *vive* en un apartamento.)

2. Nosotros...*escribimos*...(escribir) las palabras nuevas varias veces.
3. Tú...*sufres*...(sufrir) de anemia.
4. Yo...*abro*...(abrir) las ventanas del cuarto.
5. Nosotros...*asistimos*...(asistir) a clases todos los días.
6. El gobierno...*asiste*...(asistir) a los veteranos.
7. Los indios...*viven*...(vivir) de la caza.
8. Nosotros...*subimos*...(subir) la escalera.
9. El dinero no...*cubre*...(cubrir) los gastos.
10. El barco...*parte*...(partir) a las nueve en punto.
11. El maestro no...*permite*...(permitir) excusas.
12. Usted...*vive*...(vivir) una vida muy agitada.
13. El presidente...*recibe*...(recibir) mucha correspondencia.
14. Tú...*recibes*...(recibir) una pensión del gobierno.
15. Yo no...*permito*...(permitir) ruido excesivo.
16. Elena...*cubre*...(cubrir) la mesa con un mantel.
17. El secretario...*asiste*...(asistir) al presidente.
18. Ellos...*abren*...(abrir) la puerta de la tienda por la mañana.
19. Nosotros...*escribimos*...(escribir) una composición.
20. El ministro...*vive*...(vivir) como un rey.
21. Los precios de todo...*suben*...(subir) en tiempo de guerra.
22. Ellos...*viven*...(vivir) en el campo.

REVIEW

Verbs of the first, second, and third conjugations—Change the subject of each of the sentences below, substituting in its place the six different subjects listed underneath. Make corresponding change in verb where necessary. Follow example.

1. *Ellos* viven en la Avenida Miranda.
   1. Juan ....

   (Example: Juan *vive* en la Avenida Miranda).

   2. Nosotros .... 4. Usted .... 6. Yo.......................
   3. El profesor .... 5. Ella .... 7. Juan y usted ....

2. *El* lee el periódico todos los días.
   1. Yo .... 3. Los profesores .... 5. Usted ....
   2. Ellos .... 4. Usted y yo .... 6. Nosotros ....

3. *Ellas* tocan el piano bien.
   1. Elena .... 3. Nosotros .... 5. Ella y yo ....
   2. Yo .... 4. Tú .... 6. Ustedes ....

4. *Yo* abro la puerta.
   1. Ellas .... 3. Juan .... 5. Nosotros ....
   2. Tú .... 4. Ustedes .... 6. La enfermera ....

5. *Nosotros* comemos tarde.
   1. Los empleados .... 3. El Sr. Pérez y usted 5. Los niños ....
   2. La sirvienta .... 4. Nosotros .... 6. Usted y yo ....

6. *Alberto* fuma cigarrillos americanos.
   1. Ustedes .... 3. Ellas .... 5. Usted ....
   2. Tú .... 4. Yo .... 6. Los Pérez ....

7. *Yo* subo las escaleras.
   1. Nosotros .... 3. Tú .... 5. El doctor ....
   2. Usted .... 4. Ellos .... 6. María y yo ....

8. ¿Dónde trabaja usted?
   1. Tú .... 3. El papá de Juan ...... 5. Alberto García ......
   2. Ustedes .... 4. Usted .... 6. Ellos ....

18

Change the subjects of these sentences from YO to USTED. Follow example.

1. Yo recibo muchas cartas.

   (Example: *Usted recibe* muchas cartas.)

2. Yo como mucha carne.

3. Yo leo novelas de detectives.

4. Yo camino mucho.

5. Yo hablo español bien.

6. Yo estudio dos horas todos los días.

7. Yo escribo las palabras nuevas varias veces.

8. Yo subo las escaleras tres veces al día.

9. Yo paso mucho tiempo en la biblioteca.

10 Yo necesito más tiempo para los estudios.

11. Yo no como mucho en el desayuno.

12. Yo compro mi ropa en El Encanto.

13. Yo no comprendo la explicación del profesor.

14. Yo creo que el español es difícil.

15. Yo bebo mucha agua en el verano.

16. Yo respondo a las preguntas del profesor.

17. Yo vivo en la calle principal.

18. Yo gasto mucho dinero.

19. Yo descanso los domingos.

20. Yo fumo poco.

21. Yo tomo mucho café.

NOTE: For further practice with these verbs, repeat the above exercise changing YO to TU (*Tú lees* el periódico todos los días etc.). Repeat again, changing YO to NOSOTROS (*Nosotros leemos* el periódico todos los días, etc.).

POSSESIVE FORM

Possession in Spanish can only be expressed by the preposition *de**, followed by the possessor.

el libro *de Juan* (John's book)

la pluma *de la muchacha* (the girl's pen)

Note that the preposition *de* and the definite article *el* always contract to *del* (Examples: el libro *del* muchacho, la carta *del* profesor). *De la, de los, de las,* do not contract (Examples: el libro de la muchacha, la carta de los muchachos, etc.).

Supply the preposition *de* with or without the article, as required. Where no article is necessary, simply omit. (Remember that *de* plus *el* contracts to *del*).

1. La pluma es....................María.
2. Los colores....................bandera son rojo, blanco y azul.
3. El nombre....................profesor es José García.
4. La bicicleta es....................Carlos.
5. La mamá....................niño es maestra.
6. El automóvil....................Juan es nuevo.
7. El color....................cielo es azul.
8. La capital....................Bolivia es La Paz.
9. Las paredes....................sala son blancas.
10. Carlos es amigo....................profesor.
11. El significado....................palabras nuevas.
12. Nosotros leemos los ejercicios....................libro.
13. El precio....................libro es alto.
14. Ellos hablan....................juego de pelota.
15. El profesor contesta las preguntas....................estudiantes.
16. Los hijos....................Juan son obedientes.
17. Las causas....................accidentes son claras.
18. La Casa Blanca es la residencia....................presidente.
19. El señor López es el presidente....................corporación.
20. Las estaciones....................año son cuatro.
21. La casa....................familia López es grande.
22. En Chile los trenes son propiedad....................estado.
23. El león es el rey....................selva.

---

* The preposition *de,* in addition to showing possession, has other important uses in Spanish; it is often used to indicate the kind of an object or person, place of origin, etc. (Examples: Necesito un libro *de* español. La mesa es *de* madera. Ella es *de* Cuba).

SER and ESTAR

There are two verbs in Spanish, *ser* and *estar,* which are equivalent to the English verb *to be.* We have already studied the conjugation of *ser* (soy, eres, es, etc. - see page 8). The forms of *estar* in the present are:

yo	estoy	nosotros	estamos
tú	estás	(vosotros	estáis)
usted)	está	ustedes)	están
él, ella)		ellos)	

SER: The verb *ser* is used to indicate existence or some permanent situation (Examples: El señor López *es* profesor de español. La camisa de Juan *es* blanca).
ESTAR: The verb *estar* is used to indicate an accidental or temporary condition. Examples: El señor López *está* enfermo hoy. La camisa de Juan *está* sucia). It is also used to indicate situation or location (Examples: El libro *está* en el estante. Marta *está* en su casa).

In the blanks, supply the correct form of ESTAR.

1. Yo...*estoy*....en la clase.

    (Example: Yo *estoy* en la clase.)

2. Nosotros...*estamos*...cansados.
3. Esa palabra no...*esta*......en el diccionario.
4. El dinero....*esta*....en el banco.
5. Tú...*estar*.....enfermo.
6. Juan y María...*estan*...en Europa.
7. La escuela....*esta*....a diez millas.
8. Nosotros...*estamos*en la clase de español.
9. ¿Dónde...*esta*.....María?
10. La casa de los García.............*esta*.....en los suburbios.
11. El café....*esta*....caliente.
12. Yo...*estoy*.....de vacaciones.
13. El libro....*esta*....sobre la mesa.
14. Juan y tú...*estan*...en la clase del señor García.
15. Yo...*estoy*...contento con el nuevo profesor.
16. El policía...*esta*......en la esquina.
17. Ellos...*estan*..de viaje por la América del Sur.
18. La América...*esta*......entre dos océanos.
19. La oficina....*esta*.....en el último piso.
20. Carlos y Elena...*estan*......en el trabajo.
21. La fuerza...*esta*...en la unión. (force, strength)
22. Usted...*esta*....equivocado.
23. Ellos...*estan*....cansados de esperar.

In the blanks, supply the necessary form of either SER or ESTAR, whichever is required by the meaning of the sentence.

1. El señor García.........*es*.........profesor.

   (Example: El señor García *es* profesor.)

2. El...*está*....en la clase con nosotros.

3. Tú........*eres*......cubano.

4. Nosotros...*estamos*...contentos con las clases.

5. El clima de Bogotá....*está*.......muy húmedo.

6. El señor Rivas....*está*......en el hospital.

7. ¿El.......*es*.......médico o abogado?

8. Ustedes....*están*...muy amables.

9. Yo.......*soy*.......amigo del gerente.

10. Las noches......*son*.....largas en invierno.

11. San José........*es*.........la capital de Costa Rica.

12. El domingo....*es*.........día de fiesta.

13. Juan......*es*.......hermano del jefe de policía.

14. Ellos...*están*....muy estudiosos.

15. La puerta.........*está*...abierta.

16. El profesor...*está*.....enfermo hoy.

17. Yo......*soy*.....veterano de la guerra.

18. El perro......*es*.......un amigo fiel del hombre.

19. Los zapatos de Juan...*están*...muy sucios.

20. La comida...*está*.......muy buena hoy.

21. La casa........*es*.......de madera.

22. El costo de vida.......*está*....muy alto.

23. La familia entera....*está*.....en el comedor.

24. ¿Cuál.......*es*.....el nombre del abogado?

22

For practice with the various verb forms studied so far, change the
subject of each sentence from YO to EL. Then make corresponding
change in verb, as required. Follow example.

1. Yo estudio todas las noches.

   (Example: *El* estudia todas las noches.)

2. Yo soy amigo de él.

3. Yo debo mucho dinero al banco.

4. Yo gasto mucho en taxis.

5. Yo leo el periódico todas las mañanas.

6. Yo no comprendo esta lección.

7. Yo vivo lejos de la familia.

8. Yo como poco en el desayuno.

9. Yo camino varias cuadras todos los días.

10. Yo sufro mucho con el calor.

11. Yo no creo en supersticiones.

12. Yo abro la oficina a las ocho de la mañana.

13. Yo no respondo bien a las preguntas.

14. Yo fumo demasiados cigarrillos.

15. Yo vendo automóviles usados.

16. Yo no necesito más dinero.

17. Yo recibo muchas llamadas telefónicas.

18. Yo descanso todos los domingos.

19. Yo escribo pocas cartas.

20. Yo estoy muy preocupado.

21. Yo corro mucho en los juegos de pelota.

22. Yo subo las escaleras varias veces al día.

23. Yo no hablo español bien.

24. Yo toco el violín.

NOTE: For further practice with these verbs, repeat the above exercises
orally, this time changing YO to NOSOTROS (*Nosotros* estudiamos español todos los días). Repeat, changing YO to USTEDES (*Ustedes* estudian español todos los días). Repeat again, changing YO to TU (*Tú* es-
tudias español todos los días).

The verb TENER

The verb *tener* (to have) is conjugated in the present tense as follows:

yo	*tengo*	nosotros	tenemos
tú	*tienes*	(vosotros	tenéis)
usted } él, ella }	*tiene*	ustedes } ellos }	*tienen*

Tener is used exactly like the verb *to have* in English, to express possession (Example: Yo *tengo* una pluma nueva—I have a new pen. Juan *tiene* muchos amigos en la escuela—John has many friends in the school). *Tener* has other important uses (see pages 25 and 26).

In the blanks, supply the correct form of TENER.

1. María...*tiene*.....un vestido nuevo.

   (Example: María *tiene* un vestido nuevo.)

2. Tú...*tienes*...el pelo negro.

3. Mi amiga...*tiene*....una cartera muy linda.

4. Nosotros...*tenemos*...trajes nuevos.

5. Los maestros...*tienen*....vacaciones.

6. Ella...*tiene*.....un automóvil grande.

7. Yo....*tengo*...dos hermanos.

8. Nosotros...*tenemos*...muchos amigos en la escuela.

9. La casa...*tiene*......las puertas grises.

10. La niña...*tiene*...el pelo largo.

11. ¿....*Tiene*....usted muchos amigos en Cuba?

12. ¿...*Tienes*...tú una bicicleta?

13. El ejercicio de Elena...*tiene*.....un error.

14. El señor no....*tiene*....pluma para escribir.

15. Cada alumno....*tiene*.....un libro.

16. La casa no...*tiene*....muchas ventanas.

17. El maestro....*tiene*...muchas revistas.

18. Ustedes no...*tienen*...problemas.

19. Ellos...*tienen*...una semana de vacaciones.

20. El colegio....*tiene*...cinco pisos.

21. ¿...*Tienen*...ustedes muchos cuadernos?

22. Nosotros...*tenemos*...lápices nuevos.

23. Roberto también...*tiene*.....muchos libros de español.

The verb TENER — *Continued*

Note that the verb *tener* (to have) has various idiomatic uses in Spanish.

    (a) It is used with certain nouns to indicate physical or mental condition.

> Yo *tengo* hambre. (I am hungry)
> El *tiene* frío. (He is cold)

Other phrases with *tener,* similarly used, are: *tener calor* (to be warm or hot), *tener sed* (to be thirsty), *tener miedo* (to be afraid), *tener sueño* (to be sleepy), *tener razón* (to be right).

    (b) *Tener* is also used in Spanish to express age.

> El *tiene* diez años. (He is ten years old).
> La catedral *tiene* 100 años. (The cathedral is 100 years old).

In the blanks, supply the correct form of TENER.

1. Yo....................mucha hambre.

    (Example: Yo *tengo* mucha hambre.)

2. La casa....................un balcón.

3. El libro de español....................diez capítulos.

4. Tú....................una corbata roja.

5. ¿Cuántos años....................usted?

6. El árbol....................muchas frutas.

7. La semana....................siete días.

8. Nosotros....................una fábrica.

9. Ellos....................una bandera americana.

10. La señora Gómez....................treinta años.

11. El cielo....................nubes grises.

12. Las iglesias....................muchas lámparas.

14. Ustedes siempre....................trabajo.

15. ¿Cuántos años....................la niña?

16. Ella....................siete años.

17. El primo de Elena....................un violín.

18. ¿....................usted mucho calor?

19. Nosotros....................camisas blancas.

20. Cuba....................un clima caluroso.

21. Tú....................guantes nuevos.

22. La compañía....................muchos trenes.

23. Yo no....................cigarrillos.

MUST

TENER QUE

Note that _tener_ followed by _que_ and an infinitive is used in Spanish to express obligation or necessity.

> Yo _tengo que_ estudiar mucho.
> _Tenemos que_ aprender muchas palabras nuevas.

(Compare the similar use in English of _to have_ plus an accompanying infinitive: I have to study, you have to learn, etc.).

Supply the proper form of TENER QUE. Also include the infinitive which appears in parentheses.

1. Juan _tiene que_ (estudiar) mucho.

   (Example: Juan _tiene que_ estudiar mucho.)

2. Yo _tengo que_ (escribir) una composición.
3. Usted _tiene que_ (estudiar) bien la lección.
4. María _tiene que_ (pasar) las vacaciones en New York.
5. Ustedes _tienen que_ (aprender) muchas palabras nuevas.
6. El señor García _tiene que_ (escribir) cartas en español.
7. Tú _tienes que_ (manejar) con cuidado.
8. ¿ _Tiene que_ (gastar) mucho dinero?
9. Ellos _tienen que_ (estudiar) más.
10. Nosotros _tenemos que_ (contestar) al maestro en español.
11. Yo _tengo que_ (mirar) a la pizarra.
12. Ustedes _tienen que_ (fumar) menos.
13. Nosotros _tenemos que_ (contestar) las preguntas del profesor.
14. Nosotros _tenemos que_ (estar) en el baile a las diez de la noche.
15. Yo _tengo que_ (terminar) el trabajo hoy.
16. Usted _tiene que_ (viajar) por todo el país.
17. Todos los alumnos _tienen que_ (escribir) en español.
18. La secretaria del señor Martínez _tiene que_ (contestar) el teléfono.
19. Ella _tiene que_ (leer) el periódico todos los días.
20. Ellos _tienen que_ (ser) _POLITE_ corteses con los vecinos. _NICE_
21. Tú _tienes que_ (estar) en el trabajo todo el día.
22. Nosotros _tenemos que_ (practicar) los ejercicios muchas veces.
23. La señora Gómez _tiene que_ (preparar) la comida temprano. _early_

ADJECTIVES — *Continued*

The student, no doubt, will already have observed that while descriptive adjectives such as *rojo, alto, bello* usually follow the noun they modify, indefinite or limiting adjectives (mucho, poco, cuanto, mismo, junto, otro) always precede the noun. Furthermore, such adjectives have number and gender, and must agree in these details with the nouns which they modify.

mucho dinero	*mucha* ropa	*muchos* libros	*muchas* personas
poco dinero	*poca* ropa	*pocos* libros	*pocas* personas

Note, however, that *cada,* whether used with either a masculine or feminine noun, has no other form (Example: *cada* libro, *cada* mesa).

Note also that *todo,* when a definite article accompanies the noun, always precedes the article (Example: *todo* el mes *toda* la semana; *todos* los meses, *todas* las semanas).

In the blanks, supply the correct form of the adjectives given in parentheses.

1. Raquel tiene (mucho) amigas en la escuela.

   (Example: Raquel tiene *muchas* amigas en la escuela.)

2. ¿(Cuánto) revistas lee usted cada semana?
3. Juan tiene (otro)* amiga.
4. Ellos estudian en la (mismo) escuela.
5. Tengo (poco) amigas en la clase.
6. Los niños pasan (todo) la mañana en el patio.
7. Enrique y yo trabajamos (junto).
8. (Cada) muchacha tiene un compañero de baile.
9. Todos tenemos (mucho) sed en el verano.
10. Elena y Roberto caminan (junto) por la calle.
11. ¿(Cuánto) hermanos tiene usted?
12. Tenemos que aprender (otro) palabras nuevas.
13. El profesor tiene (poco) días de vacaciones.
14. (Cada) alumno tiene una silla.
15. Ella tiene dos automóviles (nuevo).
16. Ustedes estudian a la (mismo) hora.
17. Yo tengo (otro) cartera nueva.
18. ¿Lee usted los (mismo) libros todos los días?
19. Ellos tienen un examen (cada) semana.
20. Nosotros siempre tenemos (mucho) trabajo.
21. Todos los profesores comen (junto) los domingos.
22. El cuaderno de María tiene (poco) ejercicios.
23. Los abogados tienen (mucho) problemas.

---

* Note that *otro* is used in Spanish without an indefinite article. (Example: Yo tengo *otro* lápiz. Necesito *otra* pluma).

POSSESSIVE ADJECTIVES

Like all other adjectives in Spanish, the possessive adjectives agree in gender and number with the nouns which they modify (Examples: *mi* libro, *mis* libros; *tu* perro, *tus* perros; *su* mesa, *sus* mesas; *nuestro* cuarto, *nuestros* cuartos, etc.) Presented in tabular form, the possessive adjectives appear as follows:

	SINGULAR		PLURAL	
	Masculino	Femenino	Masculino	Femenino
(my)	mi	mi	mis	mis
(your-familiar)	tu	tu	tus	tus
(your)	su	su	sus	sus
(his, her, its)	su	su	sus	sus
(our)	nuestro	nuestra	nuestros	nuestras
(your)	su	su	sus	sus
(their)	su	su	sus	sus

In the blanks, supply the possessive adjective which corresponds to the subject of the sentence.

1. Juan prepara............lección bien.

   (Example: Juan prepara *su* lección bien.)

2. Yo tengo el dinero en............bolsillo.
3. ¿Escribe usted los ejercicios en............cuaderno?
4. Tú escuchas a............maestro.
5. Todos los alumnos estudian bien............lecciones.
6. Yo llevo el libro de español a............clase(s).
7. Nosotros pasamos............vacaciones en el campo.
8. Ellos trabajan en............escritorios.
9. Ustedes tienen que cuidar............casas.
10. Nosotros pasamos todo el día en............escuela.
11. Yo escribo muchas cartas a............primos de Cuba.
12. Cada niño escribe............composición.
13. La señorita Gómez está en............oficina.
14. Los ingenieros estudian en............cuartos.
15. Tú tienes............lápiz y............pluma.
16. Nosotros vamos a............clases todas las tardes.
17. Nosotros vendimos............casa.
18. Tú gastas todo...............sueldo.
19. Tenemos que estudiar bien............ejercicios.
20. El maestro pone............libros sobre la mesa.
21. Nosotros vamos a............club todos los sábados.
22. Ella escribe muchas notas en............libro.
23. Nosotros paseamos mucho en............automóvil.

---

* Note that poss. adj. *tu* is not accented, whereas pers. pronoun *tú* must always be accented.

For further practice with possessive adjectives plus a general review of plural form, change each of the italicized words below to the plural. Make whatever changes are then necessary in the rest of the sentence. Follow example.

1. Mi *libro* es nuevo.

   (Example: Mis libros son nuevos.)

   [handwritten: ? Descriptivo adjectivos plural?]

2. Nuestra *lección* es privada. *Nuestras lecciones son privadas.*

3. Su* *primo* es joven. *Los primos son jóvenes.*

4. Nuestro *cuarto* es cómodo. *Nuestros cuartos son cómodos.*

5. Mi *hermana* es profesora. *Mis hermanas son profesoras.*

6. Tu *amigo* está enfermo. *Tus amigos están enfermos.*

7. Nuestra *casa* es grande. *Nuestras casas son grandes.*

8. Mi *alumno* es muy gentil. *Mis alumnos son muy gentiles.*

9. Tu *reloj* está roto. *Tus relojes están rotos.*

10. Nuestro *árbol* está bonito. *Nuestros árboles están bonitos.*

11. Nuestra *escuela* es moderna. *Nuestras escuelas son modernas.*

12. Su *gato* es blanco y negro. *Sus gatos son blancos y negros.*

13. Mi *vestido* es muy viejo. *Mis vestidos son muy viejos.*

14. Nuestro *patio* es grande. *Nuestros patios son grandes.*

15. Su *guitarra* es española. *Sus guitarras son españolas.*

16. Nuestra *ciudad* es moderna. *Nuestras ciudades son modernas.*

17. Mi *cigarrillo* es corto. *Mis cigarrillos son cortos.*

18. Tu *hija* es inteligente. *Tus hijas son inteligentes.*

19. Nuestro *ejercicio* es fácil. *Nuestros ejercicios son fáciles.*

20. Nuestra *lámpara* es nueva. *Nuestras lámparas son nuevas.*

21. Mi *perro* es muy fiel. *Mis perros son muy fieles.*

22. Nuestra *música* es famosa. *Nuestras músicas son famosas.*

23. Nuestro *negocio* es bueno. *Nuestros negocios son buenos.*

* Since *su* may mean your, his, her, its, their, ambiguity is avoided by use of the phrases *de él, de ella, de usted, de ellos*, etc. Thus, *Su primo es joven* becomes, if necessary for reasons of clarity: *El primo de ella es joven* or: *El primo de usted es joven*, etc.

[handwritten: dos interpretaciones]

Irregular verbs IR, VER

There are many irregular verbs in Spanish whose conjugations differ slightly, in one way or another, from those of regular verbs. Generally, each of those irregular verbs must be studied separately. *Ir* and *ver* are conjugated (present tense) as follows:

yo	*voy*	nosotros	*vamos*
tú	*vas*	(vosotros	*váis*)
usted, él, ella	*va*	ustedes, ellos	*van*

yo	*veo*	nosotros	vemos
tú	ves	(vosotros	véis)
usted, él, ella	ve	ustedes, ellos	ven

Change the subject of each sentence below, substituting in its place the nine different subjects given. Make whatever changes in verb are necessary. Follow example.

1. Yo voy a la iglesia los domingos.
   1. *Juan*....................
      (Example: Juan *va* a la iglesia los domingos.)
   2. Nosotros ....
   3. Elena ....
   4. Ellos ....
   5. Usted ....
   6. Juan y yo ....
   7. Mis padres ....
   8. El hermano de Juan
   9. Los alumnos............

2. *Ellos* siempre van al * campo en las vacaciones.
   1. Yo ....
   2. Usted ....
   3. Ellas ....
   4. Tú ....
   5. Mis amigos ....
   6. El señor Pérez ....
   7. Ustedes ....
   8. Los ingenieros ....
   9. La mamá de Luis ....

3. *Los estudiantes* no van a la escuela los sábados.
   1. Nosotros ....
   2. Ellos ....
   3. El profesor ....
   4. Ustedes ....
   5. Los hermanos de ......
   6. Usted ....
   7. Los niños ....
   8. Los hijos del señor
   9. Los empleados ....

4. *Nosotros* vemos los errores en los ejercicios.
   1. Yo ....
   2. Usted ....
   3. Ellos ....
   4. Ustedes y yo ....
   5. Todos los alumnos ..
   6. Cada estudiante ....
   7. Tú ....
   8. Mis alumnos ....
   9. Ellas ....

5. *Yo* veo muchas películas nuevas
   1. Nosotros ....
   2. El y yo ....
   3. Usted ....
   4. Juan y Enrique ......
   5. Las primas de Luis
   6. Mis amigos ....
   7. Ellos ....
   8. Tú ....
   9. Mis hijas ....

6. *El* ve las nubes en el cielo.
   1. Ellos ....
   2. Los estudiantes ....
   3. El hombre ....
   4. María y su hijo ....
   5. ¿Quién ....?
   6. Usted y yo ....
   7. Nosotros ....
   8. Tú ....
   9. Yo ....

---

* Note that the preposition *a* and the definite article *el* contract to *al*. *A la, a los, a las* do not contract. Compare with similar contraction of *de* and *el* to *del*. See page 20.

IR A and an infinitive

Note carefully how the verb *ir* is used together with the preposition *a* and an infinitive to express intention or simple future action. (This construction is similar to the English *to be going to*).

> Juan *va a estudiar* francés el año próximo.
> (John is going to study French next year).
> Ellos *van a pasar el* verano en Méjico.
> (They are going to spend the summer in Mexico).

Supply the correct form of IR plus A and the accompanying infinitive.

1. Yo *voy a* (comer) en casa de Elena hoy.

   (Example: Yo *voy a comer* en casa de Elena hoy.)

2. Los niños *van a* (ir) al cine el domingo.

3. El *va a* (estudiar) para abogado.

4. ¿ *va a* (comprar) usted un automóvil nuevo?

5. Yo *voy a* (ir) a España el próximo año.

6. Todos los alumnos *van a* (recibir) muy buenas notas.

7. Nosotros *vamos a* (ver) una película mañana.

8. ¿Dónde *van a* (bailar) ustedes el domingo?

9. Yo *voy a* (pasar) las vacaciones en la playa.

10. ¿ *vas a* (viajar) tú por Europa el año próximo?

11. ¿Quién *va a* (cambiar) su cheque?

12. Todos los estudiantes *van a* (asistir) a la conferencia.

13. Enrique y yo *vamos a* (comprar) una bicicleta grande.

14. La hermana de María *va a* (cantar) en la fiesta.

15. Nosotros *vamos a* (pasar) bien los exámenes.

16. Ellos *van a* (aprender) muchas palabras nuevas.

17. ¿Qué lección *vas a* (estudiar) tú hoy?

18. La prima de Elena *va a* (cocinar) una comida española mañana.

19. Los alumnos *van a* (tener) una fiesta el sábado.

20. Nosotros *vamos a* (ver) el juego de pelota.

21. ¿Quién *va a* (ser) la maestra hoy?

22. Usted *va a* (recibir) buenas noticias en diciembre.

23. Los jugadores *van a* (tener) trajes blancos.

Demonstrative adjectives ESTE and ESE

The demonstrative adjectives in Spanish are *este* (this) and *ese* (that). Like other adjectives in Spanish, they agree in gender and number with the nouns they modify. The different forms of *este* and *ese* follow:

SINGULAR		PLURAL	
(Masculine)	(Feminine)	(Masculine)	(Feminine)
este	*esta*	*estos*	*estas*
ese	*esa*	*esos*	*esas*

Examples:

Este (this) libro es nuevo.   *Esa* (that) pluma es de Juan.
Estos (these) libros son nuevos.   *Esas* (those) plumas son de Juan.

In the blanks below, supply the correct form of ESTE.

1. este árbol
2. .... cuaderno
3. .... bicicleta
4. .... ventana
5. .... muchacho
6. .... zapatos
7. .... bandera
8. .... calle
9. .... campesinos
10. .... enfermero
11. .... esquina
12. .... cajas
13. .... errores
14. .... flores
15. .... colegio
16. .... fuentes
17. .... gato
18. .... comida
19. .... avión
20. .... hospitales

In the blanks, supply the correct form of ESE.

1. esa casa
2. .... señor
3. .... jóvenes
4. .... sistema
5. .... león
6. .... música
7. .... lámpara
8. .... noticias
9. .... papeles
10. .... rey
11. .... negocios
12. .... pared
13. .... regalo
14. .... naciones
15. .... sala
16. .... revistas
17. .... personas
18. .... residencia
19. .... rosas
20. .... soldados

ESTE, ESE, AQUEL

In addition to *este* (this) and *ese* (that), studied in the previous lesson (page 32), there exists in Spanish a third demonstrative adjective *aquel,* which also has the meaning of *that. Aquel,* however, serves to indicate things at considerable distance from the speaker. Thus, while *ese* describes things near the person to whom one is speaking, *aquel* is used to indicate things at a distance from both speaker and listener. (Examples: *Aquel* automóvil al otro lado de la calle es del señor Gómez. *Aquellas* flores en el jardín son muy bonitas). The four forms of *aquel* are: *aquel, aquella, aquellos, aquellas.*

Change each of the following to plural form.

1. este lápiz   (*estos* lápices)
2. ese joven   (*esos* jóvenes)
3. aquel día   *aquellos días*
4. esta mujer   *estas mujeres*
5. esa flor   *esas flores*
6. aquella tarde   *aquellas tardes*
7. esa noche   *esas noches*
8. esta nación   *estas naciones*
9. aquel paseo   *aquellos paseos*
10. ese camino   *esos caminos*
11. este perro   *estos perros*
12. esta niña   *estas niñas*
13. aquel soldado   *aquellos soldados*
14. aquella casa   *aquellas casas*
15. ese piano   *esos pianos*
16. esa guitarra   *esas guitarras*
17. este año   *estos años*
18. aquel plato   *aquellos platos*
19. aquella pared   *aquellas paredes*
20. esa pelota   *esas pelotas*

21. este automóvil   *estos automóviles*
22. esta pregunta   *estas preguntas*
23. aquel maestro   *aquellos maestros*
24. esa señora   *esas señoras*
25. aquella planta   *aquellas plantas*
26. ese árbol   *esos árboles*
27. este sistema   *estos sistemas*
28. esta semana   *estas semanas*
29. aquel agente   *aquellos agentes*
30. aquella sala   *aquellas salas*
31. este accidente   *estos accidentes*
32. ese tren   *esos trenes*
33. esa bandera   *esas banderas*
34. este ciudadano   *estos ciudadanos*
35. aquel cuarto   *aquellos cuartos*
36. esta muchacha   *estas muchachas*
37. aquella ama de casa   *aquellas amas de casa*
38. aquel periódico   *aquellos periódicos*
39. esa rosa   *esas rosas*
40. ese patio   *esos patios*

Change the italicized words below to plural form. Then make whatever other changes are necessary in each sentence.

1. Este *libro* es nuevo.

   (Example: *Estos libros* son nuevos.)

2. Este *avión* es de mi padre.

3. *Ese** es de Alberto.

4. Esta *puerta* está abierta.

5. Este *patio* es pequeño.

6. *Aquél* es grande.

7. Esa *casa* es de un abogado.

8. *Aquélla* gris es de Juan.

9. Esta *lección* es nueva.

10. Este *libro* es bonito

11. Aquel *sombrero* es de la señora.

12. *Esa* es la bandera española.

13. *Esta* es la americana.

14. Aquella *bicicleta* es de mi primo.

15. Aquel *soldado* es americano.

16. Ese *señor* es muy gentil.

17. Esa *maestra* está de vacaciones.

18. Aquel *bote* rojo está roto.

19. *Este* no está roto.

20. ¿Es difícil este *ejercicio*?

21. Esa *exhibición* es famosa.

22. Esta *pluma* no es muy buena.

23. *Esa* de usted es muy bonita.

24. *Aquélla* es del maestro.

---

* Note that *este, ese* and *aquel*, although generally used as adjectives, may also be used alone as pronouns. (*Examples*: Este es de Juan. Esa de usted es muy bonita.) Compare similar use in English of this and that. (This book is Mary's. That is John's. This is Helen's—etc.)

Irregular verbs HACER, PONER

The verbs *hacer* and *poner,* which are verbs of the second conjugation (see page 16), are regular except in the first person singular, present tense, where some irregularity occurs.

	hacer				poner		
yo	*hago*	nosotros	hacemos	yo	*pongo*	nosotros	ponemos
tú	haces	(vosotros	hacéis)	tú	pones	(vosotros	ponéis)
usted él, ella }	hace	ustedes ellos }	hacen	usted él, ella }	pone	ustedes ellos }	ponen

Change the subject of each sentence below, substituting in its place the nine given subjects. Make all necessary changes. Follow example.

1. *Ricardo* hace muchos ejercicios en casa.
   1. Nosotros . . .
      (Example: *Nosotros hacemos* muchos ejercicios en casa.)

2. Yo . . .	4. Usted . . .	7. María y yo . . .
3. Tú . . .	5. Ustedes . . .	8. Los niños . . .
	6. Ellos . . .	9. El estudiante . . .

2. ¿Qué hace *usted* después de la clase todos los días?

1. Ellos . . .	4. Ustedes . . .	7. Nosotros . . .
2. Los muchachos . . .	5. Tú . . .	8. Su amigo . . .
3. Las niñas . . .	6. El . . .	9. Los hijos de María

3. *El enfermero* hace bien el trabajo.

1. Yo . . .	4. Usted . . .	7. Usted y su hijo . . .
2. Ellos . . .	5. El joven . . .	8. Usted y yo . . .
3. Tú . . .	6. Las primas de Juan	9. Nosotros . . .

4. *El profesor* pone las preguntas en la pizarra.

1. Ella . . .	4. Tú . . .	7. Usted . . .
2. Nosotros . . .	5. ¿Quién . . . ?	8. Mi hermana . . .
3. Usted y yo . . .	6. Juan y Enrique . . .	9. La muchacha . . .

5. *Yo pongo* los libros en el escritorio.

1. El ingeniero . . .	4. Los niños . . .	7. Usted . . .
2. La secretaria . . .	5. Tú . . .	8. Ellos . . .
3. Nosotros . . .	6. Su amigo . . .	9. Ustedes . . .

6. ¿Dónde pone *la maestra* su libro?

1. Nosotros . . .	4. Ustedes . . .	7. Los empleados . . .
2. Ellos . . .	5. Mis amigos . . .	8. Ellas . . .
3. Tú . . .	6. Los estudiantes . . .	9. Usted y su hermano

Irregular verbs SABER, TRAER

Like the verbs *hacer* and *poner,* studied in the previous lesson (page 35), *saber* and *traer* are also verbs of the second conjugation with just one irregularity. They are irregular only in the first person singular of the present tense. Study these conjugations carefully.

saber				traer			
yo	sé	nosotros	sabemos	yo	traigo	nosotros	traemos
tú	sabes	(vosotros	sabéis)	tú	traes	(vosotros	traéis)
usted él, ella	sabe	ustedes ellos	saben	usted él, ella	trae	ustedes ellos	traen

---

Change the subject of each sentence below, substituting in its place the nine given subjects. Make all necessary changes. Follow example.

1. *Yo* no sé bien la lección de hoy.
   1. Nosotros . . .
      (Example: *Nosotros* no *sabemos* bien la lección de hoy.)
   2. Elena . . .
   3. Usted . . .
   4. Ustedes . . .
   5. Ninguno de ellos .
   6. Los estudiantes . . .
   7. Enrique . . .
   8. Tú . . .
   9. El hermano de Juan

2. La *profesora* sabe español muy bien.
   1. Ellos . . .
   2. Nosotros . . .
   3. Usted y yo . . .
   4. Mis padres . . .
   5. Los empleados . .
   6. Ustedes . . .
   7. Mis vecinos . . .
   8. Tú . . .
   9. La señora Gómez

3. *Carlos* no sabe donde vive la maestra.
   1. Ustedes . . .
   2. Ellas . . .
   3. Los alumnos . . .
   4. Nosotros . . .
   5. Tú . . .
   6. Los estudiantes . . .
   7. Ellos . . .
   8. Los muchachos . . .
   9. Los niños . . .

4. *Yo* traigo el libro de español a la escuela todos los días.
   1. Usted . . .
   2. Ellos . . .
   3. Ellas . . .
   4. Nosotros . . .
   5. El profesor . . .
   6. ¿Quién . . . ?
   7. Usted y yo . . .
   8. La muchacha . . .
   9. Los hijos del señor

5. *Elena* siempre trae regalos a la maestra.
   1. Nosotros . . .
   2. Ustedes . . .
   3. Todos los niños . . .
   4. Usted . . .
   5. Yo . . .
   6. Tú . . .
   7. Mis amigas . . .
   8. Roberto y María .
   9. El señor Rodríguez

6. *Nosotros* no traemos nuestros diccionarios a la clase.
   1. Yo . . .
   2. Tú . . .
   3. Todos los niños . . .
   4. El maestro . . .
   5. La señora Fernández
   6. Ellos . . .
   7. Mis padres . . .
   8. Usted . . .
   9. Mi amigo . . .

Irregular verbs DAR, SALIR

Like the verbs *hacer, poner, saber,* and *traer,* studied in the two previous exercises (see pages 35, 36), the verbs *dar* and *salir* have just one slight irregularity in the present tense. They are irregular in the first person singular only. Now study their conjugations.

dar	***salir***
yo *doy* nosotros (as) damos	yo *salgo* nosotros (as) salimos

---

Change the subject of each sentence below, substituting in its place the nine given subjects. Make all necessary changes. Follow example.

1. *Ella* da muchas fiestas en el invierno.
   1. Nosotros *damos*
      (Example: *Nosotros damos* muchas fiestas en el invierno.)
   2. Usted *da*
   3. La señora López. *da*
   4. Ustedes *dan*
   5. Ellos. *dan*
   6. Yo. *doy*
   7. Tú *das*
   8. Los americanos *dan*
   9. Mis vecinos. *dan*

2. *Los muchachos* dan siempre un paseo en automóvil los domingos.
   1. Nosotros *damos*
   2. Usted *da*
   3. Ustedes y yo *damos*
   4. Ellos *dan*
   5. Mis primos *dan*
   6. Los hemanos de . . . *dan*
   7. Mis padres *dan*
   8. Yo. *doy*
   9. Tú *das*

3. *La señora García* da mucho dinero a los pobres.
   1. El padre de Juan *da*
   2. Usted. *da*
   3. Los alumnos *dan*
   4. Yo. *doy*
   5. Ellas *dan*
   6. Nosotros. *damos*
   7. Mi hermano *da*
   8. El ciudadano *da*
   9. Los comerciantes. *dan*

4. *Los estudiantes* salen de la escuela a las cuatro de la tarde.
   1. Los enfermeros *salen*
   2. Ellas *sale*
   3. Yo *salgo*
   4. Mi hijo. *sale*
   5. Nosotros *salimos*
   6. Usted. *sale*
   7. Tú *sales*
   8. La maestra. *sale*
   9. Los hombres *salen*

5. *Los niños* no salen de paseo durante las clases.
   1. Yo *salgo*
   2. Tú *sales*
   3. Usted. *sale*
   4. Nosotros *salimos*
   5. Juan. *sale*
   6. Ustedes *salen*
   7. Usted y yo. *salimos*
   8. Los alumnos. *salen*
   9. Los estudiantes *salen*

6. ¿A qué hora sale *usted* del trabajo todos los días?
   1. las empleadas *salen*
   2. el hermano de Pedro *sale*
   3. el jefe. *sale*
   4. las mujeres. *salen*
   5. ustedes. *salen*
   6. tú. *sales*
   7. ellos. *salen*
   8. nosotros. *salimos*
   9. el padre de Enrique *sale*

Use of preposition A

The preposition *a* is generally used before the indirect object* in Spanish, that is, before the person to whom or for whom something was done (*Example*: Ella da el libro *a* Juan. ¿A quién da el profesor lecciones de español?).

The preposition *a* is also used in Spanish before the direct object if the direct object is a person, proper name, or intelligent animal. (Examples: El enseña *a* Juan y *a* su hermana. Yo veo *a* la muchacha en el jardín). Note, however, that after the verb *tener* the preposition *a* is not used before the direct object (Example: El tiene dos hermanas).

In the blanks, supply A where necessary. Also supply the indicated definite article where one is required.

1. Yo veo............Elena en la calle con mucha frecuencia.

   (Example: Yo veo *a* Elena en la calle con mucha frecuencia.)

2. María va a visitar............sus familiares en Washington.

3. Tú vas a recibir............Juan en el aeropuerto.

4. Usted tiene que escribir............sus padres con más frecuencia.

5. La señora viste............su hijo todos los días.

6. El baña............su perro todas las semanas.

7. Los niños quieren mucho............la maestra.

8. Usted siempre trae regalos............los estudiantes.

9. ¿Vio usted...............la profesora esta mañana?

10. El señor Gómez enseña español............los muchachos.

11. El maestro preguntó............Juan varias cosas.

12. Ellos siempre contestan............la profesora en español.

13. ¿Quién explica historia............los alumnos?

14. Ellos siempre dan buenas propinas............los camareros.

15. No veo............la secretaria en la oficina.

16. Juan y María traen............su primo a la fiesta.

17. No encuentro............mi hijo por ninguna parte.

18. ¿Por qué no traes............Elena al baile mañana?

19. Yo veo............los Rodríguez en el cine todos los sábados.

20. La hermana de María siempre trae............sus amigos a las reuniones.

21. Los estudiantes nuevos hacen muchas preguntas............la señorita Gómez.

22. Enrique siempre envía flores............su novia.

---

* In order to understand a great part of Spanish grammar, especially the use of the various pronouns, the student must be able to distinguish between a direct and an indirect object.

Some verbs such as *give, send, tell, bring,* often take two objects after them, one the name of a thing and the other the name of some person or animal. The thing which is named is called the direct object; the person or animal named is the indirect object. Example: He sent Mary (indirect object) some flowers (direct object).

38

FORMATION OF ADVERBS

Many adverbs are formed in Spanish from the corresponding adjective simply by adding the ending *mente* to the *feminine singular* of the adjective.

correcto—correctamente
fácil—fácilmente
claro—claramente

(Note that when two or more adverbs modify the same word, *mente* is added only to the last one: El habla *claro y correctamente*.)

In the blanks, supply the adverb form of the adjectives appearing in parentheses.

1. El profesor habla...*lentamente*...(lento) en la clase.

   (Examle: El profesor habla *lentamente* en la clase.)

2. Enrique toca la guitarra....................(perfecto). *perfectamente*
3. Yo camino....................(rápido). *rápidamente*
4. ....(probable) usted tiene que estudiar más. *probablemente*
5. El perro sigue....................(fiel) a su amo. *fielmente*
6. Esos niños están....................(grave) enfermos. *gravemente*
7. Nosotros aprendemos español....................(fácil). *fácilmente*
8. Mi mamá cocina....................(divino). *divinamente*
9. Los alumnos comprenden los ejercicios....................(perfecto). *perfectamente*
10. ....(general) vamos al campo los domingos. *generalmente*
11. Juan se viste....................(rápido). *rápidamente*
12. Los jóvenes hablan....................(alegre) de la fiesta. *alegremente*
13. Usted siempre escucha....................(atento) al profesor. *atentamente*
14. Ellas contestan....................(correcto) las preguntas del maestro. *correctamente*
15. Mis amigas me reciben siempre....................(alegre). *alegremente*
16. Yo estudio las palabras nuevas....................(lento). *lentamente*
17. La banda toca el himno....................(perfecto). *perfectamente*
18. Las horas pasan....................(rápido) en la escuela. *rápidamente*
19. Los estudiantes saben usar los pronombres....................(correcto). *correctamente*
20. La profesora está hoy....................(completo) cansada. *completamente*
21. El explica la gramática....................(claro). *claramente*
22. Ellos caminan....................(lento) por el parque. *lentamente*
23. Nuestros vecinos nos saludan siempre....................(cortés). *cortésmente*

Change the subject of each sentence below, substituting in its place the nine given subjects. Make all necessary changes. Follow example.

1. *Pedro* sale de la escuela a las tres.
   1. Yo . . .
      (Example: *Yo salgo* de la escuela a las tres.)

	4. Usted . . .	7. Jorge y Julio . . .
2. Nosotros . . .	5. Tú . . .	8. Mis hermanos . . .
3. Ella . . .	6. Los maestros . . .	9. Ustedes . . .

2. *Nosotros* vamos al cine todos los domingos.

1. Mis primos . . .	4. Nuestro profesor. .	7. El alumno . . .
2. Sus vecinos . . .	5. Yo . . .	8. Ellas . . .
3. Usted . . .	6. Elena y Juan . . .	9. ¿Quién . . . ?

3. *Ellos* ven todas las películas nuevas.

1. Los niños . . .	4. El señor Gómez . .	7. Los empleados . .
2. Los hermanos . . .	5. Nosotros . . .	8. Tú . . .
3. María y su hijo . .	6. Mis amigos . . .	9. Usted y yo . . .

4. *Ella* hace todos los ejercicios correctamente.

1. Tú . . .	4. Las primas de José	7. Nosotros . . .
2. Cada estudiante . .	5. Usted . . .	8. Los alumnos . . .
3. ¿Quiénes . . . ?	6. Yo . . .	9. Ese joven . . .

5. *El maestro* pone los libros sobre el escritorio.

1. Nosotros . . .	4. Mis alumnos . . .	7. ¿Quién . . . ?
2. Usted . . .	5. Los estudiantes . . .	8. Los ingenieros . . .
3. Los muchachos . . .	6. Tú . . .	9. Mis padres . . .

6. *Juan* siempre sabe bien sus lecciones.

1. El . . .	4. Ustedes y yo . . .	7. Tú . . .
2. Ustedes . . .	5. Los estudiantes . . .	8. Ellas . . .
3. Yo . . .	6. Los niños aplicados	9. Las muchachas . . .

7. *Los alumnos* traen regalos a la maestra.

1. Tú . . .	4. Ustedes . . .	7. Sus hijos . . .
2. Cada estudiante. . .	5. Mis compañeros . .	8. Nuestros vecinos · ·
3. Los profesores . . .	6. Ese señor . . .	9. El . . .

8. *Yo* caigo.

1. Nosotros . . .	4. Usted . . .	7. ¿Quiénes . . . ?
2. Las señoras . . .	5. El anciano . . .	8. La muchacha . . .
3. Los niños . . .	6. Ellos . . .	9. Usted y yo . . .

The verbs *valer* and *caer* belong to the same group as *hacer, poner, saber* and *traer* (see pages 35, 36); they are verbs of the second conjugation, irregular **in the** first person singular only. *Valer* is conjugated *valgo, vale, vale, valemos, valen.* **Caer** is conjugated *caigo, cae, cae, caemos, caen.*

Irregular verbs DECIR, OIR

The verbs *decir* and *oír* are somewhat more irregular than the irregular verbs studied previously. *Decir* and *oír* change in the first person singular and also in the vowel of the stem. Study these conjugations carefully.

	decir				oír		
yo	digo	nosotros	decimos	yo	oigo	nosotros	oímos
tú	dices	(vosotros	decís)	tú	oyes	(vosotros	oís)
usted él, ella	dice	ustedes ellos	dicen	usted él, ella	oye	ustedes ellos	oyen

---

Change the subject of each sentence below, substituting in its place the nine given subjects. Make all necessary changes. Follow example.

1. *Yo* siempre digo la verdad.

   1. El . . .

     (Example: *El* siempre *dice* la verdad.)

	4. El y yo . . .	7. Tú . . .
2. Mi hermano . . .	5. Enrique . . .	8. Los niños . . .
3. Nosotros . . .	6. Ellos . . .	9. Ustedes . . .

2. *Juan* dice que entiende bien el español.

1. Tú . . .	4. Mis amigos . . .	7. Ustedes . . .
2. Usted y él . . .	5. Sus hijos . . .	8. Las muchachas . . .
3. Nosotros . . .	6. Nuestros vecinos . .	9. Ese señor . . .

3. *Nosotros* decimos las oraciones en voz alta.

1. Nuestra profesora . .	4. Los estudiantes . . .	7. Mis alumnos . . .
2. Ellos . . .	5. Quién . . . ?	8. Usted . . .
3. El maestro nuevo . .	6. Aquel niño . . .	9. El señor García . . .

4. *Nosotros* oímos las noticias por radio todos los días.

1. Mis hermanos . . .	4. ¿Quién . . . ?	7. Tú . . .
2. El y su primo . . .	5. Ustedes . . .	8. Los maestros . . .
3. Usted . . .	6. La enfermera . . .	9. Los hijos de María

5. *Enrique* no oye bien al profesor desde ahí.

1. Los niños . . .	4. Tú . . .	7. ¿Quiénes . . . ?
2. Nosotros . . .	5. Ese joven . . .	8. Ellos . . .
3. Usted . . .	6. Ustedes . . .	9. Pedro y Carlos . . .

6. *Los niños* oyen los consejos de sus padres.

1. Las niñas . . .	4. Juan y Eduardo . . .	7. Tú . . .
2. Ustedes . . .	5. Mis amigos . . .	8. Mis primos . . .
3. El . . .	6. Yo . . .	9. Este hombre . . .

Irregular verbs VENIR, QUERER

The verbs *venir* and *querer*, like the verbs *decir* and *oír*, are irregular in that they change in the first person singular and also in the vowel of the stem. Study these conjugations carefully.

	venir				*querer*		
yo	vengo	nosotros	venimos	yo	quiero	nosotros	queremos
tú	vienes	(vosotros	venís)	tú	quieres	(vosotros	queréis)
usted, él, ella	viene	ustedes, ellos	vienen	usted, él, ella	quiere	ustedes, ellos	quieren

---

Change the subject of each sentence below, substituting in its place the nine given subjects. Make all necessary changes. Follow example.

1. *Lolita* viene aquí todos los días.

   1. Ellos . . .

      (Example: *Ellos vienen* aquí todos los días.)

	4. Sus vecinos . . .	7. Mi médico . . .
2. Mi familia . . .	5. Mi secretaria . . .	8. María y Elena . . .
3. Ella . . .	6. El director . . .	9. El señor García . .

2. *Mis primos* vienen de España el próximo mes.

1. Enrique . . .	4. Los abogados . . .	7. Los niños . . .
2. Enrique y María . . .	5. ¿Quién . . . ?	8. El maestro . . .
3. Ellas . . .	6. Mi médico . . .	9. Mis alumnos . . .

3. *Yo* vengo a la escuela todas las tardes.

1. Nosotros . . .	4. El padre de Marta	7. Ellos . . .
2. Usted . . .	5. La señorita Gómez	8. La hija de Juan . .
3. Tú . . .	6. Mi maestra . . .	9. Ustedes . . .

4. *Elena* no quiere estudiar para enfermera.

1. Yo . . .	4. Ellas . . .	7. Esta muchacha . .
2. Nosotros . . .	5. Mi hija . . .	8. Usted . . .
3. Ustedes . . .	6. Tú . . .	9. La prima de José . .

5. *Nosotros* queremos ir a la conferencia esta noche.

1. Ellos . . .	4. Ella . . .	7. El . . .
2. ¿Quién . . . ?	5. Ustedes . . .	8. Los comerciantes . .
3. Los estudiantes . . .	6. Mi mamá . . .	9. Ustedes y yo . . .

6. ¿Quiere *usted* dar un paseo en mi automóvil?

1. ustedes . . .	4. Enrique . . .	7. las muchachas . . .
2. ella . . .	5. los niños . . .	8. aquella señorita . .
3. él . . .	6. tú . . .	9. este señor . . .

Auxiliary Verbs PODER

Auxiliary (helping) verbs are not used as extensively in Spanish as in English, yet there are a few auxiliaries such as *deber* and *poder* which are very frequently met. *Deber* (must) is regular in its conjugation. *Poder* (can) is quite irregular. Study the following conjugation of poder.

yo	*puedo*	nosotros	podemos
tú	*puedes*	(vosotros	podéis)
usted		ustedes	
él, ella	*puede*	ellos	*pueden*

In the blanks supply the correct form of PODER.

1. Pedro no................ver bien la pizarra desde su asiento.

   (Example: Pedro no *puede* ver bien la pizarra desde su asiento.)

2. Los alumnos................hacer los ejercicios perfectamente.

3. Nosotros no................entrar al cine sin pagar.

4. Yo................hacer el trabajo sin dificultad.

5. Mis hermanos no................venir hoy a la escuela.

6. Creo que ellos no................entrar en aquella casa.

7. Los estudiantes................comprender bien las explicaciones.

8. El señor González no................manejar bien después del accidente.

9. ¿................ustedes ir a la fiesta esta noche?

10. ¿Quién................contestar la pregunta?

11. Los ancianos no................trabajar mucho.

12. Tú no................comprender bien al maestro nuevo.

13. Cada muchacho................copiar su lección nuevamente.

14. Juan no................escribir con la mano derecha.

15. María no................llegar al colegio antes de las nueve.

16. La secretaria................copiar las cartas ahora.

17. Una buena enfermera................ayudar mucho al paciente.

18. Mis amigos no................venir hoy a mi casa.

19. Usted................pasar bien todos los exámenes.

20. Muchos................adelantar mucho en la escuela.

21. Nosotros................adelantar mucho en la escuela.

22. ¿Por qué ustedes no................ir a la universidad hoy?

---

* Note that *mano*, although it terminates in *o,* is feminine.

For practice with the irregular verbs studied up to the present, change the following verbs forms from first to third person by changing YO to EL in each sentence.

1. Yo voy a la escuela en autobús.

   (Example: *El va* a la escuela en autobús.)

2. Yo oigo muchas noticias por radio.

3. Yo traigo mis cuadernos al colegio,

4. Yo soy alumno de esta escuela.

5. Yo doy muchos regalos a mis amigos.

6. Yo tengo que estudiar las palabras nuevas.

7. Yo pongo mucho cuidado cuando hago mis tareas.

8. Yo tengo que estudiar los ejercicios en español.

9. Yo veo muy bien el televisor desde aquí.

10. Yo voy al cine todos los domingos.

11. Yo estoy muy adelantado en mis clases de música.

12. Yo no digo siempre la verdad.

13. Yo doy consejos a mis hermanos.

14. Yo estoy muy apurado ahora.

15. Yo no sé bailar muy bien.

16. Yo soy hermano de Juan.

17. Yo vengo temprano a la escuela.

18. Yo voy a pasear en bote este fin de semana.

19. Yo no veo bien sin lentes.

20. Yo salgo todos los sábados.

21. Yo sé tocar el piano.

22. Yo tengo que enviar un cable a España.

NOTE: For further practice with these verbs, repeat the above exercise orally, this time changing YO to NOSOTROS (Nosotros vamos a la escuela en autobús). Repeat again, changing YO to USTEDES (Ustedes van a la escuela en autobús), etc.

Past tense of verbs EL PRETERITO

The preterite (*el pretérito*) in Spanish corresponds exactly to the simple past tense in English; thus it is used to describe any completed* action or event in the past. (Examples: *Yo hablé* (I spoke); *él comió* (he ate); *ellos vendieron* (they sold). With verbs of the first conjugation (verbs terminating in —*ar,* see page 11) this tense is conjugated as follows:

yo	hablé	nosotros	habl*amos*
tú	habl*aste*	(vosotros	habl*asteis*)
usted } él, ella }	habl*ó*	ustedes } ellos }	habl*aron*

Supply the correct form of the verb.

1. El señor García no (enseñar) en nuestra clase ayer.   *enseñó.*

   (*Example:* El señor García no *enseñó* en nuestra clase ayer.)

2. Los alumnos (pasar) muy bien los exámenes.   *pasaron*
3. María (saludar) al maestro.   *saludó*
4. Nosotros (comprar) una casa en la playa.   *compramos*
5. Yo (invitar) a mis amigas a la fiesta.   *invité*
6. Los maestros (hablar) sobre el nuevo curso.   *hablaron*
7. ¿Dónde (trabajar) tú antes?   *trabajaste.*
8. Los estudiantes (practicar) el ejercicio varias veces.   *practicaron*
9. ¿Por qué no (hablar) con su amigo en español?   *habló*
10. Mi padre (trabajar) en una fábrica de automóviles.   *trabajó*
11. La secretaria (enviar) muchas cartas ayer.   *envió*
12. El (comprar) ese televisor la semana pasada.   *compró*
13. La señora Gómez (cocinar) toda la tarde.   *cocinó*
14. Ustedes (revisar) ayer las tareas atrasadas.   *revisaron*
15. Enrique (llamar) al policía después del accidente.   *llamó*
16. Los muchachos (limpiar) sus zapatos después del paseo.   *limpiaron*
17. ¿Dónde (encontrar) usted a mi hermano?   *encontró*
18. La criada (lavar) los platos después de la reunión.   *lavó*
19. ¿Quién (encontrar) la respuesta correcta?   *encontró*
20. Los comerciantes españoles (viajar) mucho por la América del Sur.   *viajaron*
21. El maestro (mirar) el reloj antes de terminar la clase.   *miró*
22. Ellos no (pasear) a causa de la lluvia.   *pasearon.*

---

* Just as in English, for continuing past action a second past tense is used, the so-called imperfect past tense (el imperfecto). This will be studied in a later exercise (see page 92).

Past tense of verbs EL PRETERITO — *Continued*

In the previous lesson (page 45), we studied the past tense (*el pretérito*) of verbs of the first conjugation The preterite of verbs of the second and third conjugations (verbs terminating in —*er* and —*ir*, see pages 16 and 17) is as follows:

(Second Conjugation) *vender*				(Third Conjugation) *vivir*			
yo	vend**í**	nosotros	vend**imos**	yo	viv**í**	nosotros	viv**imos**
tú	vend**iste**	(vosotros	vend**isteis**)	tú	viv**iste**	(vosotros	viv**isteis**)
usted} él, ella}	vend**ió**	ustedes} ellos}	vend**ieron**	usted} él, ella}	viv**ió**	ustedes} ellos}	viv**ieron**

Supply the correct form of the verb.

1. Yo no (aprender) nada* en esa clase el año pasado. *aprendí*

   (Example: Yo no *aprendí* nada en esa clase el año pasado.)

2. La secretaria (abrir) las puertas de la oficina esta mañana. *abrió*
3. Yo (comer) en ese restaurante anoche. *Comí*
4. El avión (salir) a las tres. *salió*
5. Ellos (abrir) el sobre inmediatamente. *abrieron*
6. Nosotros (comprender) muy bien la clase anterior. *comprendimos*
7. Los españoles (descubrir) varias islas en América. *descubrieron*
8. Juan (recibir) malas noticias la semana pasada. *recibió*
9. Mi padre (abrir) una botella de vino durante la comida. *abrió*
10. Mis amigos (salir) a pasear temprano. *salieron*
11. Nosotros (vivir) en el campo muchos años. *vivimos*
12. Mi maestra (escribir) muchas palabras nuevas en la pizarra. *escribió*
13. El niño (beber) mucha leche. *bebió*
14. ¿(Vender) usted su casa el mes pasado? *Vendió*
15. Los alumnos (aprender) una lección muy bonita. *aprendieron*
16. ¿Quién (escribir) esas cartas en español? *escribió*
17. Nuestro mejor cliente (salir) para España ayer. *salió*
18. Ellos (comprender) bien la explicación del maestro. *comprendieron*
19. Nosotros (ver) cuadros famosos en el museo. *vimos*
20. La señorita Smith (vivir) en Cuba cinco años. *vivió*
21. La hermana de Carlos (ofrecer) una comida a sus amigos. *ofreció*

---

* Note that a double negative in Spanish is frequently used, especially for purposes of emphasis. The use of the double negative will be studied in a later exercise.

Change the subject of each of these past tense (*pretérito*) sentences, substituting in its place the nine given subjects. Make all necessary changes. Included are sentences with verbs from the first, second, and third conjugations. Follow example.

1. Ellos comieron anoche en el Country Club.

   1. Yo . . .

     (Example: Yo *comí* anoche en el Country Club.)

	4. Mis amigos . . .	7. Tú . . .
2. Nosotros . . .	5. Ustedes . . .	8. El . . .
3. Usted . . .	6. Elena y yo . . .	9. Los profesores . . .

2. Ese señor *estudió* español en Chile el año pasado.

1. Usted y yo . . .	4. Esta muchacha . . .	7. Juan y Luis . . .
2. Mi hijo . . .	5. El . . .	8. Yo . . .
3. Nosotros . . .	6. Nosotros . . .	9. Tú . . .

3. Enrique *recibió* una carta de España ayer.

1. Nosotros . . .	4. Ellos . . .	7. Mi amiga Rosa . . .
2. El hermano de Luis	5. Usted . . .	8. Sus vecinos . . .
3. Mis primos . . .	6. Yo . . .	9. El señor Pérez . . .

4. Los estudiantes *compraron* muchos libros.

1. Ustedes . . .	4. Mis hermanos . . .	7. Usted y ella . . .
2. Los niños . . .	5. Ella . . .	8. Nosotros . . .
3. Yo . . .	6. Tú . . .	9. El alumno nuevo . .

5. El señor Fernández *vendió* su automóvil ayer.

1. Mis vecinos . . .	4. Ellos . . .	7. El hijo de José . . .
2. El médico . . .	5. Ustedes . . .	8. Tú . . .
3. Usted . . .	6. Juan . . .	9. Esta muchacha . . .

6. Anoche nosotros *recibimos* buenas noticias.

1. Ellos . . .	4. Tú . . .	7. La señora Gómez
2. Mis padres . . .	5. Los empleados . . .	8. El maestro . . .
3. Yo . . .	6. Usted . . .	9. Los profesores . . .

For further practice in forming the preterite of regular verbs change each of the following from present to the past tense.

1. Usted compra *compró*

   (Ex. Usted compró.)

2. Ellos venden *vendiero*

3. Tú escribes *escribiste*

4. El estudia *estudió*

5. Enrique aprende *aprendió*

6. Yo vivo *viví*

7. Nosotros hablamos *hablamos*

8. Ustedes beben *bebieron*

9. Ella sube *subió* [come up-climb]

10. Nosotros esperamos *esperamos* [hope]

11. María comprende *comprendió*

12. Yo abro *abrí*

13. Ustedes preguntan *preguntaron*

14. Usted responde *respondió*

15. El sale *salió*

16. Yo fumo *fumé*

17. Ella come *comió*

18. Nosotros vivimos *vivimos*

19. Ellos saludan *saludaron*

20. Juan vende *vendió*

21. Nosotros asistimos *asistimos*

22. Tú gastas *gastaste* [spend]

23. ~~El tiene~~

24. Ella recibe *recibió*

25. Ellos tratan *trataron* [to try to]

26. Usted teme *temió* [fear]

27. Yo salgo *salí* [go out]

28. Nosotros tomamos *tomamos*

29. Ustedes corren *corrieron* [run]

30. Ellos insisten *insistieron*

31. Alberto saluda *saludó*

32. Carlos responde *respondió*

33. Tú vives *viviste*

34. Usted camina *caminó*

35. Yo vendo *vendí*

36. Nosotros decidimos *decidimos*

37. El necesita *necesitó*

38. Ustedes cosen *cosieron* [sew]

39. Nosotros discutimos *discutimos* [ir] [discuss]

40. El perro ladra *ladró* [ar] [bark]

41. Ustedes ven *vieron*

42. El descubre *desubrió*

43. Yo invito *invité* [ar]

44. Nosotros montamos *montamos* [ar] [mount]

45. ~~Usted viene~~ [ar] [mount]

46. Tú viajas *viajaste* [ar]

48

PERSONAL PRONOUNS — Prepositional form

In Spanish, the personal pronouns have the same form when used as subjects of the sentence as when used as objects of a preposition—except in the first person singular. In the first person singular, the subject pronoun *yo* becomes *mí* after a preposition. The prepositional forms of the personal pronouns are thus: *mí, ti, usted, él, ella, nosotros (as), ustedes, ellos (as).*

Yo compré este libro para *usted.*

Este regalo este para *mí.*

Voy con *ella* al cine.

No podemos ir sin *ellos.*

Change the word in italics to the prepositional form of the pronoun.

1. Juan siempre habla mucho de *su hermano.*

   (Example: Juan siempre habla mucho de *él.*)

2. Ella está en casa de *sus primos.*

3. Nosotros vivimos en el edificio de *la señora Gómez.*

4. María habla mucho de *sus tíos.*

5. Ustedes trabajan con *el señor García* todo el año.

6. Mi tío siempre trae regalos para *mis hermanos.*

7. Este joven habla mucho de *su amiga Elena.*

8. Yo voy al baile con *mis amigas.*

9. El niño va al parque con *su hermana mayor.*

10. Mis padres viajan con *los González* muy a menudo.

11. ¿Qué sorpresa tiene el maestro para *sus alumnos?*

12. Mi hermana estudia con *Marta y con Elena.*

13. El señor García vive cerca de *mi maestra.*

14. Ud. trabaja con *José y con Manuel.*

15. Yo vengo a la escuela con *Ana y con María.*

16. Esta señora es amiga de *mi mamá.*

17. El profesor escribe los ejercicios para *Enrique y para mí.*

18. ¿Estudian ellas con *usted y con Mario?*

19. Vamos a la playa con *nuestros vecinos.*

20. Los alumnos escriben composiciones sobre *Simón Bolívar.*

21. El amigo de Elena vive en frente de *mis primos.*

22. La muchacha habla por teléfono con *su novio* todos los días.

23. Mi hermana estudia con *su amiga* en la biblioteca.

PERSONAL PRONOUNS — Prepositional form — *Continued*

In the last lesson (page 49), we learned that the prepositional forms of the personal pronous are *mí,** *usted, él,** *ella, nosotros (as), ustedes, ellos (as).* The present exercise will provide further practice with these forms.

Note that when *mí* and *ti* are used as objects of the preposition *con,* they are joined with *con* to form single words. The ending *go* is also added (Examples: El quiere ir *conmigo.* Ellos van a estudiar *contigo*).

Change the following pronouns from singular to plural form. Include the preposition in each case.

1. con él ....*con ellos*............
2. para usted ......*para ustedes*......
3. por mí ....*por nosotros*......
4. sobre ella ....
5. conmigo ....
6. de usted ....
7. detrás de él ....
8. contigo ....
9. hacia usted ....
10. sin mí ....

11. según ella ....
12. sobre usted ....
13. de usted ....
14. hacia él ....
15. para ti ....
16. para mí ....
17. ante usted ....
18. con él ....
19. por ella ....
20. en mí ....

Change the following pronouns from plural to singular form. Include the preposition in each case.

1. para nosotros ..*para mí*...............
2. con ellos ....*con él*................
3. sobre ustedes ..*sobre usted* ....
4. ante ellos ....
5. por ellos ....
6. sin ustedes ....
7. con nosotras ....
8. en ellos ....
9. de ustedes ....
10. para ellas ....

11. hacia nosotros ....
12. sobre ellos ....
13. por ustedes ....
14. según ellas ....
15. sin ustedes ....
16. de nosotros ....
17. para ellos ....
18. con ustedes ....
19. sin ustedes ....
20. por ellos ....

---

* Note that pronouns *mí* and *él* are accented to distinguish from the adjective *mi* and the article *el.*

50

PERSONAL PRONOUNS — Direct object forms

When used as direct objects of the verb, the personal pronouns have the following forms:

singular		Plural	
(yo)	me	(nosotros)	nos
(tú)	te	(vosotros)	os
(usted)	lo, la*	(ustedes)	los, las*
(él)	lo	(ellos)	los
(ella)	la	(ellas)	las

Observe carefully that in Spanish, direct object pronouns always precede the verb.

Compró el libro.   Llamaron a (nosotros).
Lo compró.   *Nos* llamaron.
Llamé a la profesora.   Vendí los libros.
La llamé.   *Los* vendí.

In each of these sentences, substitute the correct direct object pronoun for the words in italics. Follow example.

1. Yo veo *el libro* sobre la mesa.
   (Example: Yo *lo* veo sobre la mesa.)
2. Tú escribiste *la carta* con mucho cuidado.
3. Yo preparo *las lecciones* todos los días.
4. Juan llama por teléfono *a Marta* con mucha frecuencia.
5. Vemos *a los Fernández* muy a menudo.
6. El profesor pone *el periódico* en el escritorio.
7. El médico llamó *a la enfermera* varias veces.
8. Nosotros necesitamos *esos libros.*
9. Ella no tiene *su licencia* aquí.
10. Mis alumnos hacen *las tareas* cuidadosamente.
11. ¿Quién robó *tu dinero?*
12. Usted no necesita *esta pluma.*
13. ¿Vende usted *sus libros* cuando termina el curso?
14. Ellos traen *a sus primas* a la reunión.
15. La maestra siempre cierra *la puerta del aula.*
16. María abrió *las ventanas.*
17. Mi madre mandó *a mis hermanos* para el colegio.
18. Esa señora busca *a sus niñas* por todas partes.
19. Juan compró *ese sombrero* muy barato.
20. El envió *las flores* a Elena.

---

* The form *le* is sometimes substituted for the second and third person direct object pronouns *lo* and *la;* similarly *les* is substituted for *los* and *las.* Examples: Yo *le* llamé (a usted) ayer dos veces. Yo *les* veo (a ellos) en la calle con frecuencia. However, these extra forms are sometimes confusing to the student; consequently it seems advisable, at least at first, to concentrate on the more logical *lo, la los, las* as direct object forms, reserving *le* and *les* for use as indirect object forms—see following exercise, page 52.

PERSONAL PRONOUNS — Indirect object forms

In the first person singular and plural, and the second person (familiar), the forms of the personal pronouns used as indirect objects (i.e., showing to whom or for whom something is done) are the same as those used as direct objects* —namely *me, te* and *nos.* (Examples: El *me* da muchos regalos. El *te* enseña. Ellos *nos* mandaron flores.) The personal pronouns used as indirect objects for the second and third person, however, are as follows:

Singular	Plural
le	*les*

Juan *le* da (a usted, a él, a ella) muchos regalos.
Ellos *les* mandaron (a ustedes, a ellos, a ellas) flores.

Supply the correct indirect object pronouns corresponding to the words in parentheses.

1. Enrique.....*le*.....~~bring~~ trae muchos regalos (a ella).

    (Example: Enrique *le* trae muchos regalos.)

2. Mi hermano siempre.....*te*.....manda flores (a ti).

3. ¿.....*les*.....explica la maestra las clases en inglés o en español? (a ustedes)

4. Mi madre.....*le*.....escribe a menudo (a mi tía). = *ella*

5. La señorita Guzmán.....*nos*.....habla lentamente (a nosotros).

6. Juan.....*me*.....mandó un regalo desde Europa (a mí).

7. Ud.....*les*.....enseña gramática española (a ellos).

8. El siempre.....*les*.....dice la verdad (a Carlos y a ti)). *ellos*

9. El padre de María.....*le*.....compró una finca (a ella).

10. El señor González siempre.....*nos*.....trae regalos (a nosotros).

11. Mi vecina.....*me*.....enseñó el vestido nuevo (a mí).

12. .....*le*.....preguntan ellos en español o en inglés (a la maestra).

13. El jefe.....*les*.....trae muchos regalos (a los empleados).

14. El hijo de Enrique.....*te*.....manda saludos (a ti).

15. Ella también.....*le*.....trae flores (a la maestra).

16. Mi amigo Eduardo.....*me*.....escribió una tarjeta (a mí).

17. Los Fernández.....*nos*.....compraron la fábrica (a nosotros).

18. Algunas veces mi hijo.....*les*.....dice mentiras (a ustedes).

19. María.....*nos*.....enseñó su automóvil nuevo (a nosotros).

20. ¿Quién.....*le*.....prepara las tareas? (a usted).

21. Pedro.....*le*.....vendió su libro al final del curso (a él).

22. ¿.....*le*.....hablan los alumnos (al director) en español o en inglés?

---

* For definitions of direct and indirect objects, see footnote, page 38.

PERSONAL PRONOUNS — Redundant construction

Since the meaning of the indirect object pronouns *le* and *les* may mean *to him, to her, to you, to them,* etc. (see previous exercise, page 52), confusion is avoided, when necessary, by use of the so-called "redundant construction." In this construction the following forms are added to the sentence: *a él, a ella, a usted, a ustedes, a ellos,* etc.

> El le da *a ella* muchos regalos.
> Yo les escribí *a ustedes* una carta ayer.

This same redundant construction is also used on occasion with pronouns of the first and second person, in order to direct a certain emphasis toward the person or persons indicated. Generally, the prepositional phrase goes at the beginning of the sentence. (Examples: *A nosotros* no *nos* engaña nadie. *A mí* no *me* importa su apariencia.)

Supply the indicated personal pronoun.

1. El............escribió a ella dos cartas ayer.

   (Example: El *le* escribió a ella dos cartas ayer.)

2. A nosotros no............interesan las películas de vaqueros.

3. A mí............gusta mucho el clima de California.

4. Ellos............mandan a mi familia tarjetas de Navidad.

5. A ellos............gusta el juego de pelota.

6. ¿A quién............sorprende que mi hermano sea policía?

7. A tu mamá............sorprende la noticia.

8. A Elena y a Marta............gusta mucho pasear.

9. ¿Quién............explica a ella los ejercicios?

10. Los alumnos............mandaron una cesta de flores a la directora.

11. A mis hermanos y a mí............encanta la playa.

12. A mí............gusta mucho Nueva York.

13. El médico............ordenó a Juan reposo absoluto.

14. El jefe............compró a los empleados nuevos escritorios.

15. El primo de Elena............envió una tarjeta desde París.

16. Enrique siempre............trae dulces a los niños.

17. A tu hija............gusta ir a la escuela.

18. Ella............escribió a ustedes una bonita composición

19. ¿Qué............importa a nosotros lo que ellos piensen?

20. A mí no............agradan las películas de vaqueros.

21. El............dice a mí que está bien.

22. Ellos nunca............envían a nosotros noticias de Cuba.

The verb GUSTAR

The use in Spanish of the verb *gustar* (to like) is more readily undestood if *gustar* is translated literally into English as "to please". Thus *I like this book* becomes in Spanish *This book pleases me*. (A mí me gusta *este libro*). Other examples of the use of *gustar* follow:

> A Juan le gusta bailar (John likes to dance—literally, to dance pleases John.)
>
> No nos gustan estos ejercicios. (We don't like these exercises—literally, these exercises don't please us.)

Note that, as in the case of all verbs, the form of *gustar* is determined by the number and person ~~of the subject~~. The tense, of course, will vary with the particular situation (Examples: *A mí me gustan estos libros. A Juan no le gustó la película anoche*).

In the blanks, supply the correct form of GUSTAR.

1. A María no le..*gusta*...este libro.

   (Example: A María no le *gusta* este libro.)

2. A mí me..*gusta*..mucho escribir composiciones.

3. A ellos no les *gusta*....el clima de Alaska.

4. A este joven le...*gustan*..todas las muchachas del club.

5. A los animales les.*gusta*.....la carne cruda.

6. A Eneida no le..*gustan*..los perros.

7. No nos..*gustan*..las ciudades que visitamos ayer. YESTERDAY

8. A mis primas les..*gusta*..mucho ir a los bailes.

9. ¿Te..*gustan*..a ti las clases de español?

10. A nosotros no nos..*gustan*..los exámenes.

11i No me..*gusta*....estudiar los sábados.

12. A mis vecinos les..*gusta*..mucho viajar.

13. A nosotros no nos.*gustan*..los viajes muy largos.

14. Al maestro le..*gusta*..escribir los ejercicios en la pizarra.

15. ¿Le.*gusta*....a Enrique trabajar en esa tienda?

16. A mi médico le..*gusta*..mucho estudiar idiomas.

17. A mí me..*gusta*..mucho la película de anoche.

18. A mi madre le..*gusta*..sembrar flores.

19. No me.*gusta*...el discurso del señor Gómez en el mitin de ayer.

20. A ellos no les..*gusta*..el paseo de la semana pasada.

GUSTAR — *Continued*

The purpose of this exercise is to provide further practice with *gustar* (to like) as well as with the various object pronouns recently studied which are generally used together with *gustar*. Some practice sentences of a similar grammatical form also appear with *parecer, importar, agradar*.

Supply the necessary object pronoun required by the meaning of the particular sentence.

1. A Elena no...*le*....gusta estudiar matemáticas.

   (Example: A Elena no *le* gusta estudiar matemáticas.)

2. A nosotros...*nos*..gusta mucho ir al cine.

3. A mi prima no...*le*...gusta bailar.

4. A todos los alumnos.......*les*......gusta la nueva maestra.

5. ¿A quién...*le*...agrada visitar una clínica?

6. A ellos no...*les*...importa el tiempo que pierden cada día.

7. A nadie...*le*....gusta trabajar de noche.

8. Al hermano de Carlos...*le*....parece fácil escribir una composición en español.

9. A tus padres no...*les*...agrada el clima de New York.

10. A mí...*me*...gusta recibir cartas de mis amigos.

11. A ella no...*le*.....pareció correcta la respuesta de Enrique.

12. A ustedes...*les*...extrañó mi ausencia en la conferencia de ayer.

13. A mí no...*mi*...gustan las películas de vaqueros.

14. A nosotros...*nos*...gustó mucho la fiesta de la semana pasada.

15. A ellos...*les*...agrada conversar en español.

16. A ti...*te*...encantan las fiestas.

17. A mí no...*me*...gusta viajar de noche.

18. ¿Qué...*les*..importa a ustedes si ellos pasan el examen o no?

19. ¿No...*le*...parece a usted muy buena la idea del profesor?

20. El cree que a mí...*me*...gusta vivir en el campo.

21. Yo no creo que a ellos...*les*...agrade trabajar allí.

22. ...*Les*...parecen a ustedes difíciles las prácticas orales.

23. A nosotros...*nos*...importa mucho la opinión del profesor.

55

REFLEXIVE VERBS

A reflexive verb is one where the subject acts upon itself. The reflexive pronouns in Spanish are placed directly before the verb. The reflexive pronouns are *me* (myself), *nos* (ourselves), and *se* (yourself, himself, herself, yourselves, themselves). The conjugation of a typical reflexive verb *lavarse* (to wash oneself) follows:

yo	me lavo		nosotros	nos lavamos
tú	te lavas		(vosotros	os laváis)
usted} él, ella}	se lava		ustedes} ellos}	se lavan

The student should observe carefully that many verbs are reflexive in Spanish which are not used reflexively in English —Examples: *Yo me levanto* (I get up); *Yo me desayuno* (I eat breakfast); *Yo me quedo* (I remain), etc.

Supply the reflexive pronoun required in each sentence.

1. Juan...*se*...levanta a las seis todas las mañanas.

   (Example: Juan *se* levanta a las seis todas las mañanas.)

2. María siempre...*se*...arregla con mucho esmero.

3. Yo...*me*...canso mucho en el trabajo.

4. ¿A qué hora...*se*...levantan ustedes?

5. La maestra...*se*...enoja si no practicamos el español.

6. Parece que este señor nunca...*se*...viste bien.

7. ¿A qué hora...*te*...levantas tú los domingos?

8. ¿Cómo...*se*...llama esa enfermera?

9. Yo...*me*...baño en la playa todos los sábados.

10. Aquella señora...*se*...llama María Luisa.

11. Nosotros...*nos*...bañamos en la playa muy a menudo.

12. ¿Por qué...*se*...cansa usted tan pronto cuando camina?

13. ¿Cómo...*te*...llamas?

14. ¿Cómo...*se*...llama el director de la escuela?

15. Ellas...*se*...quedaron a comer en mi casa anoche.

16. ¿Cómo...*se*...llama el alumno nuevo?

17. Ayer nosotros...*nos*...aburrimos mucho en el cine.

18. Yo...*me*...arreglo las uñas todas las semanas.

19. Ellos...*se*...vistieron rápidamente y salieron a pasear.

20. Yo...*me*...baño con agua fría.

21. El...*se*...levanta muy tarde cuando no tiene que trabajar.

22. Yo...*me*...desayuno siempre muy temprano.

56

Supply the correct present tense form of the verbs in parentheses. Follow example.

1. Ellos *(levantarse)* a la seis todas las mañanas. *[se levantan]*

(Example: Ellos *se levantan* a las seis todas las mañanas.)

2. Yo *(cansarse)* cuando camino mucho. *[me canso]*

3. Nosotros *(quedarse)* en la escuela después de las clases. *[nos quedamos]*

4. Mi amiga Elena *(peinarse)* siempre muy bien. *[se peina]*

5. Este niño *(bañarse)* todos los días en la piscina. *[se baña]*

6. Mi hijo *(desayunarse)* siempre muy temprano. *[se desayuna]*

7. El *(llamarse)* Juan Fernández. *[se llama]*

8. ¿A qué hora *(levantarse)* ustedes todos los días? *[se levantan]*

9. Mi padre *(quedarse)* siempre en el comedor después de comer. *[se queda]*

10. María y su hermana *(pintarse)* el pelo. *[se pintan]*

11. Yo *(bañarme)* en la playa muy a menudo. *[me baño]*

12. Ella *(llamarse)* Marta. *[se llama]*

13. Nosotros *(aburrirse)* mucho en la reunión de anoche. *[nos aburrimos]*

14. Mi hijita ya *(vestirse)* sola. *[se viste]*

15. La maestra nueva *(llamarse)* señorita Guzmán. *[se llama]*

16. Ellos nunca *(levantarse)* temprano. *[se levantan]*

17. Ese joven *(vestirse)* muy bien. *[se viste]*

18. Yo creo que Enrique *(aburrirse)* en el cine. *[se aburre]*

19. ¿Cómo *(llamarse)* usted? *[se llama]*

20. Los niños pequeños *(enfermarse)* con frecuencia. *[se enferman]*

21. Mi maestra nunca *(equivocarse)* en los ejercicios. *[se equivoca]*

22. Carlos *(ponerse)* su traje nuevo cuando viaja. *[se pone]*

Note that in Spanish, when we refer to some action associated with parts of the body or articles of clothing, we use the definite article after all reflexive verbs rather than a possessive adjective. Study these examples:

Yo me limpio *los* (not *mis*) dientes tres veces al día.
Elena se quitó *los* (not *sus*) guantes.

In the blanks, supply the necessary definite article.

1. Juan se lava...*las*...manos antes de cada comida.

   (Example: Juan se lava *las* manos antes de cada comida.)

2. Elena se puso...*el*...abrigo. *coat*

3. El se quitó...*el*...sombrero cuando llegó a la oficina.

4. Ellos se lavan...*la*...cara con un jabón especial. *soap*

5. Mi hermano se lastimó...*el*...brazo izquierdo. *arm* *left*

6. La secretaria no se pinta...*los*...labios. *lips*

7. Los niños se lavan...*los*...dientes tres veces al día.

8. ¿Por qué no se pone...*los*...guantes? *glove* *m*

9. Yo me cepillo mucho...*el*...pelo. *m* *brush*

10. La hermana de Pedro se lava...*la*...cabeza con champú. *shampoo*

11. Mi hermana siempre se pinta...*las*...cejas. *eyebrow*

12. ¿Cómo se seca ella...*el*...pelo? *dry*

13. Ella siempre se seca...*el*...pelo al sol.

14. Tú te pones...*los*...lentes para escribir. *m* *male*

15. ¿Se quitan ustedes...*el*...sombrero al entrar?

16. El se quitó...*la*...chaqueta porque tenía calor. *jacket*

17. Nosotros nos lavamos...*las*...manos antes de comer.

18. Yo me pongo...*la*...ropa.

19. Mi amiga María se quitó...*los*...zapatos para bailar. *m*

20. El se lava...*la*...cara varias veces al día.

21. Esta niña se corta...*las*...uñas con mucho cuidado. *cut* *some* *care*

REFLEXIVE VERBS Infinitive form

Note that the reflexive pronoun which is attached to the infinite of all reflexive verbs is not constant, but varies with the person or persons to which it refers. Study the following carefully:

yo	deseo *peinarme*	nosotros	deseamos *peinarnos*
tú	deseas *peinarte*	(vosotros	deseáis *peinaros*)
usted} él, ella}	desea *peinarse*	ustedes} ellos}	desean *peinarse*

quitar + remove

Supply the infinitive form of the verbs in parentheses, together with the correct reflexive pronoun attached.

1. María no quiere (quitar) el sombrero.

   (Example: María no quiere *quitarse* el sombrero.)

2. A ti te gusta (levantar) temprano. *levantarte*

3. La niña quiere (peinar) sola. *peinarse*

4. La profesora tiene que (quedar) en el aula después de la clase. *quedarse*

5. María usa una toalla grande para (secar) la cara. *secarse*

6. A nosotros nos gusta mucho (bañar) en la playa. *bañarnos*

7. Parece que no quieres (mudar). *seems* *change* *mudarte*

8. El niño no quiere (quitar) los zapatos nuevos. *quitarse*

9. Nosotros debemos (limpiar) los dientes con mucho cuidado. *limpiar arma*

10. ¿Le gusta a usted (acostar) tarde? *acostarse*

11. Mi hermana quiere (poner) el vestido nuevo. *ponerse*

12. Ese niño puede (bañar) solo. *bañarse*

13. Marta no quiere (quitar) el sombrero. *quitarse*

14. Ella tiene que (lavar) la cabeza con champú. *lavarse*

15. Mi hijo es muy pequeño para (peinar) solo. *small* *comb* *peinarse*

16. Mis amigos dicen que no pueden (quedar) en Miami. *stay* *quedarse*

17. Ella debe (vestir) con más cuidado. *vestirse*

18. ¿A qué hora deben (acostar) los niños? *acostarse*

19. Ellos deben (lavar) las manos con mucha frecuencia. *lavarse*

20. Ustedes tienen que (limpiar) las uñas todos los días. *limpiarse*

21. El profesor tiene que (poner) los lentes para leer. *ponerse*

deber must

uñas nails

For further practice with reflexive verbs, change the subject of each sentence from YO to TU. Follow example.

1. Yo me lavo las manos muchas veces al día.

   (Example: *Tú te lavas* las manos varias veces al día.)

2. Yo me peino antes de salir de casa.

3. Yo me baño muy temprano.

4. Yo me aburro en el juego de pelota.

5. Yo me limpio las uñas todos los días.

6. Yo me afeito con mucho cuidado.

7. Yo me canso muy poco.

8. Yo me llamo Isabel.

9. Yo no me enfermo a menudo.

10. Yo me arreglo el pelo cada quince días.

11. Yo me pongo nerviosa al cruzar la calle.

12. Yo me quito los guantes cuando regreso a casa.

13. Yo me desayuno muy temprano.

14. Yo me levanto antes que mis hermanos.

15. Yo me acuesto después de las diez.

16. Yo me equivoco bastante cuando escribo en la pizarra.

17. Yo me seco el pelo con una toalla grande.

18. Yo me apuro mucho cuando voy a pie a la escuela.

19. Yo me quedo en casa todas las noches.

20. Yo me asusto con los ruidos grandes.

21. Yo me visto elegantemente cuando viajo al extranjero.

NOTE: For further practice with these reflexive verbs, repeat the above exercise orally, this time changing YO to NOSOTROS (*Nosotros nos lavamos las manos muchas veces al día.*) Repeat changing YO to EL (*El se lava las manos muchas veces al día.*) Repeat again, changing YO to ELLOS (*Ellos se lavan las manos muchas veces al día.*) etc.

Change the following reflexive verbs from present tense to past tense (el pretérito). →

1. Yo me cansó *Yo me cansé* ~fatigue~

2. Usted se asusta ...asustó... ~scare~

3. El se quita .....quitó..... ~remove~

4. Ustedes se aburren ..aburrieron ~annoy~

5. Ella se enferma ...enfermó... ~fall ill~

6. Nosotros nos quedamos .quedamos. ~remain~

7. El se limpia .....limpió..... ~clean~

8. Yo me apuro ....apuré... ~use up, drain~

9. Tú te desayuna desayunaste ~eat brk.~

10. Ustedes se peinan ..peinaron.. ~comb~

11. Ella se arregla ..arregló.. ~settle~

12. Usted se enoja.. .enojó... ~anger~

13. Yo me baño ......bañé..... ~bothe~

14. Ellos se cansan ..cansaron ~rais~

15. Tú te levantas ...levantaste

16. Ella se acuesta ....acostó....

17. Ustedes se quedan .quedaron ~remain~

18. El se llama .....llamó..... ~call~

19. Yo me quito ....quité....

20. Nosotros nos ponemos .pusimos

21. Usted se enferma .enfermó.

22. Ellos se aburren ..aburrieron

23. Nosotros nos apuramos ..apuramos ~drain~

24. Ellos se afeitan ...afeitaron

25. Yo me desayuno desayuné

26. Juan se baña ......bañó......

27. Usted se quita .....quitó....

28. Elena se pinta ...pintó... ~paint~

29. Tú te vistes ...vestiste

30. Ustedes se enojan enojaron

31. Nosotros nos cansamos cansamos

32. Yo me arreglo ...arreglé...

33. El se peina .....peinó....

34. Ella se levanta ...levantó...

35. Ellos se acuestan ...acostaron

36. Usted se apura ....apuró...

37. Ustedes se lavan ...lavaron ~wash~

38. Nosotros nos ponemos pusimos

39. Isabel se maquilla maquilló

40. El se seca .... secó... ~dry up~

41. Tú te llamas .....llamaste

42. Usted se preocupa ..preocupó ~worry~

43. Ellos se cansan ..cansaron

44. José se enferma ....enfermó

USE OF INFINITIVES

As in English, some verbs in Spanish do not require a preposition before an accompanying infinitive. Such verbs, for example, as *querer* and *desear* do not require a preposition (Examples: *Juan quiere estudiar inglés. Elena desea hablar con usted.*) Other verbs, however, require a definite preposition before the infinitive which accompanies them. Study the following examples.

El aprende a leer	*Tratamos de venir temprano*
El nos enseña a escribir	*El insiste en esperar*

Note further that, not only after prepositions accompanying certain verbs, but after all prepositions in Spanish, an infinitive is used and not a gerund. (Examples: *antes de comer, cansado de estudiar, interesdo en ver,* etc.).

Supply the necessary preposition where required, together with the infinitive in parentheses. In those sentences where no preposition is necessary, simply include the infinitives.

1. El profesor trata............(ayudar) a los estudiantes.
   (Example: El profesor trata *de ayudar* a los estudiantes.)
2. María terminó............(estudiar) el año pasado.
3. Yo no sé............(bailar) bien.
4. Nosotros nos lavamos las manos antes............(comer)
5. El se desayuna antes............(salir) para la escuela.
6. Ellos tratan............(hablar) español en casa.
7. Ustedes quedaron*............(llamar) por teléfono ayer.
8. ¿Quién le enseño a usted............(nadar)?
9. Nosotros vamos............(visitar) al profesor esta noche.
10. Ellos aprendieron............(escribir) el curso pasado.
11. Mis tíos van............(hacer) un viaje en el invierno.
12. Los niños quieren............(ir) a la fiesta conmigo.
13. Este joven aprendió............(leer) en español rápidamente.
14. Mi hermano está interesado............(comprar) una casa.
15. Pedro desea............(cambiar) su automóvil.
16. Elena dice que se cansa............(mirar) la película.
17. Yo no me canso............(estudiar) español.
18. Mi hijo aprendió............(correr) solo enseguida.
19. Nosotros sabemos............(bailar) muy bien.
20. La criada le enseño............(caminar) a la niña.
21. El quiere............(hablar) por teléfono con su padre.

Quedar en is to be translated as "to agree". *Dejar de* means to stop or to terminate. *Acabar de* is to be translated as "just". All three of these phrases are idiomatic. (Examples: Nosotros *quedamos en* ir a la playa hoy. Juan *dejó de* fumar. Ellos *acaban de* salir en este momento.)

Irregular verbs Past tense (el pretérito) of SER and IR

The verbs *ser* and *ir* are both irregular in the past tense (*el pretérito*). Moreover, both verbs are exactly the same form in this tense.

	Ser				Ir		
yo	fui	nosotros	fuimos	yo	fui	nosotros	fuimos
tú	fuiste	(vosotros	fuisteis)	tú	fuiste	(vosotros	fuisteis)
usted } él, ella }	fue	ustedes } ellos }	fueron	usted } él, ella }	fue	ustedes } ellos }	fueron

---

Supply the past tense (el pretérito) of SER.

1. Nosotros..*fuimos*..los primeros en salir de la fiesta.

   (Example: Nosotros *fuimos* los primeros en salir de la fiesta.)

2. Ayer..*fue*..el primer día de clase.
3. Juan..*fue*..quién abrió la puerta.
4. El baile del club...*fue*...un éxito.
5. ¿Quién...*fue*...el alumno que perdió su libro?
6. Mi cumpleaños..*fue*..el mes pasado.
7. Nosotros..*fuimos*..los últimos en salir de la clase.
8. Ellos..*fueron*..los muchachos más elegantes del baile.
9. ¿...*fue*...María quién ganó el premio?
10. Usted...*fue*...el mejor alumno del curso.
11. ¿Cuándo..*fue*..su cumpleaños?
12. Tú..*fuiste*..al cine.

In the blanks, supply the past tense (*el pretérito*) of IR.

1. Yo...*fui*...a la playa el domingo pasado.
2. Mis padres..*fueron*..a Washington en avión.
3. Mi hermano...*fue*...al cine con su novia.
4. ¿Quién...*fue*...con María al baile?
5. Nosotros..*fuimos*..a pasear anoche.
6. Tus primos..*fueron*..al juego de pelota.
7. La semana pasada yo no...*fui*...a la escuela.
8. Ellos no..*fueron*..a la iglesia el domingo pasado.
9. Mis vecinos..*fueron*..a la fiesta del club.
10. Yo...*fui*...con mis amigos a la conferencia..
11. El profesor...*fue*...a Hollywood en su automóvil nuevo.
12. ¿...*fue*...usted al hospital muy temprano?

Irregular verbs Past tense (el pretérito) of DAR and VER

The verb *dar*, although a verb of the first conjugation, is conjugated in the past tense (*el pretérito*) like a verb of the second or third conjugation. It is similar in this tense to VER.

	dar				*ver*		
yo	di	nosotros	dimos	yo	vi	nosotros	vimos
tú	diste	(vosotros	disteis)	tú	viste	(vosotros	visteis)
usted} él, ella}	dio	ustedes} ellos}	dieron	usted} él, ella}	vio	ustedes} ellos}	vieron

---

Change the subject of each sentence below, substituting in its place the nine given subjects. Make all necessary changes. Follow example.

1. *Juan* le dio a Elena ayer un regalo muy bonito.

   1. Ellos ...*dieron*...

   (Example: Ellos le dieron a Elena un regalo muy bonito.)

   2. Nosotros *dimos* 4. Usted ...*dio*... 7. Tú ...*diste*...
   3. Yo ...*di*... 5. Su novio ...*dio*... 8. Ustedes *dieron*
   6. Sus amigos *dieron* 9. Mi hermana ...*dio*...

2. *Los alumnos* dieron una fiesta al terminar el curso.

   1. Ellos ...*dieron*... 4. Ustedes y yo *dimos* 7. Los muchachos *dieron*
   2. Nosotros *dimos* 5. Ellas *dieron* 8. Yo ...*di*...
   3. Ustedes ...*dieron*... 6. Tú ...*diste*... 9. La maestra ...*dio*...

3. *Nosotros* le dimos un ramo de flores a la profesora.

   1. Juan y Enrique *dieron* 4. Mis amigos *dieron* 7. Tú ...*diste*...
   2. El señor Gómez *dio* 5. El director ...*dio*... 8. Estos niños *dieron*
   3. Yo ...*di*... 6. Aquel joven ...*dio*... 9. Usted ...*dio*...

1. Anoche *nosotros* vimos a los González en el club.

   1. yo ...*vi*... 4. Juan ...*vio*... 7. mis primos *vieron*
   2. él ...*vio*... 5. ustedes *vieron* 8. tú ...*viste*...
   3. mis amigos ...*vieron*... 6. usted y yo *vimos* 9. el padre de Elena *vio*

2. ¿*Vieron ustedes* mi automóvil nuevo?

   1. ellos *vieron* 4. Carlos ...*vio*... 7. el profesor ...*vio*...
   2. las muchachas *vieron* 5. ustedes ...*vieron*... 8. usted ...*vio*...
   3. tú ...*viste*... 6. mis compañeros ...*vieron*... 9. Juan y Enrique *vieron*

3. Ayer *yo* vi al primo de Eduardo en el autobús.

   1. él ...*vio*... 4. ellos ...*vieron*... 7. la señorita Guzmán *vio*
   2. nosotros ...*vimos*... 5. usted y yo ...*vimos*... 8. usted ...*vio*...
   3. mi hermano ...*vio*... 6. el señor Díaz *vio* 9. mi amigo ...*vio*...

Past tense (el pretérito) of LEER and CAER

When the stem of a verb of the second or third conjugation ends in *a, e,* or *o,* the past tense (el pretérito) is formed as follows:

	leer				*caer*		
yo	leí	nosotros	leímos	yo	caí	nosotros	caímos
tú	leíste	(vosotros	leísteis)	tú	caíste	(vosotros	caísteis)
usted} él, ella}	leyó	ustedes} ellos}	leyeron	usted} él, ella}	cayó	ustedes} ellos}	cayeron

---

Change the subject of each sentence below, substituting in its place the nine given subjects. Make all necessary changes. Follow example.

1. Yo leí la noticia en el periódico ayer.
   1. El ...*leyó*...

      (Example: El *leyó* la noticia en el periódico ayer.)
   2. Nosotros *leímos* 4. Juan *leyó* 7. Juan y Enrique *leyeron*
   3. Ellos *leyeron* 5. La maestra *leyó* 8. Ustedes *leyeron*
      6. Tú *leíste* 9. Mi madre *leyó*

2. *Yo* leí los ejercicios en la clase.
   1. Usted *leyó* 4. Todos los alumnos *leyeron* 7. Los niños *leyeron*
   2. El señor Gómez *leyó* 5. ¿Quién *leyó*? 8. María *leyó*
   3. Mi amigo José *leyó* 6. Nosotros *leímos* 9. Usted y Juan *leyeron*

3. *Nosotros* leímos esa novela el año pasado.
   1. Mis hermanos *leyeron* 4. Mi secretaria *leyó* 7. Mi hijo *leyó*
   2. Elena *leyó* 5. Los amigos de Rosa *leyeron* 8. El maestro *leyó*
   3. Los alumnos *leyeron* 6. Tú *leíste* 9. Ustedes *leyeron*

4. *La* niña se cayó* en el parque y se rompió la pierna.
   1. Tú *caíste* 4. Usted *cayó* 7. Mi prima *cayó*
   2. Mi hija *cayó* 5. Yo *caí* 8. La señora Cruz *cayó*
   3. El *cayó* 6. ¿Quién *cayó*? 9. Ese hombre *cayó*

5. *Yo* me caí al pasar la calle Independencia.
   1. Ella *cayó* 4. Usted *cayó* 7. La niña *cayó*
   2. Ellos *cayeron* 5. Mi padre *cayó* 8. El amigo de Juan *cayó*
   3. Nosotros *caímos* 6. Las dos señoras *cayeron* 9. Ustedes *cayeron*

6. *Ellos* cayeron en una situación económica muy difícil.
   1. Nosotros *caímos* 4. Los dueños del *cayeron* 7. Ustedes *cayeron*
   2. Usted *cayó* 5. Mis amigos *cayeron* 8. El padre de José *cayó*
   3. Mi familia *cayó* 6. Yo *caí* 9. Los comerciantes *cayeron*

---

* *Caer* is generally used in reflexive form (*caerse*) to describe the actual, physical act of falling (*Juan se cayó de la escalera. El cuadro se cayó.*) When used in a figurative sense, *caer* is usually non-reflective (*Juan cayó en la trampa. Ellos cayeron enfermos ayer.*) These, however, are general tendencies. To the confusion of both students and teachers, exceptions to both usages may be frequently found in everyday speech.

Irregular verbs Past tense (el pretérito) of OIR and TRAER

In the last lesson (page 65), we studied the conjugation in the past tense of *leer* and *caer*, two verbs belonging to a group whose stems end in *a, e,* or *o*. *Oír* belong to this same group and is thus similary conjugated. Note, however, that *traer,* although its stem ends in *a,* is irregular in that the letter *i* is added to its stem in the past.

	oír				traer		
yo	oí	nosotros	oímos	yo	*traje*	nosotros	*trajimos*
tú	oíste	(vosotros	oísteis)	tú	*trajiste*	(vosotros	*trajisteis*)
usted él, ella }	oyó	ustedes ellos }	oyeron	usted él, ella }	*trajo*	ustedes ellos }	*trajeron*

Change the subject of each sentence below, substituting in its place the nine given subjects. Make all necessary changes. Follow example.

1. *Yo* oí el discurso del presidente ayer.
   1. Juan ......*oyó*..........
      (Example: Juan *oyó* el discurso del presidente ayer.)
   2. Usted ....*oyó*.......   4. Enrique ....*oyó*.....   7. Ellos ....*oyeron*........
   3. Ustedes ...*oyeron*...   5. Tú ....*oíste*......   8. Los estudiantes *oyeron*......
                      6. Nosotros ...*oímos*....   9. Mis amigos *oyeron*.....

2. *Los niños* no oyeron el despertador esta mañana.
   1. Yo ......*oí*.........   4. Nosotros ....*oímos*.....   7. Mi hermano ...*oyó*....
   2. Ustedes ...*oyeron*.....   5. Mis padres *oyeron*....   8. ¿Quién ....*oyó*........
   3. Tú ...*oíste*..........   6. Ellos ....*oyeron*.......   9. La criada ...*oyó*.......

3. *La señora García* oyó las noticias del mediodía.
   1. Todos nosotros *oímos*   4. Mi vecina ...*oyó*.....   7. El director ...*oyó*.....
   2. Los empleados *oyeron*   5. Usted y yo ...*oímos*...   8. Ellos ...*oyeron*......
   3. El jefe.....*oyó*......   6. Elena e Isabel *oyeron*   9. El policía ...*oyó*...

4. *El jefe* trajo muchos regalos de Europa para los empleados.
   1. Tú ...*trajiste*......   4. Yo ....*traje*.....   7. El hermano de **Ana** *trajo*
   2. Usted ...*trajo*.......   5. Nosotros *trajimos*   8. Ustedes *trajeron*
   3. Ellos ...*trajeron*...   6. La secretaria *trajo*   9. El señor Gómez *trajo*

5. *Yo* traje el libro de español a la clase.
   1. Mis padres *trajeron*   4. ¿Quién ...*trajo*......   7. Nosotros ...*trajimos*
   2. Usted ...*trajo*.......   5. Tú ...*trajiste*.....   8. Los estudiantes *trajeron*
   3. Ellos ...*trajeron*...   6. La profesora *trajo*..   9. Ese joven ...*trajo*...

6. *Estos* niños no trajeron las composiciones a la clase.
   1. Mis alumnos *trajeron*   4. El hijo de Elena ...*trajo*...   7. La señora Díaz *trajo*
   2. El ....*trajo*.......   5. Tú ...*trajiste*.....   8. Ustedes *trajeron*
   3. El muchacho *trajo*.   6. Nosotros ...*trajimos*   9. Yo ...*traje*.........

Change the subject of each sentence below, substituting in its place the nine given subjects. Make all necessary changes. Follow example.

1. *Yo* vi a Elena en la playa ayer.

   1. Juan ....

   (Example: Juan vio a Elena ayer en la playa.)

2. Nosotros	4. Ellos	7. Mi amiga ....
3. Tú	5. Mi madre	8. Usted ....
	6. Ustedes	9. Mis padres ....

2. *Yo* fui el primero en felicitar a María.

1. Usted	4. Nosotros	7. Enrique y yo ....
2. Mi hermano	5. Ustedes	8. Tú ....
3. El	6. Ellos	9. Este señor ....

3. *Mis padres* fueron a Europa el año pasado.

1. Nosotros	4. ¿Quiénes ....?	7. El ....
2. Yo	5. Mi familia	8. Los médicos ....
3. Ustedes	6. Los estudiantes	9. Mi maestra ....

4. *El jefe* le dio una buena propina al camarero.

1. Usted	4. Este señor	7. El ingeniero ....
2. Nosotros	5. Juan	8. Los socios del club ..
3. Ellos	6. Mi primo	9. Yo ....

5. *Los niños* leyeron los ejercicios en la clase.

1. Ellos	4. El hijo del señor	7. Yo ....
2. Usted	5. Los hermanos de	8. Mi compañero ....
3. Nosotros	6. Tú	9. Ese muchacho ....

6. Ayer *una alumna* se cayó en el patio de la escuela.

1. Mi hermana	4. José	7. El padre de Juan ....
2. Yo	5. Nosotros	8. Los empleados ....
3. Usted	6. Ellos	9. El jardinero ....

7. *Mis padres* oyeron la noticia por radio.

1. Nosotros	4. Tú	7. Ustedes ....
2. Juan y María	5. Los muchachos	8. ¿Quién..................?
3. Ellos	6. El padre de Pedro ...	9. Mi secretaria ....

When a verb has two pronoun objects, the indirect object precedes the direct object.

Juan me *lo* dio (*lo* is the direct object pronoun)
Ella nos *la* regaló (*la* is the direct object pronoun)

Supply the necessary direct object pronoun in place of words in italics.

1. El me mandó *los libros.*

   (Example: El me *los* mandó.)

2. El cartero me trae *cartas* muy a menudo.

3. Ellos nos enviaron *el regalo* por vía aérea.

4. El maestro me mandó *el mensaje* con Enrique.

5. Mi padre me prometió *el primer premio.*

6. Mis primos nos enseñaron *un juego muy interesante.*

7. Tu amigo nos explicó *los ejercicios.*

8. La criada me trajo *el abrigo* de la lavandería.

9. Ellos me mandaron *los últimos libros de español.*

10. El padre de Elena me mandó *un vestido* de México.

11. Mis vecinos me enseñaron *su automóvil nuevo.*

12. El amigo de María nos trae *flores* con mucha frecuencia.

13. El jefe me dio *los cheques firmados.*

14. Mis padres me trajeron *esta guitarra* de España.

15. El médico me envió *muestras de la nueva medicina.*

16. Mis hermanos me trajeron *el regalo de cumpleaños* esta mañana.

17. El director nos dio *órdenes diferentes.*

18. Ellos nos mandaron *los abrigos* de Nueva York.

19. Mis tíos me trajeron *una maleta* de regalo.

20. La criada le cuenta al niño *muchas historias.*

21. La señorita García nos enseña *gramática española.*

22. Nuestros vecinos nos mandan *dulces* muy a menudo.

We learned in the last lesson (page 68), that when a verb in Spanish has two object pronouns, the indirect object precedes the direct object (Examples: *Juan me lo dio. Ella nos la regaló*). Note, however, that if the two pronouns are both in the third person, *se* is used instead of indirect object pronouns *le* and *les* in order to avoid repetition of the *l* sound.

Juan *se* lo dio.
Ella *se* las *regaló*.

Supply the necessary indirect object pronoun, which must precede the verb and correspond to the words in parentheses.

1. Juan las mandó (a mí).

   (Example: Juan *me* las mandó.)

2. Juan las mandó (a ella).

   (Example: Juan *se* las mandó.

3. Yo lo llevé la semana pasada (a ti).
4. Nosotros la mandamos ayer (a usted).
5. El maestro la explicó muy bien (a ella).
6. Los niños lo contaron todo esta mañana (a nosotros).
7. El nunca lo presta (a nosotros).
8. La maestra siempre la lee en español (a nosotros).
9. Yo lo traje de España (a ti).
10. Jorge lo llevó el año pasado (a ella).
11. El no lo regaló (a mí), yo lo compré en Cuba.
12. ¿Quién lo envió? (a usted).
13. El mensajero los trajo esta mañana (a ustedes).
14. Yo lo entregué (a Norma).
15. Ella las mandó el mes pasado (a ti).
16. El señor Gómez los explicó lentamente (a ellos).
17. El lo dio (al médico).
18. Ustedes las prestaron (a nosotros).
19. Nosotros lo dimos ayer (a ustedes).
20. La criada lo llevó esta mañana (a ella).
21. Ellos los mandaron ayer (a usted).
22. Mi amiga lo contó todo (a mí).

Note that when personal pronouns are used as direct objects of an infinitive, they follow the infinitive and are joined to it to form a single word.

El no quiere *mandar* el paquete.
El no quiere *mandarlo.*
Voy a *traer* la composición mañana.
Voy a *traerla* mañana.

Supply the correct object pronoun, adding it to the infinitive, in place of the words in parentheses. Follow example.

1. Yo quiero leer *el libro.*

   (Example: Yo quiero *leerlo.*)

2. Ellos no se cansan de estudiar *estas composiciones.*

3. ¿Por qué el niño trató de romper *el vaso?*

4. Nosotros tenemos que comprar *el automóvil* urgentemente.

5. ¿Quién va a mandar *esos regalos?*

6. ¿Cuándo van a enviar *el contrato?*

7. Carlos quiere hacer *sus ejercicios* en la escuela.

8. El quiere hacer *sus tareas* ahora.

9. A mi madre no le gusta leer *libros de cuentos.*

10. Ella quiere comprar *un automóvil nuevo.*

11. La criada no quiere llevar *la carta* al correo.

12. Yo voy a ver *la película* mañana.

13. Ellos no quieren enviar *todos los regalos.*

14. Ella dice que está cansada de oir *las mismas noticias*

15. La criada va a servir *el postre* inmediatamente.

16. Nosotros podemos hacer *las tareas* sin errores.

17. Usted tiene que enviar *esa carta* por vía aérea.

18. Vamos a tratar de hacer *el trabajo* en un día.

19. Ellos pueden terminar *el libro de español* en corto tiempo.

20. ¿Cuándo vas a comprar *la casa nueva?*

21. Usted debe estudiar *estas lecciones* con mucho cuidado.

22. Me gusta mucho ver *películas* en español.

23. La maestra quiere explicar *la tarea* nuevamente.

In the last exercise (page 70), we learned that when personal pronouns are used as objects of an infinitive, they follow the infinitive and are joined to it to form a single word (Examples: *El no quiere mandarlo. Voy a traerla mañana.*) Note that if there are two objects, the indirect object precedes the direct object (see page 68).

El no quiere *mandármelo.*
Ella no puede *traérnoslo* hoy.

Also note that if the two objects are in third person, *se* is used instead of the indirect object pronouns *le* and *les* (see page 69). (Examples: El no quiere *mandárselo.* Tenemos que *dárselos.*)

Supply the correct indirect object pronoun, adding it to the infinitive, in the place of the words in parentheses. Follow example.

1. El no desea mandarlo (a mí).

   (Example: El no desea *mandármelo.*)

2. Juan no quiere darlo (a ella).

   (Example: Juan no quiere *dárselo.*)

3. Mis amigos no quieren prestarlo (a nosotros).
4. ¿Por qué tengo que mandarlo (a él) hoy?
5. El niño no quiere contarlo (a ti).
6. El trató de hacerlo (a nosotros) en seguida.
7. ¿Por qué quieren ustedes darlo? (a mí.)
8. Nosotros vamos a llevarlas (a ellas).
9. La maestra está cansada de explicarlo (a usted).
10. Ellos están muy interesados en enviarlo (a nosotros).
11. ¿Cuándo va usted a darlo? (a él)
12. ¿Cuándo van ustedes a darlo? (a nosotros).
13. Mi amigo Eduardo puede traerlo (a mí).
14. Yo voy a leerla (a ti) mañana temprano.
15. Ellos trataron de prepararlo (a ustedes) rápidamente.
16. Ustedes pueden traerlo (a nosotros) ahora mismo.
17. ¿Por qué no quiere el enviarlo (a ella) temprano?
18. Después de prepararlo (a él) ustedes pueden salir.
19. Mi madre está cansada de decirlo (a nosotros).
20. Yo voy a traerlo (a ellos) después de la clase.
21. ¿Puede usted prestarlo? (a mí).
22. Yo no quiero comprarlos (a ellos).
23. Yo no quiero venderlo (a usted).
24. Nosotros podemos hacerlos (para él) muy baratos.

Irregular verbs HACER, DECIR Past tense

The verbs *hacer* and *decir* are both irregular in the past tense (el pretérito). They belong to a group which changes the root vowel to *i* in the past tense. Study these conjugations.

	hacer				decir		
yo	hice	nosotros	hicimos	yo	dije	nosotros	dijimos
tú	hiciste	(vosotros hicisteis)		tú	dijiste	(vosotros dijisteis)	
usted} él, ella}	hizo	ustedes} ellos}	hicieron	usted} él, ella}	dijo	ustedes} ellos}	dijeron

---

Change the subject of each sentence below, substituting in its place the nine given subjects. Make all necessary changes. Follow example.

1. *Mi padre* hizo un viaje a México el año pasado.

   1. Ellos *hicieron*

   (Example: Ellos hicieron un viaje a México el año pasado.)

   2. Yo *hice*   4. Enrique *hizo*   7. Mario y yo *hicimos*
   3. María y Marta *hicieron* 5. Mis padres *hicieron* 8. Ustedes *hicieron*
                        6. Mi amigo *hizo*   9. La maestra *hizo*

2. *Nosotros* hicimos las tareas con mucho cuidado.

   1. Tú *hiciste*   4. Ustedes *hicieron*   7. Esa señora *hizo*
   2. Las niñas *hicieron* 5. Mi hermano *hizo*   8. Mis hijos *hicieron*
   3. Yo *hice*   6. El señor Gómez *hizo* 9. El hijo de María . . . *hizo*

3. *Ellos* hicieron todo el trabajo perfectamente.

   1. Ustedes . . .   4. Mis alumnos . . .   7. La enfermera . . .
   2. Nosotros . . .   5. La criada . . .   8. Los empleados . . .
   3. Usted y Juan . . . 6. El . . .   9. El jardinero . . .

4. *Yo* le dije que el maestro lo explicó ayer.

   1. Ella *dijo*   4. Ustedes *dijeron*   7. Ese señor *dijo*
   2. Nosotros *dijimos* 5. Juan *dijo*   8. La directora *dijo*
   3. Usted *dijo*   6. Ellos *dijeron*   9. El *dijo*

5. *El niño* no le dijo la verdad a su mamá.

   1. Carlos *dijo*   4. La hija de Pepe *dijo* 7. Ellas *dijeron*
   2. Tú *dijiste*   5. Mi primo *dijo*   8. Ustedes *dijeron*
   3. Ellos *dijeron*   6. Usted *dijo*   9. Mi amiga *dijo*

6. *Mi amigo* me dijo donde vive ahora.

   1. Ellos . . .   4. Teresa . . .   7. Ellas . . .
   2. Usted . . .   5. Juana y Marta . . .   8. El . . .
   3. Tú . . .   6. Mis alumnos . . .   9. La señorita Pérez . . .

Irregular verbs QUERER, VENIR Past tense

Querer and venir also belong to the group of verbs which change their root vowel to i in the past tense (el pretérito) (see previous exercise on hacer and decir, page 72). Study the following conjugations.

querer		venir	
yo quise	nosotros quisimos	yo vine	nosotros vinimos
tú quisiste	(vosotros quisisteis)	tú viniste	(vosotros vinisteis)
usted, ella} quiso	ustedes, ellos} quisieron	usted, él, ella} vino	ustedes, ellos} vinieron

Change the subject of each sentence below, substituting in its place the nine given subjects. Make all necessary changes. Follow example.

. *Elena* no quiso decirme la verdad.

1. Ellos *quisieron* .

(Example: Ellos no *quisieron* decirme la verdad.)

2. Los niños *quisieron*   4. La muchacha *quiso*   7. La criada *quiso*
3. Ustedes *quisieron*   5. Enrique *quiso*   8. Usted *quiso*
       6. La niña *quiso*   9. Las muchachas *quisieron*

. *Yo* quise explicarles la lección nuevamente.

1. Usted *quiso*   4. La maestra *quiso*   7. Los profesores *quisieron*
2. Ustedes *quisieron*   5. La señora García *quiso* 8. Tú *quisiste*
3. El *quiso*   6. El director *quiso*   9. Mi amiga *quiso*

3. *Ellos* no quisieron darme la nueva dirección.

1. Ustedes . . .   4. El . . .   7. Los profesores . . .
2. Mis vecinos . . .   5. Eduardo . . .   8. La criada . . .
3. Tú . . .   6. Mis primos . . .   9. El hijo de Elena . . .

4. *Ellos* vinieron a visitarme el domingo pasado.

1. El *vino*   4. El maestro *vino*   7. El hijo de Marta *vino*
2. Ella *vino*   5. Mi primo *vino*   8. Tú *viniste*
3. Mis amigos *vinieron*   6. Los primos de José *vinieron*   9. Mi novia *vino*

5. *Yo* vine a la escuela en un automóvil nuevo.

1. Usted *vino*   4. El *vino*   7. El señor González *vino*
2. Nosotros *vinimos*   5. Ellos *vinieron*   8. Jorge y Manuel *vinieron*
3. Ustedes *vinieron*   6. El maestro *vino*   9. Ella *vino*

6. ¿Por qué no vino *usted* a la escuela la semana pasada?

1. ustedes . . .   4. sus hermanos . . .   7. esa muchacha . . .
2. tú . . .   5. los niños . . .   8. él . . .
3. Juan . . .   6. los hijos del señor ?   9. la señorita Díaz . . .

Irregular verbs PONER, SABER Past tense

The verbs *poner* and *saber* belong to a group whose root vowel changes to *u* in the preterite. Study the following conjugations:

	poner				saber		
yo	puse	nosotros	pusimos	yo	supe	nosotros	supimos
tú	pusiste	(vosotros	pusisteis)	tú	supiste	(vosotros	supisteis)
usted } él, ella }	puso	ustedes } ellos }	pusieron	usted } él, ella }	supo	ustedes } ellos }	supieron

---

Change the subject of each sentence below, substituting in its place the nine given subjects. Make all necessary changes. Follow example.

1. *Ella* no puso su sombrero sobre la mesa.

   (Example: *Yo* no puse mi sobrero sobre la mesa.)

   1. Usted ...*puso*...... 4. Mi tío ...*puso*...... 7. El y yo ...*pusimos*...
   2. Nosotros .*pusimos*. 5. Tú ...*pusiste*...... 8. Elena y Juan *pusieron*
   3. Ellos *pusieron*... 6. La criada ..*puso*.... 9. Ellas .*pusieron*...

2. *Yo* supe contar hasta cien.

   1. Nosotros *supimos* 4. Ustedes *supieron* 7. Mi hermana *supo*
   2. El estudiante *supo* 5. Tú *supiste* 8. Mis amigos *supieron*
   3. La muchacha *supo* 6. Usted ...*supo*.. 9. Usted y él *supimos* *supieron*

3. *Nosotros* pusimos los acentos correctamente.

   1. El ...*puso*...... 4. Ustedes *pusieron* 7. Usted y él *pusieron*
   2. Usted ...*puso*... 5. Ella ..*puso*...... 8. Tú ...*pusiste*....
   3. Yo ......*puse*.... 6. Los alumnos *pusieron* 9. Mi padre ..*puso*..

4. *Usted* supo los nombres de las ciudades.

   1. Ella ...*supo*...... 4. El estudiante *supo* 7. Usted y él *supieron*
   2. Ustedes *supieron* 5. Nosotros *supimos* 8. Mi primo ..*supo*....
   3. Yo ......*supe*.... 6. Un cartero .*supo*.. 9. Ellos *supieron*

5. *Yo* puse un cuadro en la pared.

   1. Usted .... 4. El estudiante .... 7. Todos nosotros ......
   2. Tú .... 5. La señora .... 8. Luis y Pedro ....
   3. Nosotras .... 6. Ustedes .... 9. Ellos

6. *Ustedes* supieron la noticia antes que ella.

   1. Yo .... 4. María .... 7. La madre ....
   2. Usted .... 5. Nosotros .... 8. Juan y Tomás ....
   3. Juanita .... 6. Ustedes .... 9. Tú ....

74

Irregular verbs TENER, PODER Past tense

Tener and *poder* also belong to the group of verbs whose root vowel changes to *u* in the preterite (see previous exercise on *poner* and *saber*, page 74). The conjugations of *tener* and *poder* in the preterite are:

tener				poder			
yo	tuve	nosotros	tuvimos	yo	pude	nosotros	pudimos
tú	tuviste	(vosotros	tuvisteis)	tú	pudiste	(vosotros	pudisteis)
usted / él, ella	tuvo	ustedes / ellos	tuvieron	usted / él, ella	pudo	ustedes / ellos	pudieron

Change the subject of each sentence below, substituting in its place the nine different subjects listed underneath. Make corresponding change in verb, where necessary. Follow example.

1. *Ella* tuvo un accidente con su automóvil.

> (Example: *El* tuvo un accidente con su automóvil.)

1. Nosotros *tuvimos*   4. Ernesto *tuvo*   7. El policía *tuvo*
2. Ellos *tuvieron*   5. Mi padre *tuvo*   8. La profesora *tuvo*
3. Tú *tuviste*   6. Ustedes *tuvieron*   9. El y ella *tuvieron*

2. *Nosotros* pudimos traducir el párrafo.

1. El *pudo*   4. Tú *pudiste*   7. Mi hermana *pudo*
2. Ustedes *pudieron*   5. El profesor *pudo*   8. Tú y yo *pudimos*
3. Yo *pude*   6. Los estudiantes *pudieron*   9. Ellos *pudieron*

3. *Yo* tuve que hacer un viaje a Europa.

1. Nosotros *tuvimos*   4. Carmen *tuvo*   7. Daniel y José *tuvieron*
2. Ustedes *tuvieron*   5. Los soldados *tuvieron*   8. El general *tuvo*
3. El *tuvo*   6. Tú *tuviste*   9. Usted *tuvo*

4. *Yo* pude resolver los problemas de Aritmética.

1. Nosotros *pudimos*   4. El matemático *pudo*   7. Tú y el Sr. García *pudieron*
2. Ellas *pudieron*   5. Los arquitectos *pudieron*   8. Ricardo *pudo*
3. Mi primo *pudo*   6. Usted *pudo*   9. El y ella *pudieron*

5. *María y Alberto* no tuvieron tiempo para terminar el ejercicio.

1. Yo   4. El estudiante   7. Nosotros
2. Ella   5. La maestra   8. Emilia
3. Usted   6. Ellos   9. Tú

6. *Usted* pudo comprar un automóvil nuevo.

1. Yo   4. El chofer   7. Nosotros
2. Ustedes   5. Mi amigo   8. Pablo
3. El   6. Ellos   9. Los hermanos Díaz .

For practice with the preterite of the irregular verbs recently studied, change the subject of the following sentences from YO to EL. Follow example.

Yo fui anoche al cine con Juan.

(Example: *El* fue al cine anoche con Juan.)

1. *Yo* leí un libro de cuentos muy interesante.
2. *Yo* traje un ramo de flores para María.
3. *Yo* dije que ella es muy bonita.
4. *Yo* me caí de una escalera anoche.
5. *Yo* vi una buena película.
6. *Yo* hice una composición sobre la lluvia.
7. *Yo* estuve en París el año pasado.
8. *Yo* no quise comprar esos libros antiguos.
9. *Yo* supe que ella había llegado anoche.
10. *Yo* oí la noticia por la radio.
11. *Yo* fui a visitar a mi tía Juana.
12. *Yo* quise ir a trabajar por la noche.
13. *Yo* puse el sombrero en la silla.
14. *Yo* no pude traducir el párrafo.
15. *Yo* creí que ella era soltera.
16. *Yo* les di dinero a los estudiantes.
17. *Yo* no tuve mucho tiempo para saludarlo.
18. *Yo* vine a esta ciudad a buscar trabajo.
19. *Yo* anduve por la carretera.
20. *Yo* no dije ninguna mentira a la maestra.
21. *Yo* no vine sin zapatos a la escuela.
22. *Yo* no fui a molestar a los vecinos.

NOTE: For further practice with these verbs, repeat the above exercise orally, this time changing YO to NOSOTROS. Repeat again, changing YO to ELLOS, and YO to TU, etc.

For further practice with the irregular verbs recently studied, change the following from present tense to the preterit.

1. Ella hace   (Ella *hizo*)
2. Juan lee   (Juan *leyó*)
3. Tú estás ... *estuviste*
4. Carlos se cae ... *cayó*
5. Usted trae ... *trajo*
6. Ellos se van ... *fueron*
7. Nadie va ... *fue (a)*
8. Ellas no ven ... *vieron*
9. El es ... *fue*
10. Usted la trae ... *trajo*
11. Tú das ... *diste*
12. Ellos no saben ... *supieron*
13. Tú quieres ... *quisiste*
14. Ricardo oye ... *oyó*
15. Ustedes tienen ... *tuvieron*
16. Nosotros traemos ... *trajimos*
17. Julio viene ... *vino*
18. Pedro tiene ... *tuvo*
19. Juan sabe ... *supo*
20. Ellos hacen ... *hicieron*
21. Usted es ... *fue*
22. Ella viene ... *vino*

23. Tú vas ... *fuiste*
24. El tiene ... *tuvo*
25. Ella anda ... *anduvo*
26. Emilio quiere ... *quiso*
27. Ustedes dicen ... *dijeron*
28. Alguién llama ... *llamó*
29. Yo lo pongo ... *puse*
30. Nosotros venimos ... *vinimos*
31. El está ... *estuvo*
32. Nosotros hacemos ... *hicimos*
33. Tomás puede ... *pudo*
34. Usted tiene ... *tuvo*
35. Yo sé ... ~~fut~~ *supe*
36. Ernesto dice ... *dijo*
37. Ellas dan ... *dieron*
48. Yo estoy ... ~~fut~~ *estuve*
39. Augusto anda ... *anduvo*
40. Enrique no está ... *estuvo*
41. Ustedes son ... *fueron*
42. Tú eres ... *fuiste*
43. Angel tiene ... *tuvo*
44. Tú andas ... *anduviste*

VOWEL CHANGING VERBS

In the present tense of certain verbs of the first conjugation, the vowel of the stem changes from *o* to *ue,* and from *e* to *ie* whenever the accent falls upon this vowel. The endings remain regular. Study the following conjugations:

contar (*o* to *ue*)			pensar (*e* to *ie*)		
yo *cuento*	nosotros	contamos*	yo *pienso*	nosotros	pensamos*
tú *cuentas*	(vosotros	contáis)	tú *piensas*	(vosotros	pensáis)
usted ⎫ *cuenta* él, ella ⎭	ustedes ⎫ *cuentan* ellos ⎭		usted ⎫ *piensa* él, ella ⎭	ustedes ⎫ *piensan* ellos ⎭	

Change the subjects of each sentence below, substituting in its place the nine given subjects. Make all necessary changes. Follow example.

1. *María* cuenta las estrellas del cielo.

   (Example: Nosotros *contamos* las estrellas del cielo.)

   1. Yo ....
   2. Ustedes ....
   3. Tú ....
   4. Ellos ....
   5. Julio ....
   6. Luis y Elena ....
   7. Los astrónomos ......
   8. El profesor ....
   9. Ella ....

2. *Yo* pienso estudiar el idioma francés.

   1. Nosotros ....
   2. Ellos ....
   3. El ....
   4. Tú ....
   5. Ustedes ....
   6. Octavio ....
   7. La muchacha ....
   8. El médico ....
   9. Los capitanes ....

3. *Yo* cuento** una anécdota interesante.

   1. El ....
   2. Tú ....
   3. Usted ....
   4. Nosotros ....
   5. Ella ....
   6. Ernesto y yo ....
   7. El profesor ....
   8. Los padres ....
   9. El abuelo ....

4. *Ella* piensa hacer un viaje a la Argentina.

   1. Ustedes ....
   2. Ellos ....
   3. Nosotros ....
   4. Yo ....
   5. Tú ....
   6. Nosotros ....
   7. La joven ....
   8. Los estudiantes ....
   9. El ingeniero ....

5. *El* cuenta el dinero que tiene en el bolsillo.

   1. Yo ....
   2. Usted ....
   3. Ella ....
   4. Nosotros ....
   5. Tú ....
   6. Ellos ....
   7. El muchachito ....
   8. Los trabajadores ....
   9. Pedro ....

6. *Ustedes* piensan divertirse mucho durante las vacaciones.

   1. Yo ....
   2. Tú ....
   3. Nosotros ....
   4. Ella ....
   5. El y Luisa ....
   6. Usted ....
   7. Los estudiantes ....
   8. La criada ....
   9. El empleado ....

* No change takes place in the first person plural of these verbs, because the accent does not fall upon the vowel of the stem but upon the first syllable of the verb ending.

** Note that *contar* means to relate or tell, and to count.

Here are addional verbs of the first conjugation belonging to the same group as those studied in the previous exercise. These particular verbs change the vowel of their stem from *o* to *ue* whenever the accent falls upon this vowel. They are thus conjugated exactly like *contar* (see previous exercise, page 78).

— AR   o → ue

almorzar   (yo *almuerzo*, tú *almuerzas*, usted *almuerza*, él *almuerza*, etc.).
encontrar   (yo *encuentro*, tú *encuentras*, usted *encuentra*, él *encuentra*, etc.).
mostrar   (yo *muestro*, tú *muestras*, usted *muestra*, él *muestra*, etc.).
acordarse   (yo me *acuerdo*, tú te *acuerdas*, usted se *acuerda*, él se *acuerda*, etc.).
acostarse   (yo me *acuesto*, tú te *acuestas*, usted se *acuesta*, él se *acuesta*, etc.).

recordar   recuerdo

Supply the proper present tense form of the verbs in parentheses.

1. El nunca (almorzar) en ese restaurante.

   (Example: El nunca *almuerza* en ese restaurante.)

2. Yo siempre (mostrar) mis libros a mis compañeros.

3. Ellos frecuentemente (acostarse) tarde.

4. Luis y Daniel (encontrarse) en el parque diariamente.

5. Usted no (acordarse) de su dirección.

6. El (encontrar) muy simpática a esa señorita.

7. Yo sí (acostarse) en la cama nueva.

8. El no (mostrar) la cicatriz que tiene en la espalda.

9. Enrique y María (almorzar) juntos todos los días.

10. Tú no (encontrar) la llave de tu automóvil.

11. El no (acordarse) de pagarme lo que me debe.

12. Usted sí (almorzar) con sus padres los sábados.

13. Nosotros* (acordarse) de él con mucha frecuencia.

14. Nosotros* (mostrar) nuestros retratos de la infancia.

15. Ellos (almorzar) muy bien todos los días.

16. Ellas (acostarse) en el suelo de madera de la habitación.

17. Usted (encontrar) dinero siempre en la calle.

18. Ella (mostrar) sus calificaciones a sus padres.

19. El y yo (almorzar) arroz con pollo y ensalada.

20. Antonio y Federico (acordarse) de felicitarme en la Navidad.

* NOTE: Remember, no change takes place in the first person plural of these verbs.

The following verbs also belong to the group first studied in the exercise on page 79. These verbs change the vowel *e* to *ie* in the present tense whenever the accent falls upon this vowel. They are thus conjugated exactly like *pensar* (see page 79).

$E \rightarrow ie$

empezar	(yo *empiezo*, tú *empiezas*, usted *empieza*, él *empieza*, etc.).
cerrar	(yo *cierro*, tú *cierras*, usted *cierra*, él *cierra*, etc.).
sentarse	(yo me *siento*, tú te *sientas*, usted se *sienta*, él se *sienta*, etc.).
despertarse	(yo me *despierto*, tú te *despiertas*, usted se *despierta*, él se *despierta*, etc.).

Supply the proper present tense form of the verbs in parentheses.

1. Yo (empezar) a trabajar a las ocho de la mañana.

   (Example: Yo *empiezo* a trabajar a las ocho de la mañana.)

2. Ella (cerrar) la ventana porque siente mucho frío.

3. Usted (sentarse) cómodamente en ese sofá verde.

4. Yo (despertarse) siempre muy temprano.

5. Ellos (empezar) los ejercicios por la tarde.

6. Nosotros* (cerrar) bien la caja donde guardamos el dinero.

7. Tú (sentarse) siempre en el mismo asiento.

8. Jorge (despertarse) cuando siente un pequeño ruido.

9. El (empezar) a estudiar después de la tarde.

10. La profesora (cerrar) los ojos porque le molesta esa luz.

11. Isabel y Eugenia no (sentarse) ahí porque no ven bien la película.

12. Ellos (despertarse) cuando oyen el despertador.

13. Sus padres (empezar) a sufrir mucho cuando su hijo se enferma.

14. Los empleados (cerrar) las tiendas los días de fiesta.

15. El (sentarse) incómodo en esa silla porque es muy gordo.

16. La criada (despertarse) siempre por la madrugada.

17. El lunes (empezar) las clases en esa academia.

18. Lucía (cerrar) la boca cuando otros hablan.

19. Nosotros (sentarse) delante del televisor a poca distancia.

20. Tú y ella (despertarse) muy tarde todos los días.

* REMEMBER: no change takes place in the first person plural: nosotros *empezamos;* nosotros *cerramos;* nosotros nos *sentamos;* nosotros nos *despertamos.*

VOWEL CHANGING VERBS

In the present tense of a few verbs of the second conjugation, the vowel of the stem also changes from *o* to *ue*, and from *e* to *ie* when the accent falls upon this vowel. Again, as with the verbs of the first conjugation undergoing these same changes (see pages 78 - 80), the endings remain regular. Study the following conjugations:

	volver				*perder*		
yo	*vuelvo*	nosotros	volvemos	yo	*pierdo*	nosotros	perdemos
tú	*vuelves*	(vosotros	volvéis)	tú	*pierdes*	(vosotros	perdéis)
usted él, ella }	*vuelve*	ustedes ellos }	*vuelven*	usted él, ella }	*pierde*	ustedes ellos }	*pierden*

Supply the proper present tense form of the verbs in parentheses.

1. Ellos nunca (perder) en el juego.

   (Example: Ellos nunca *pierden* en el juego.)

2. Yo (volver) a copiar todos mis ejercicios.

3. Los alumnos no (entender)* muy bien a su maestro de español.

4. (Llover)* mucho durante la estación del año.

5. Luisa (perder) su sortija con frecuencia.

6. (Volver) pronto cuando llaman a Francisco.

7. Esos trabajadores (perder) mucho tiempo fumando.

8. Elena y Juana (volver) a sus respectivos países mañana.

9. Ese lindo bebé (entender) a su mamá.

10. Ustedes (perder) el dinero porque tienen rota la cartera.

11. En ese país casi nunca (llover)*.

12. El estudiante no (entender) esa letra tan mal escrita.

13. Ella (perder) su trabajo porque tiene muchas ausencias.

14. Yo (volver) a equivocarme porque no veo bien con esos espejuelos.

15. Los amigos de Fernández (volver) el próximo año de Panamá.

16. Yo no (perder) el tiempo enseñando a esos malos estudiantes.

17. Si (volver) tarde otra vez, te despediré.

18. Tú siempre (perder) porque no te fijas bien.

19. Yo bien sé que tú (volver) mañana porque te interesa.

20. Hay animales que (entender) muy bien a las personas.

---

* *Entender* changes the *e* of its stem to *ie;* it is thus conjugated exactly like *perder*: *entiendo, entiendes, entiende, entendemos, entienden.* *Llover* changes the *o* of its stem to *ue;* it is conjugated like *volver*, except that *llover* is a defective (impersonal) verb and exists only in the third person singular. It thus has only the one form *llueve* in the present tense.

VOWEL CHANGING VERBS

As already indicated, all of the vowel changing verbs studied so far (*contar, pensar, almorzar, encontrar, mostrar, acordarse, acostarse, empezar, cerrar, sentarse, despertarse, volver, perder, entender* (see pages 78 - 81) have been verbs of the first and second conjugations. All of these verbs, although changing the vowel *e* of their stem to *ie*, or *o* to *ue* in the present tense, suffer no such changes in the past tense (*el pretérito*). In the past tense they remain completely regular.

> Yo *volví* a las ocho.
> El no *entendió* lo que dije.
> Ellos *perdieron* mucho dinero.

Supply the past tense (*el pretérito*) of the verbs in parentheses.

1. Ella (acostarse) el sábado a las doce de la noche.

   (Example: Ella *se acostó* el sábado a las doce de la noche.)

2. Usted (entender) muy bien lo que yo le dije.

3. Los profesores (entender) al visitante extranjero.

4. Regino (despertarse) muy temprano esta mañana.

5. Yo (perder) mis libros cuando fui a la playa.

6. Ustedes no (acordarse) de invitar a su amigo Ernesto.

7. Horacio y Moisés (almorzar)* conmigo en el restaurante chino.

8. Yo (almozar) huevos fritos con jamón y café con leche.

9. Nosotros (empezar) a trabajar hace tres meses.

10. Yo (empezar)* mis tareas por la mañana muy temprano.

11. Los pájaros no (volver) al árbol hasta la tarde.

12. Yo (volver) a visitar a tu hermana Inés.

13. Ella (sentarse) en una silla delante de la ventana.

14. Mis hijos (contar) todo lo que sucedió en la escuela.

15. Durante el viaje (llover) mucho.

16. Ellos (mostrar) mucho interés en conocer la exposición.

17. Martín (perder) mucho tiempo esperando la llamada por teléfono.

18. Yo me (encontrar) una cartera con cien pesos.

19. La criada (cerrar) muy bien la puerta de la cocina.

20. La explosión me (despertar) a media noche.

---

* Note that the *z* of the root changes to *c* before the *e* (or *i*) of verb endings.

VOWEL CHANGING VERBS

In the present tense, certain verbs of the third conjugation also change the root of the stem, when stressed, from *e* to *ie* and from *o* to *ue* (see pages 78 - 81 for similar changes* in verbs of the first and second conjugations).

	sentir				*dormir*		
yo	siento	nosotros	sentimos	yo	*duermo*	nosotros	dormimos
tú	sientes	(vosotros	sentís)	tú	*duermes*	(vosotros	dormís)
usted} él, ella}	siente	ustedes} ellos}	sienten	usted} él, ella}	*duerme*	ustedes} ellos}	*duermen*

Supply the proper present tense of SENTIR.

1. Yo no me** (sentir) bien hoy.

   (Example: Yo no me *siento* bien hoy.)

2. Ellos...................mucho que ella se encuentre enferma.
3. Margarita no se...................muy bien después del ejercicio.
4. ¿Cómo se...................usted hoy, señor Rodríguez?
5. Ricardo...................mucho ruido en esa habitación.
6. Nosotros...................mucho frío en el invierno.
7. Los abuelos se...................muy tristes sin sus nietos.
8. El profesor y los alumnos se...................cansados de tanto trabajo.
9. Yo lo...................mucho; pero no puede ayudarle.
10. Nosotros...................no poder acompañarlos.

Supply the proper form, present tense, of DORMIR:

1. Yo no...................bien por la tarde.

   (Example: Yo no *duermo* bien por la tarde.)

2. El enfermo tomó la píldora y se***...................enseguida.
3. Ella se...................cuando oye a ese orador.
4. Cuando me acuesto yo no me...................enseguida.
5. Mi hermanito siempre...................diez horas.
6. Nosotros...................en el hotel de la esquina.
7. Tú y yo...................muy bien abrigados.
8. Ese trabajador...................demasiadas horas.
9. Esa música melodiosa me...................
10. La mamá................... al bebé con canciones de cuna.

---

* Although undergoing the same changes in the present tense, these verbs are treated separately here from those of the first and second conjugations because, as will be studied shortly, these verbs also undergo additional changes in the past tense (*el pretérito*). As has been already studied, such verbs of the first and second conjugations remain regular in the past tense (see page 82).

** *Sentir* used reflexively (*sentirse*) means *to feel.* Used non-reflexively, *sentir* means to sense or to be aware of (Sentence 5 above), also to be sorry (Sentences 9 and 10 above). Also note that *"yo me siento"* may be used to mean I feel or I sit down*.

*** *Dormir* used reflexively (*dormirse*) means to fall asleep. Used non-reflexively, *dormir* means simply to sleep (Sentences 5-6-7-8-10 above).

VOWEL CHANGING VERBS — *Continued*

The verbs *preferir, mentir, divertirse,* and *morir* belong to the same group as *sentir,* and *dormir,* studied in the previous lesson. The first three of these verbs (*preferir, mentir, divertirse*) change the vowel *e* of their stem to *ie* when the accent falls upon this vowel; they are thus conjugated exactly like *sentir.* *Morir* changes the vowel *o* of its stem to *ue; morir* is thus conjugated exactly like *dormir* (see page 83).

preferir (yo *prefiero,* usted *prefiere,* él *prefiere,* etc.).
mentir (yo *miento,* usted *miente,* él *miente,* etc.).
divertirse (yo me *divierto,* usted se *divierte,* él se *divierte,* etc.).
morirse (yo me *muero,* usted se *muere,* él se *muere,* etc.).

Supply the correct present tense for of the verbs in parentheses.

1. Ella siempre (divertirse) en las fiestas de Francisco.

   (Example: Ella siempre *se divierte* en las fiestas de Francisco.)

2. Yo (preferir) ir al campo con María.

3. Usted (morirse) de risa con los cuentos de Juan.

4. Esos jóvenes (divertirse) en el baile de máscaras.

5. Ellos (preferir) ir al cine con sus amigas.

6. El nunca le (mentir) a su profesor.

7. Mi amigo Luis (mentir) mucho, pero en broma.

8. Ustedes (divertirse) jugando a la pelota.

9. Tú siempre (preferir) ir al cine en vez de ir al baile.

10. Nosotros (mentir) para disculparnos.

11. Esos animalitos (morirse) si no comen.

12. Yo (morirse) de miedo oyendo esos cuentos fantásticos.

13. Guillermo (preferir) comer en su propia casa.

14. Los estudiantes (divertirse) jugando al balompié.

15. Ustedes (preferir) descansar hoy antes de viajar mañana.

16. Tú no (mentir) porque sabes que te criticarán.

17. La madre (morirse) de sufrimiento por la ausencia de su hijo.

18. Tus tonterías no me (divertir).

19. Julio (preferir) la vida en la ciudad a la vida en el campo.

20. Si tú (mentir) te castigarán.

84

VOWEL CHANGING -IR VERBS (PEDIR, REPETIR)

A special group of third conjugation verbs change the vowel *e* of their stem to *i* in the present tense when the stress or accent falls upon this vowel. The verbs *pedir* and *repetir* are both typical of this group.

	pedir				*repetir*		
yo	pido	nosotros	pedimos*	yo	repito	nosotros	repetimos*
tú	pides	(vosotros	pedís)	tú	repites	(vosotros	repetís)
usted, él, ella	pide	ustedes, ellos	piden	usted, él, ella	repite	ustedes, ellos	repiten

---

Supply the correct present tense form of PEDIR.

1. Yo nunca (pedir) favores a nadie.

   (Example: Yo nunca *pido* favores a nadie.)

2. Ustedes siempre (pedir) prestados los libros.
3. El empleado (pedir) aumento de sueldo al dueño.
4. Carlos no (pedir) ayuda a sus vecinos.
5. Nosotros (pedir) varios artículos por correo.
6. Tú no (pedir) limosnas a nadie.
7. Elena y Tomasa (pedir) dinero a su mamá para la merienda.
8. Ud. (pedir) más respeto para los ancianos.
9. El médico no (pedir) muy altos honorarios.
10. Ella algunas veces (pedir) prestado un sombrero a su amiga.

Supply the correct present tense form of REPETIR:

1. Yo (repetir) los ejercicios varias veces.

   (*Example*: Yo *repito* los ejercicios varias veces.)

2. En esa canción se (repetir) el tema varias veces.
3. El loro (repetir) todo lo que oye.
4. Nosotros (repetir) la noticia por la radio.
5. Horacio siempre (repetir) ese cuento tan pesado.
6. Yo (repetir) algunas veces las lecciones difíciles.
7. ¿Por qué (repetir) ella todo lo que le cuentan?
8. En ese anuncio (repetir) el número del teléfono.
9. Ustedes nunca (repetir) nada de lo que oyen.
10. Los malos estudiantes (repetir) los errores.

---

* Note again that, as in the case of all vowel-changing verbs, the first person plural remains regular since the accent does not fall upon the vowel of the stem but, instead, upon the first syllable of the ending.

VOWEL CHANGING ·IR VERBS — *Continued*

Other verbs belonging to the same group as *pedir* and *repetir*, studied in the previous lesson, are *servir, reírse, vestirse, despedirse*. All of these verbs change the vowel of their stem from *e* to *i* in the present tense when the accent falls upon this vowel. They are thus conjugated exactly like *pedir* and *repetir* (see page 85).

– servir	(yo *sirvo*, usted *sirve*, él *sirve*, etc.).	
reírse	(yo me *río*, usted se *ríe*, él se *ríe*, etc.).	PEDIR
vestirse	(yo me *visto*, usted se *viste*, él se *viste*, etc.).	
despedirse	(yo me *despido*, usted se *despide*, él se *despide*, etc.).	

Supply the correct present tense form of ~~REPETIR~~.

1. Mi tía siempre (vestirse) muy despacio.

   (Example: Mi tía siempre *se viste* muy despacio.)

2. Los niños (reírse) mucho con los cuentos de su abuelo.

3. El camarero (servir) el almuerzo a esas señoras.

4. Antonio (pedir) más comida porque tiene hambre.

5. Las esposas (despedir) de sus esposos en la estación.

6. Mis amigos (reírse) en el cine con las películas cómicas.

7. Yo (vestirse) con ropa limpia todos los días.

8. Yo no (repetir) lo que me dijiste.

9. Ese traje no (servir), bótalo o regálalo.

10. Nosotros (reírse) de esos letreros tan feos.

11. El sacerdote ya no (pedir) tanto dinero para la iglesia.

12. Carmen y Lucía (vestirse) siempre a la última moda.

13. Yo (repetir) fácilmente esas fechas de memoria.

14. Cuando salimos para el Brasil (despedirse) de nuestros amigos.

15. Tu hijito siempre (pedir) más juguetes.

16. Ustedes (servir) para ese trabajo.

17. Yo nunca (vestirse) delante de otras personas.

18. (Repetir) ese chiste, Juan.

19. Yo (servir) a mis semejantes como Dios manda.

20. (Pedir) un refresco para mí, Tomás.

21. La señora (despedir) a la criada porque no trabaja bien.

22. El (reírse) mucho con los chistes de Juan.

86

Supply the correct present tense form of the verbs in parentheses. Follow example.

1. Yo (preferir) trabajar menos.

   (Example: Yo prefiero trabajar menos.)

2. Usted (repetir) todos esos verbos en voz alta.

3. Ella frecuentemente (dormirse) en el cine.

4. Nosotros (sentirse) muy impacientes sin recibir cartas.

5. Alfonso (reírse) de las gracias de su nieto.

6. Esas plantas (morirse) si no las riegan.

7. Ellos (divertirse) durante la excursión al campo.

8. Tú (preferir) quedarte en casa en vez de ir al cine.

9. Margarita no (mentir) jamás.

10. El (pedir) una llamada por teléfono a larga distancia.

11. Tus amigos (vestirse) con trajes muy raros.

12. El novio (despedirse) de su novia en el jardín.

13. Estas herramientas no (servir) para nada.

14. ¿Por qué (dormirse) usted en el sillón?

15. Enriqueta (servir) la mesa con mucho gusto.

16. Las cotorras y los loros (repetir) lo que oyen.

17. Ellas (vestirse) ante el espejo grande.

18. Juana no (sentirse) muy bien desde esta mañana.

19. Tu vecino siempre le (pedir) prestado su abrigo a José.

20. Nosotros (dormir) en la alcoba del tercer piso.

21. Mis condiscípulos (despedir) el año con una gran fiesta.

22. ¿Qué (preferir) usted, helado o fruta?

23. Yo no te (mentir), Alfredo; esa es la pura verdad.

87

VOWEL CHANGING ·IR VERBS

All of the verbs of the third conjugation which undergo a change in their root vowel in the present tense (pages 84-87) also have one slight irregularity in the preterit. They change the *e* of their stem to *i*, or the *o* of their stem to *u* in the third person singular and plural of the past tense (*el pretérito*). The following conjugations of *sentir* and *dormir* are typical; that is, *sentir* is typical of those verbs changing *e* to *i* in the third person singular and plural of the past tense; *dormir* is typical of those verbs changing *o* to *u*.

	sentir			*dormir*	
yo sentí	nosotros sentimos		yo dormí	nosotros dormimos	
tú sentiste	(vosotros sentisteis)		tú dormiste	(vosotros dormisteis)	
usted él, ella } *sintió*	ustedes ellos } *sintieron*		usted él, ella } *durmió*	ustedes ellos } *durmieron*	

Supply the preterit of SENTIR.

1. Yo no (sentirse) bien ayer.

   (Example: Yo no *me sentí* bien ayer.)

2. Roberto no (sentirse) bien en toda la semana.
3. Yo no (sentirse) bien en toda la semana.
4. Nosotros nunca (sentirse) bien durante el invierno.
5. Usted (sentir) muchas molestias durante el viaje a la Florida.
6. Ellas (sentirse) muy tristes por la ausencia de la madre.
7. Jorge y Fernando (sentirse) cansados después del juego de béisbol.
8. El (sentir) mucho no vernos cuando fue a México.
9. Ellos (sentir) mucho ruido durante la noche pasada.
10. El profesor (sentir) mal esta mañana.

Supply the preterit of DORMIR.

1. El niño (dormir) muy mal anoche.

   (Example: El niño *durmió* muy mal anoche.)

2. Ellos (dormirse) hasta muy tarde.
3. Las muchachas no (dormirse) durante el largo viaje.
4. Mi amigo Jaime (dormirse) al oír el discurso del candidato.
5. ¿Cuándo (dormir) la siesta ei pobre anciano?
6. La abuela (dormirse) sentada en el sillón.
7. Mi padre (dormir) dos horas en la hamaca.
8. Yo (dormirse) enseguida cuando tomé una píldora antes de acostarme.
9. El centinela no (dormir) en toda la noche.
10. Nosotros (dormirse) enseguida que apagaron la luz.

VOWEL CHANGING -IR VERBS (el pretérito) — *Continued*

In the previous exercise we studied the preterite of *sentir* and *dormir*, typical of all vowel-changing -*ir* verbs in their conjugation in this tense. Other vowel changing verbs of this conjugation which are conjugated in the same way as *sentir* or *dormir* are *preferir, mentir, divertirse, morir, pedir, repetir, servir, reírse, vestirse, despedirse* (pages 84-86). The chief irregularity to be noted in the preterite of all these verbs is that *e* of the stem changes to *i*, and *o* changes to *u* in the third person singular and plural (see previous exercise, page 88).

> Juan *se divirtió* mucho en la fiesta anoche.
> Todos *repitieron* el mismo cuento.

Supply the preterite of the verbs in parentheses.

1. Muchos soldados (morir) en la última guerra.

   (Example: Muchos soldados *murieron* en la última guerra.)

2. Aquellos niños (divertirse) en la fiesta de los Reyes Magos.
3. Esos automóviles viejos no (servir) para nada.
4. Yo no creo que ella (mentir).
5. Julián (dormir) la siesta los sábados y domingos.
6. Mi profesor me (pedir) la tarea.
7. Ella (preferir) el vestido rosado al vestido azul.
8. Ustedes (sentir) mucho la desgracia ocurrida a su vecino.
9. Todos (vestirse) con trajes raros en el carnaval.
10. El niño (repetir) muy bien la tabla de multiplicar.
11. Abrahán Lincoln (morir) en el año 1865.
12. El (preferir) el anillo de oro que vio en la vidriera.
13. La señorita y su mamá (sentirse) muy cansadas después de las compras.
14. ¿Tú (despedirse) de tus compañeros de la escuela?
15. Ayer ellos no (dormir) en su habitación.
16. Las niñas de Lucía (divertirse) mucho jugando con sus muñecas.
17. ¿Por qué usted no (divertirse), amigo?
18. Yo creo que todos (mentir).
19. Rafael (pedir) un aumento de sueldo al patrón.
20. Miguel no (reírse) de los chistes del payaso.
21. Esa joven (vestirse) con mucha elegancia.
22. ¿Qué plato (servir) a Ud. el camarero?

Change the following form the present tense to the preterit.

1. El pide (El _pidió_)
2. Yo miento (Yo _mentí_)
3. Ella se muere _se murió_
4. Usted sirve _sirvió_
5. Tú repites _repetiste_
6. Ustedes se ríen _rieron_
7. Nosotros sentimos _sentimos_
8. Ellas se visten _vistieron_
9. Nadie siente _sintió_
10. Usted se despide _despidió_
11. Alguien repite _repitió_
12. Yo prefiero _preferí_
13. Ella se viste _vistió_
14. ¿Quién se ríe? _rió_
15. Andrés miente _mintió_
16. Antonia se despide _despidió_
17. Ellos prefieren _prefirieron_
18. Todos ríen _rieron_
19. Yo no me duermo _dormí_
20. ¿Quiénes sirven? _sirvieron_
21. ¿Por qué se divierte? _divirtió_
22. Ella repite todo _repitió_
23. María se duerme _durmió_

24. Nosotras servimos _servimos_
25. ¿Por qué no sirve? _sirvió_
26. Algunos duermen _durmieron_
27. Rafael se despide _despidió_
28. Yo nunca pido _pedí_
29. Usted lo prefiere _prefirió_
30. Tú lo sientes _sentiste_
31. El niño no se viste _vistió_
32. ¿Quién no pide? _pidió_
33. ¿Quién se muere? _murió_
34. Yo me río _reí_
35. Ellas no sirven _sirvieron_
36. El médico miente _mintió_
37. Tú lo prefieres negro _preferiste_
38. Usted no se despide _despidió_
39. Yo me visto de limpio _vestí_
40. ¿Por qué muere? _murió_
41. Alguien se ríe _rió_ _rió_
42. Ella prefiere irse _prefirió_
43. Tú no duermes bien _dormiste_
44. Luis se divierte _divirtió_
45. Roberto repite mucho _repitió_
46. Yo pido más dulces _pedí_

visto

Irregular verbs ESTAR, ANDAR (el pretérito)

Estar and *andar* share the same irregularity in the preterit; the endings are irregular while the stems remain unchanged. Study the conjugations of these two high-frequency verbs.

	andar				estar	
yo	*estuve*	nosotros	*estuvimos*	yo	*anduve*	nosotros *anduvimos*
tú	*estuviste*	(vosotros	*estuvisteis*)	tú	*anduviste*	(vosotros *anduvisteis*)
usted, él, ella	*estuvo*	ustedes, ellos	*estuvieron*	usted, él, ella	*anduvo*	ustedes, ellos *anduvieron*

Change the subjects of each sentence below, substituting in its place the nine given subjects. Make all necessary changes. Follow example.

1. *Mi madre* estuvo de compras todo el día.

   (Example: *Yo* estuve de compras todo el día.)

   1. Nosotros ....
   2. Ellas ....
   3. Tú y yo ....
   4. Su hija ....
   5. Ellos ....
   6. Ustedes ....
   7. La maestra ....
   8. Tomás y Luis ....
   9. Tú ....

2. *Yo* anduve por el parque anoche.

   (Example: *El* anduvo por el parque anoche.)

   1. Usted ....
   2. Nosotras ....
   3. Yo ....
   4. María y yo ....
   5. Tú ....
   6. Juan y Elena ....
   7. Los soldados ....
   8. Antonio ....
   9. Mi profesor ....

3. ¿Dónde estuvo *ella* ayer?

   1. ellos ....
   2. yo ....
   3. los niños ....
   4. nosotros ....
   5. tú ....
   6. Roberto ....
   7. el médico ....
   8. Esther y Jesús ......
   9. el señor Pérez ....

4. ¿Anduvo *usted* por el tejado de la casa?

   1. ellos ....
   2. la paloma ....
   3. mis primos ....
   4. el pintor ....
   5. tú y él ....
   6. el mono ....
   7. los gatos ....
   8. Enrique ....
   9. ustedes ....

5. *La maestra* estuvo enferma toda la semana.

   1. Ellas ....
   2. Nosotros ....
   3. La señora López ....
   4. Inés y Felipe ....
   5. Tú ....
   6. El ....
   7. Mi vecina ....
   8. Yo ....
   9. Sus padres ....

6. *Ella* anda con su libro bajo el brazo.

   1. Tú ....
   2. El ....
   3. Los profesores ....
   4. Nosotros ....
   5. El y ella ....
   6. Margarita ....
   7. Ustedes ....
   8. El estudiante ....
   9. Los artistas ....

PAST IMPERFECT TENSE (el imperfecto)

The past imperfect tense is the easiest to form and the most regular of all tenses in Spanish. The endings for verbs of the first conjugation (-ar verbs) are *aba, abas, aba, ábamos, (abais), aban*. The conjugation of the typical first conjugation verb *hablar* follows:

yo	habl*aba*		nosotros	habl*ábamos*
tú	habl*abas*		(vosotros	habl*abais*)
usted } él, ella }	habl*aba*		ustedes } ellos }	habl*aban*

Whereas the preterit, as studied previously (see page 45), describes a single and completed past action, the past imperfect tense is used to describe a repeated or habitual action in the past. It is equivalent in this usage to the English "used to":

Yo *fumaba* mucho — I used to smoke very much.
El *habla* el francés bien — He spoke (used to speak) French well.

Supply the past imperfect tense form of the verbs in parentheses.

1. Martín siempre (contestar) las cartas.

   (Example: Martín siempre *contestaba* las cartas.)

2. Ella nunca (levantarse) antes de las diez de la mañana.
3. Mi profesor me (hablar) frecuentemente en español.
4. Nosotros (estar) muy ocupados cuando él llamaba.
5. El año pasado, Ernesto (fumar) mucho, ahora no.
6. Usted me (llamar) antes por la noche.
7. Yo no (jugar) ningún deporte en el colegio.
8. Ellos (gastar) mil pesos todos los meses.
9. La profesora (explicar) las lecciones en alta voz.
10. Antonio (tocar) el órgano en la iglesia.
11. Yo nunca (estudiar) mucho en la Universidad.
12. María (comprar) antes en esa tienda de ropas.
13. El doctor (tratar) de curar al enfermo.
14. Esos empleados (cambiar) sus cheques en el banco.
15. Juana siempre (necesitar) que le ayudaran.
16. La enferma se (cansar) al subir por las escaleras.
17. Antes, Bernardo (terminar) sus tareas a las nueve.
18. El novio (entrar) en la casa de la novia.
19. Ellas siempre (acordarse) de dar las gracias.
20. Nosotros (encontrarse) en el parque todas las tardes.

The endings for verbs of the second and third conjugations (*-er* and *-ir* verbs) in the past imperfect tense are *ia, ias, ia, iamos, (iais), ian*. The conjugations of the typical verbs *comer* and *vivir* follows:

comer				vivir			
yo	comía	nosotros	comíamos	yo	vivía	nosotros	vivíamos
tú	comías	(vosotros	comíais)	tú	vivías	(vosotros	vivíais)
usted, él, ella	comía	ustedes, ellos	comían	usted, él, ella	vivía	ustedes, ellos	vivían

---

Supply the past imperfect tense form of the verbs in parentheses.

1. El le (escribir) varias cartas a María.

   (Example: El le *escribía* a menudo a María.)

2. Ellos no (saber) traducir las oraciones.

3. Los turistas (venir) al hotel del lago todos los veranos.

4. Yo siempre (salir) temprano para mi trabajo.

5. Carmen (leer) una novela todas las semanas.

6. La maestra (leer) el periódico en el patio.

7. Los hijos (venir) a almorzar todos los domingos.

8. Yo siempre (tener) muy poco dinero en el bolsillo.

9. Juan (vender) automóviles durante sus vacaciones.

10. Carlota antes (recibir) muchas cartas de sus amigas.

11. Nosotros (salir) a pasear los domingos con Andrés.

12. Ellas (vivir) en el hotel de la colina.

13. Miguel (vivir) antes en Caracas, Venezuela.

14. Tú antes (recibir) muchos regalos en la Navidad.

15. Antonia, cuando era joven (escribir) bonitas poesías.

16. Los niños desabrigados (coger) catarro en el invierno.

17. Las muchachas (lucir) muy bonitas en los bailes.

18. Muchos estudiantes (perder) sus libros en la escuela.

19. Yo (vestir) bien todos los días.

20. El señor López (vivir) desordenadamente cuando era soltero.

21. Ellos (vender) sus joyas cuando (querer) dinero.

PAST IMPERFECT TENSE — *Continued*

We learned previously (page 92) that the past imperfect tense is used to describe a repeated or habitual past action, and is equivalent in this usage to the English *used* to (Yo *fumaba* mucho — I used to smoke very much). This tense also another use in Spanish. It is used to describe a continuing past action, partic ly an action which was continuing when something else happened. In this v ,a it has the same meaning as the past continuous tense in English.

> Ellos *hablaban** (were speaking) español cuando entré.
> Juan *leía* un libro cuando llegamos.

In the blanks, supply the past imperfect tense form of the verbs in parentheses.

1. Ellos (pasear) ayer en la playa cuando los vi.

   (Example: Ellos *paseaban* ayer en la playa.)

2. Luisa (jugar) con su gatito.
3. Nosotros (estar) en el trabajo a esa hora.
4. Ellos (estudiar) el idioma francés en París.
5. Yo (prepararse) para el examen del lunes.
6. Las clases siempre (empezar) a las ocho de la mañana.
7. Cristóbal (llamar) todas las noches a tu hermano.
8. Tú (tener) poco tiempo para trabajar.
9. Yo nunca (volver) tan tarde de la fiesta.
10. Cuando ellos (esperar) el autobús yo (pasar) por allí.
11. ¿Cuántos estudiantes (saber) un poco de español antes de comenzar el curso?
12. Ella (cantar) mientras yo (dibujar) el mapa.
13. Cuando Regino (salir) Dolores (entrar).
14. (Llover) mucho esta mañana.
15. La mamá (leer) con emoción la carta de su hijo.
16. Cuando yo lo llamé, él (estar)** para salir.
17. El pobre anciano no (sentirse) bien de salud.
18. Tu puerta (estar) abierta cuando yo llegué.
19. ¿Qué (hacer) ella cuando la llamaron por teléfono?
20. Yo (tener) cinco años cuando empecé a aprender a leer.
21. Los comerciantes (necesitar) más dinero para el negocio.
22. (Tronar) mucho durante la tormenta de anoche.

---

*The progressive form of *hablar* (*estaban hablando*) is more common in such cases but the use of the past imperfect tense is equally correct.

**Estar para, followed by an infinitive, has the meaning of "to be about to" or "to be on the point of" doing something. Thus, *ellos estaban para salir* means "they were about to leave".

The student should note that various verbs such as *creer, saber, pensar, tener, poder, deber, sentirse* are generally used in the past imperfect tense in Spanish rather than in the preterite as is done in English. The implication in Spanish is that these verbs, in most situations, suggest a state of mind or condition which prevailed for some time rather than something that took place only at a specified moment:

> Yo *creía* (I thought) que Juan estaba enfermo.*
> No *sabíamos* (we did not know) que ellos hablaban español.

Supply the past imperfect tense form of the verbs in parentheses.

1. María no (saber) que yo hablaba inglés.

   (Example: María no *sabía* que yo hablaba inglés.)

2. Yo no (poder) hacer esos ejercicios tan difíciles.

3. Juan (tener) deseos de visitar su pueblo natal.

4. Ellos son ricos y (poder) comprar un automóvil de lujo.

5. Ernesto (sentir) mucho no poder prestarme el dinero.

6. Nosotros no (saber) que ella pintaba tan bien.

7. El pueblo (creer) en las bellas promesas del candidato.

8. ¿(Conocer) ellas a ese joven tan simpático?

9. ¿(Creer) usted que él (sentirse) mal?

10. El maestro no (pensar) que tenía que repasar tanto.

11. Mis compañeros (deber) muchas atenciones a sus profesores.

12. Julio (esperar) ir con ella en la excursión al campo.

13. Domingo no (saber) que estaba desaprobado en los exámenes.

14. Nosotros no (poder) entender a ese extranjero.

15. Ellos (sentirse) muy cómodos en esos asientos.

16. Los empleados (tener) que trabajar horas extras.

17. Ellas sí (deber) dinero a sus amigas.

18. No (pensar) que yo tenía cuarenta años de edad.

19. El (creer) que Tomás y Juana estaban casados.

20. Los profesores no (saber) que él estuvo en la guerra.

---

* A literal but incorrect translation of these forms in English would be, I *"was not knowing"* that John was sick — *"We were not knowing"* that they spoke Spanish.

Past imperfect tense   SER, IR

There are only two verbs of importance* which are irregular in the past imperfect tense: *ser* and *ir*. The form of these verbs changes considerably in the past imperfect tense. Study these conjugations carefully:

	ser				ir		
yo	*era*	nosotros	*éramos*	yo	*iba*	nosotros	*íbamos*
tú	*eras*	(vosotros	*erais*)	tú	*ibas*	(vosotros	*ibais*)
usted él, ella	*era*	ustedes ellos	*eran*	usted él, ella	*iba*	ustedes ellos	*iban*

Supply the past imperfect tense form of SER.

1. Ellos................buenos estudiantes de español.

   (Example: Ellos *eran* buenos estudiantes de español.)

2. La vecina................muy atenta con todos.
3. José y Alfredo................comerciantes en Madrid.
4. Tú................antes un buen pelotero.
5. Nosotros................aficionados a la natación.
6. El policía................muy exigente con los automovilistas.
7. Rafael y Benito................mensajeros de esa farmacia.
8. Yo no................partidario de prestarle los cien pesos pero se los dimos.
9. Alberto................el secretario de ese club cuando yo ingresé.
10. Ustedes................buenos compañeros en la escuela cuando niños.

Supply the past imperfect tense form of IR.

1. Ella siempre................a su trabajo en bicicleta.
   (*Example*: Ella siempre *iba* a su trabajo en bicicleta.)
2. Yo................a pasear todos los domingos al campo cuando tenía automóvil.
3. Nosotros................con Luis para comprar naranjas.
4. Ayer yo................muy cansado para mi casa y me dormí en el autobús.
5. Ud. siempre................silbando esa bonita canción.
6. Los ingenieros................en automóvil a la mina.
7. Todas las mujeres................a la iglesia el domingo.
8. El estudiante de física................a Nueva York a ver a su familia todos los años.
9. ¿A dónde................Esteban ayer por la tarde?
10. Tú................demasiado rápido y por eso chocaste.

---

* The verb *ver* is also irregular in the past imperfect tense, although only slightly so. The letter *e* is simply added to the stem. It is thus conjugated: *veía, veías, veía, veía, veíamos, veían, veían*. Practice sentences with *ver* appear in later exercises.

Past imperfect tense (*Use of* IBA A)

Note that the past imperfect tense of *ir* (*iba, ibas, iba, íbamos,* etc.) is used together with the preposition *a* and an infinitive to express an action in the past that was planned but did not occur. It is thus used exactly like its equivalent in English *was* (or *were*) *going to.*

Nosotros *íbamos a jugar* (were going to play) tenis ayer, pero hacía mucho frío.

Yo *iba a llamarla* (was going to call you up), pero no tenía su número de teléfono.

Supply the past imperfect tense form of IR plus the preposition **A**. Also include the infinitive appearing in parentheses.

1. Ella.................(invitar) a Luis anoche, pero no tenía su dirección.

   (Example: Ella *iba a invitar* a Luis anoche, pero no tenía su dirección.)

2. Yo.................(llamar) a mi amigo Juan, pero no me acordé.

3. Ustedes.................(trabajar) por la noche si les avisaban.

4. Tú.................(estudiar) la lección equivocada.

5. El arquitecto.................(diseñar) el edificio, pero no pudo.

6. Nosotros.................(ver) cuánto dinero teníamos en el banco.

7. Enrique.................(vender) la tienda, pero no tenía autorización.

8. El.................(jugar) ajedrez, pero no tenía compañero.

9. ¿Por qué ellos.................(dejar) los estudios?

10. ¿Dónde.................(matricular) Rosa a su hija?

11. Mi tía.................(coser) un vestido, pero no tenía máquina.

12. ....(acostarse) pero llegó visita.

13. María y Julia.................(pasear) al parque por la tarde.

14. Los novios.................(casarse) después de las Navidades.

15. El.................(trabajar) en el taller pero no lo llamaron.

16. Las señoras.................(visitar) a Isabel, pero se extraviaron.

17. Yo.................(levantarse) temprano pero me quedé dormido.

18. Ernesto y Benjamín.................(comprar) una finca, pero no tenían dinero.

19. Ellos.................(cocinar) la carne, pero no sabían cómo hacerlo.

20. El médico.................(curar) al enfermo pero éste no le hacía caso.

Change the following from present tense to past imperfect tense. (Be sure to be able to explain the change in meaning in each case). Follow example.

1. Ellos *escriben* cartas a sus amigos.

   (Example: Ellos *escribían* cartas a sus amigos.)

2. Tomás nunca *estudia* en su casa.

3. Ella siempre *viene* acompañada por la noche.

4. Yo *veo* todos los días al cartero.

5. Tú *pones* el sombrero sobre la mesa.

6. Nosotros *tenemos* muchas ganas de bailar.

7. Mario *viene* a la escuela en automóvil.

8. A mí me *gusta* montar en bicicleta.

9. Ustedes *se divierten* con sus chistes.

10. Ricardo *hace* sus ejercicios muy bien.

11i Ella *sale* de la iglesia a las diez de la mañana.

12. Juana *se viste* elegantemente.

13. José y Pablo *miran* las estrellas con un telescopio.

14. Ella *sabe* recitar bonitas poesías.

15. Usted *conoce* muy bien su profesión.

16. Ella *duerme* siempre hasta las nueve de la mañana.

17. Tú *eres* un estudiante muy aplicado.

18. Nosotros *estamos* preparados para la lucha.

19. El *anda* descalzo todo el día.

20. A mí me *gusta* bañarme en la piscina.

21. Ellos *pasan* muchas horas contemplando el valle.

22. Pedro *repite* todo lo que dice el profesor.

23. ¿Por dónde *anda* la prima de Tomás?

24. Mis amigos *me saludan* el día de año nuevo.

FUTURE TENSE

The future tense of all three conjugations (*ar, er,* and *ir* verbs) is formed in the same way. To the infinitive of the verb are added the endings *é, ás, emos, án.*

hablar

yo	hablaré	nosotros	hablaremos
tú	hablarás	(vosotros	hablaréis)
usted, él, ella	hablará	ustedes, ellos	hablarán

comer

yo	comeré	nosotros	comeremos
tú	comerás	(vosotros	comeréis)
usted, él, ella	comerá	ustedes, ellos	comerán

vivir

yo	viviré	nosotros	viviremos
tú	vivirás	(vosotros	viviréis)
usted, él, ella	vivirá	ustedes, ellos	vivirán

The future tense is used exactly as in English to describe some future action. In particular, it is used to express promise, determination, or assurance regarding some future act. (Examples: Yo le *pagaré* el dinero mañana. Juan nos *ayudará* con el trabajo).

Supply the future tense of the verbs in parentheses.

1. El (trabajar) muchas horas extraordinarias hasta terminar el trabajo.
   (Example: El *trabajará* muchas horas extraordinarias hasta terminar el trabajo.)
2. Nosotros (estudiar) dos nuevas lecciones de español.
3. Ustedes (volver) muy pronto de San José.
4. María (vestirse) para ir a la iglesia el domingo.
5. ¿Qué (necesitar) ese mecánico para arreglar la máquina?
6. El profesor (dar) los resultados del examen.
7. Ellos (estar) descansando toda la tarde.
8. El profesor (hablar) en la reunión de maestros.
9. Usted (visitar) al vecino que está enfermo.
10. Yo (ir) de pesca en mis vacaciones.
11. Los García (regresar) pronto de ese corto viaje.
12. La abuela (vivir) con sus nietos en el campo.
13. Ellos (quedarse) sin empleo si no llegan a tiempo al trabajo.
14. La paloma (volver) al palomar.
15. Ella (ver) a sus hermanos en su viaje a Panamá.
16. Antonio y Juana (recibir) muchos regalos en el aniversario de bodas.
17. Las niñas del asilo (jugar) con sus nuevas muñecas.
18. Los alumnos (enseñar) los resultados de los exámenes a sus padres.
19. Ellos no (comer) hoy en el restaurante de la esquina.
20. El escritor (revisar) su libro antes de llevarlo a la imprenta.
21. Los Rodríguez (traer) sus muebles desde Caracas.

99

In the blanks, supply the preterite (*el pretérito*) and the future tense of each of the following present tense verbs.

Present Tense	Past Tense	Future Tense
1. Yo estudio	*Yo estudié*	*Yo estudiaré*
2. Ella está	ELLA estuvo	ELLA estará
3. Usted pinta	Usted pintó	pintará
4. El compra	compró	comprará
5. Ellos comen	comieron	COMERÁN
6. Julia escribe	escribió	escribirán
7. Tú hablas	hablaste	hablarás
8. Ernesto y Luis viven	VIVIERON	VIVIRÁN
9. Ustedes necesitan	NECESITARON	NECESITARÁN
10. Yo vuelvo	VOLVÍ	VOLVERÉ
11. Alguien oye	OYÓ	OIRÁ
12. Enriqueta se viste	VISTIÓ	VESTIRÁ
13. El médico cura	CURÓ	CURARÁ
14. El panadero canta	CANTÓ	CANTARÁ
15. El carpintero llega	LLEGÓ	LLEGARÁ
16. El cartero llama	LLAMÓ	LLAMARÁ
17. Los niños juegan	JUGARON	JUGARÁN
18. La peluquera peina	PEINÓ	PEINARÁ
19. Tú vendes	VENDISTE ~~VINISTE~~	VENDERÁS
20. Ustedes preparan	PREPARARON	PREPARARÁN
21. El almuerza	ALMORZÓ	ALMORZARÁ
22. Benjamín lee	LEYÓ	LEERÁ
23. Nosotras vamos	FUIMOS	IREMOS
24. El bebé se duerme	DURMIÓ	DORMIRÁ
25. La mamá se levanta	LEVANTÓ	LAVANTARÁ
26. Yo termino	TERMINÉ	TERMINARÉ

100

Future tense   SABER, PODER

All verbs have regular endings in the future tense, but a few common verbs have irregular stems. In the verbs *saber* and *poder*, the *e* of the infinite is simply dropped.

	saber					poder		
yo	*sabré*	nosotros	*sabremos*		yo	*podré*	nosotros	*podremos*
tú	*sabrás*	(vosotros	*sabréis*)		tú	*podrás*	(vosotros	*podréis*)
usted } él, ella }	*sabrá*	ustedes } ellos }	*sabrán*		usted } él, ella }	*podrá*	ustedes } ellos }	*podrán*

Two other verbs conjugated in the same way as *saber* and *poder* are *caber* and *haber*. *Caber* is conjugated: *cabré, cabrás, cabrá, cabrá, cabremos, (cabréis), cabrán, cabrán.* *Haber* is conjugated: *habré, habrás habrá, habrá, habremos, (habréis), habrán, habrán.*

Supply the future tense of the verbs in parentheses.

1. Ella no (poder) aprender muy bien ese vocabulario.   *PODRÁ*
   (Example: Ella no *podrá* aprender muy bien ese vocabulario.)
2. Samuel (saber) mañana los resultados de esos problemas. *SABRÁ*
3. Mañana (haber)* muchos estudiantes ausentes. *HABRÁ*
4. Yo creo que no (caber) tantos libros en esa caja. *CABRÁN*
5. Ustedes (poder) recoger todos esos papeles del suelo. *PODRÁN*
6. El no (saber) muy bien la tabla de multiplicar. *SABRÁ*
7. Ella cree que (haber) un gran baile mañana. *HABRÁ*
8. Nadie (saber) quien fue el autor del robo. *SABRÁ*
9. Ernesto y Octavio (poder) competir en las cárreras. *PODRÁN*
10. (Haber) varios estudiantes esperando para matricularse. *HABRÁ*
11. Todos mis amigos (saber) muy pronto mi nueva dirección. *SABRÁN*
12. Dice el policía que no (haber) más desórdenes. *HABRÁ*
13. Yo (saber) manejar avión muy pronto. *SABRÉ*
14. Ustedes no (poder) comprar esa casa tan cara. *PODRÁN*
15. El doctor sí (saber) la enfermedad que él padece. *SABRÁ*
16. ¿Crees tú que (caber) todas esas maletas en el automóvil? *CABRÁN*
17. Yo pienso que no (haber) elecciones el mes que viene. *HABRÁ*
18. Ellos no (poder) hablar bien el español en tan pocos meses. *PODRÁN*
19. Alguien (saber) donde vive ella. *SABRÁ*
20. Tú no (poder) encontrar la llave de tu casa. *PODRÁS*
21. Nosotras (caber) bien en tu auto convertible. *CABREMOS*
22. ¿(Haber) alguien en casa a esa hora? *HABRÁ*

---

* *Haber* as an independent or principal verb has the following forms in the present, past, past perfect, and future tenses: hay, hubo, había, habrá. As a principal verb, *haber* is the equivalent of the English "there is" or "there are". Thus, *Hay muchos estudiantes ausentes hoy*, means "There are many students absent today". *Habrá muchos estudiantes ausentes mañana* means "There will be many students absent tomorrow, etc."

Future tense   PONER, TENER

Two other common verbs with regular endings, but irregular stems in the future, are *poner* and *tener*. In these verbs the letter *d* replaces the characteristic *e* of the infinitive.

Two other verbs conjugated in the future in the same way as *poner* and *tener* are *salir* and *venir*. *Salir* is conjugated: *saldré, saldrás, saldrá, saldrá, saldremos, (saldreis), saldrán, saldrán.* *Venir* is conjugated: *vendré, vendrás vendrá, vendrá vendremos, (vendreis), vendrán, vendrán.*

	poner			tener	
yo *pondré*	nosotros *pondremos*		yo *tendré*	nosotros *tendremos*	
tú *pondrás*	(vosotros *pondréis*)		tú *tendrás*	(vosotros *tendréis*)	
usted} él, ella} *pondrá*	ustedes} ellos} *pondrán*		usted} él, ella} *tendrá*	ustedes} ellos} *tendrán*	

Supply the future tense of the verbs in parentheses.

1. Usted (poner) el sombrero sobre la silla. *Pondrá*
   (Example: Usted *pondrá* el sombrero sobre la silla.)

2. Yo (tener) mucho dinero. *Tendré*

3. Julia y Carmen (venir) a la fiesta de mi cumpleaños. *Vendrán*

4. Ustedes (poner) un techo al patio. *Pondrán*

5. Los Fernández (salir) de viaje para California. *Saldrán*

6. Yo (salir) muy temprano mañana para ir de pesca. *Saldré*

7. Tomás (poner) mucha atención a las explicaciones de su profesor. *Pondrá*

8. Las costureras (tener) quince días de vacaciones. *Tendrán*

9. Mis amigos (tener) que trabajar más para ganar más. *Tendrán*

10. Tú (ponerse) nervioso en el examen. *Te Pondrás*

11. Yo (venir) a las clases el próximo viernes. *Vendré*

12. Las cartas (salir) en el próximo correo. *Saldrán*

13. El cartero (poner) las cartas en el buzón. *Pondrá*

14. Las peluqueras (tener) que limpiar el salón. *Tendrán*

15. ¿Cuándo (salir) usted para España? *Saldrá*

16. ¿Dónde (poner) ella las flores que le regalaron? *Pondrá*

17. Los criados (poner) la mesa enseguida. *Pondrán*

18. Ellos (tener) que esperarme. *Tendrán*

19. El tren (venir) a las doce de la noche. *Vendrá*

20. Carlos y Josefa (poner) sus nombres en la puerta de la oficina. *Pondrán*

21. Yo (tener) que terminar este ejercicio de gramática. *Tendré*

102

Future tense   QUERER, HACER, DECIR

The three remaining verbs which are irregular in the future tense, and which we have yet to study, are *querer, hacer,* and *decir.* Again, the endings of these three verbs are regular in the future tense but their stems undergo a change. Their conjugations follow:

querer	yo *querré,* tú *querrás,* usted *querrá,* él *querrá,* nosotros *querremos,* (vosotros *querréis*), ustedes *querrán,* ellos *querrán.*
hacer	yo *haré,* tú *haras,* usted *hará,* él *hará,* nosotros *haremos,* (vosotros *haréis*), ustedes *harán,* ellos *harán.*
decir	yo *diré,* tú *dirás,* usted *dirá,* él *dirá,* nosotros *diremos,* (vosotros *diréis*), ustedes *dirán,* ellos *dirán.*

Supply the future tense of the verbs in parentheses.

1. Yo (hacer) todo ese trabajo hoy mismo.   *HARÉ*

   (Example: Yo *haré* todo ese trabajo hoy mismo.)

2. Ellos (querer) tomar algún refresco en la playa.   *QUERRÁN*

3. Usted (decir) lo que quiere.   *DIRÁ*

4. Nosotros (hacer) todos los ejercicios de la página veinte.   *HAREMOS*

5. Los padres (querer) ver a sus hijos.   *QUERRÁN*

6. Los estudiantes (decir) las conjugaciones de los verbos irregulares.   *DIRÁN*

7. Cristóbal (hacer) la comida.   *HARÁ*

8. El médico (querer) operar al enfermo enseguida.   *QUERRÁ*

9. Yo (hacer) un estudio interesante de esos insectos.   *HARÉ*

10. Juanita te (decir) los días de la semana en español correctamente.   *TE DIRÁ*

11. Andrés y Carmen (querer) casarse el mes que viene.   *QUERRÁN*

12. Tú (hacer) la comida para todos los invitados.   *HARÁS*

13. Nosotros (querer) mucho a nuestros sobrinos mejicanos.   *QUERREMOS*

14. Andrés (hacer) los trabajos del taller de pintura.   *HARÁ*

15. Usted (dar) los buenos días.   *DARÁ*

16. Nosotros (querer) ir al baile del casino.   *QUERREMOS*

17. Ellos (hacer) los adornos para la fiesta.   *HARÁN*

18. Usted (decir) los nombres de los nuevos miembros del club.   *DIRÁ*

19. Ellas (querer) que les regalen dulces y bombones.   *QUERRÁN*

20. Tú (hacer) todo el trabajo.   *HARÁS.*

EL FIN!

For practice with the future tense of the following regular and irregular verbs, change the subject of each of the sentences below, substituting in its place the nine given subjects. Make all necessary changes. Follow example.

1. *Yo* vendré aquí a las seis.

   (Example: El *vendrá* aquí a las seis.)

   1) Usted .... 4) Ellas .... 7) Nosotros ....
   2) Tú .... 5) María .... 8) Mis hermanos ....
   3) Ellos .... 6) Los muchachos ...... 9) Usted ....

2. *El* escribirá esa carta.

   1) Usted .... 4) Guillermo .... 7) La secretaria ....
   2) Elena .... 5) Ellos .... 8) Ustedes ....
   3) Yo .... 6) Tú .... 9) Los pintores ....

3. *Yo* hablaré español todo el tiempo en México.

   1) Ella .... 4) El .... 7) La muchacha ....
   2) Nosotras .... 5) Usted .... 8) El alumno ....
   3) Ellos .... 6) Samuel .... 9) Los empleados ......

4. *Yo* me quedaré aquí dos meses.

   1) Ella .... 4) Juan .... 7) Los abuelos ....
   2) Tú .... 5) El .... 8) La tía ....
   3) Nosotros .... 6) Usted .... 9) Los hijos ....

5. *Yo* iré en avión a San Francisco.

   1) El .... 4) Nosotros .... 7) Los soldados ....
   2) Ellos .... 5) Ustedes .... 8) El general ....
   3) Julia .... 6) Juana .... 9) La policía ....

6. *Yo* tendré mucho que hacer antes de salir.

   1) El .... 4) Usted .... 7) La criada ....
   2) Usted .... 5) Tú .... 8) Los trabajadores ....
   3) Nosotros .... 6) Ellos .... 9) El jefe ....

7. *Yo* estaré de vuelta a las seis.

   1) Ella .... 4) Margarita .... 7) El secretario ....
   2) El .... 5) Rafael .... 8) El sacerdote ....
   3) Usted .... 6) Luis y Pedro .... 9) Los choferes ....

8. *Yo* podré hacerlo mañana.

   1) Ella .... 4) El .... 7) La cocinera ....
   2) Usted .... 5) Tú .... 8) Los pintores ....
   3) Nosotros .... 6) Ustedes .... 9) Pérez y López ....

VERBS TENSE — *General Review*

For a review of both regular and irregular verbs in the various tenses so far studied, change the following present tense verbs to: 1) preterite, 2 past imperfect tense, 3) future tense. Follow example.

Present Tense	Preterite	Past Imperfect	Future
1. Yo vengo	*Yo vine*	*Yo venía*	*Yo vendré*
3. Ella dice	....	....	....
4. Tú estás	....	....	....
5. Ellos saben	....	....	....
6. Felipe hace	....	....	....
7. La Sra. Díaz es	....	....	....
8. Yo estoy	....	....	....
9. Julio quiere	....	....	....
10. El y ella ven	....	....	....
11. Usted pierde	....	....	....
12. Nosotros vamos	....	....	....
13. Ellos comen	....	....	....
14. Yo almuerzo	....	....	....
15. Ella empieza	....	....	....
16. Tú te acuestas	....	....	....
17. Yo puedo ir	....	....	....
18. Yo sé	....	....	....
19. Ellos tienen	....	....	....
20. Tú sales	....	....	....
21. Federico vuelve	....	....	....
22. Yo pierdo	....	....	....
23. Usted viene	....	....	....
24. Tomás es	....	....	....

ARTICLES — *Continued*

We learned earlier that most nouns which end in *o* are masculine and most nouns which end in *a* are feminine. The following are exceptions to this rule: *la* mano, *el* día, *el* mapa, *el* tranvía. Furthermore, certain words of Greek origin which terminate in *ma* are also masculine rather than feminine: *el* clima, *el* problema, *el* idioma, *el* drama, *el* programa. Finally, for reasons of euphony the article *el* instead of *la* is used in the singular before all feminine words beginning with *a* or *ha* (*el* agua, *el* alma, *el* hambre, *el* aula, etc.). Note that in all of these words (*agua, alma, hambre,* etc.) the tonic accent falls on the first syllable in the plural and the normal feminine article *las* is used (*las* aguas, *las* almas, etc.).

In the blanks, supply the correct definite article.

1. A ella no le agrada............clima de Chicago.

   (Example: A ella no le agrada *el* clima de Chicago.)

2. Ellos tienen............mano muy grande.

3. Yo no conozco............programa del concierto.

4. Carlos vendrá............día primero de agosto.

5. A mí me gusta hablar............idioma español.

6. Ella colgó............mapas en la pared.

7. ¿Cuál es............agua destilada?

8. Yo no puedo resolver............problema de álgebra.

9. Dice que............hambre lo mató.

10. Ella espera............tranvía en la esquina.

11. Yo pienso estudiar...............idioma portugués.

12. Dicen que............aguas de esa fuente son medicinales.

13. Ese niño tiene............manos sucias.

14. Siempre cobramos...............último día del mes.

15. Juan estudia............mapa de su país.

16. El examen será en............aula número 5.

17. En muchas ciudades............tranvía ha sido suprimido.

18. Rosa regresará............primer día del próximo mes.

19. Juanita tiene............manos muy delicadas.

20. Quiero a mis hijos con toda............alma.

SHORTENED FORMS OF ADJECTIVES

The following adjectives drop the final *o* when they precede the nouns which they modify: *bueno, malo, uno, alguno, ninguno, primero, tercero* (Examples: un *buen* hombre, el *primer* libro). No change is made, however, when they precede a feminine noun or nouns in the plural (Examples: una *buena* muchacha; en *ninguna* parte, los *primeros* libros).

The words *grande* and *ciento* lose their final syllable when placed before the nouns they modify. (Examples: una *gran* ciudad; un *gran* hombre; *cien* personas; *cien* libros). If, of course, they follow the nouns they modify, they retain their usual form. (Examples: una ciudad *grande;* la calle *ciento dos*).

A few adjectives such as *grande, pobre, caro,* change their meaning slightly when placed before the nouns they modify: un *gran* hombre (a great man); un hombre *grande* (a large man); una *pobre* mujer (a poor, *pitiful* woman); *una* mujer *pobre* (a poor, *poverty-stricken* woman).

In the blanks, supply the correct form of the adjective in parentheses when it is placed before the noun which it modifies.

1. ¿Cuál es el.................día de la semana? (primero).

   (Example: ¿Cuál es el *primer* día de la semana?)

2. Marzo es el.................mes del año (tercero).

3. Edison fue un.............inventor (grande).

4. Tengo más de.................libros en mi biblioteca (ciento).

5. Ayer fue el.................día de clases (primero).

6. Antonio es un.................compañero (bueno).

7. Julio y Andrés son muy............amigos (bueno).

8. Te diré.................día lo que sucedió (alguno).

9. Yo no traje............libro de ejercicios (ninguno).

10. Es posible que....................noche haga frío (alguno).

11. Me pagó...............pesos por el trabajo (ciento).

12. Ya terminamos la.................lección (tercero).

13. El pronombre *él* pertenece a la.................persona (tercer).

14. Inglaterra es un.................país (grande).

15. Hoy es el.................día de la semana (primero).

16. Rita no parece ser una............muchacha (malo).

17. Guillermo no es un............estudiante (malo).

18. Ellos necesitan............dinero para el negocio (alguno).

19. Martí fue un.................patriota cubano (grande.).

20. España fue el.................país de Europa que visité (tercero).

In this exercise, change the position of the adjective, shown here in italics, and place it after the noun which it modifies (see previous exercise, page 108). Follow example.

1. El próximo lunes será el *primer* día de febrero.

    (Example: El próximo lunes será el día *primero* de febrero.)

2. El nunca fue un *mal* alumno.

3. Su padre fue un *gran** hombre.

4. Esa *pobre** muchacha merece ayuda.

5. Busca la explicación en el *tercer* tomo de la enciclopedia.

6. Usted no tiene *ningún* libro que prestarme.

7. El nos dará una sorpresa un *buen* día.

8. El señor Hernández es un *gran** ciudadano.

9. Mercedes no tiene *ningún* deseo de viajar.

10. Juan parecía ser una *mala* persona.

11. Ayer fue el *tercer* día de clases.

12. Pronto estaremos en la *tercera* parte del libro.

13. No ha llamado *ningún* hombre por teléfono.

14. Ella es una *buena* vecina.

15. Fernando es un *buen* abogado.

16. Ya él aprobó el *primer* año de su carrera.

17. Ella no tiene *ningún* interés en casarse este año.

18. La ciudad de La Habana tiene un *buen* clima.

19. Ellos no tienen *ningún* entusiasmo por los estudios.

20. La pobre madre recibió una *mala* noticia.

21. Mañana problablemente será un *buen* día.

---

* Be able to explain the change of meaning here when this adjective is shifted to follow the noun —see page 107.

COMPARISON OF ADJECTIVES — *Comparative Degree*

The comparative degree of adjectives in Spanish is formed by placing *más* before the adjective. Generally, *que* also follows the adjective.

> Juan es *más alto que* su *hermano*.
> Esta calle es *más ancha que* la otra.

Positivo	Comparative
– pobre *(poor)*	más alto que *(taller than)*
– alto *(tall)*	más pobre que *(poorer than)*

In the blanks, supply the comparative degree of the adjectives in parentheses. (Note that all adjectives appear here in masculine singular form. If another form is required, make the necessary changes in number and gender.)

1. Antonia es...*más*...(bonito) *bonita* ...*que*...su prima.

    (Example: Antonia es *más bonita que* su prima.)

2. Julio es...*más*.....(alto)...*que*.....su hermano.

3. Estas cintas son...*más*....(largo) *largas* ...*que*.....aquéllas. (those)?

4. Tus lecciones son...*más*....(fácil)...*que*....las mías.

5. Esta casa es...*más*....(pequeño)...*que*....la de Juan.

6. Este papel es...*mejor*...(bueno)*....*que*....el de la oficina.

7. Esta tierra es...*peor*...(malo)*....*que*....la del norte

8. Tus hijos son...*más*......(alegre)....*que*....los míos.

9. Guillermo es...*más*.....(inteligente)...*que*......Clemente.

10. Yo creo que Antonio no es....*peor*....(malo)...*que*......yo.

11. Ella tiene los ojos...*más*.......(grande) *grandes* ...*que*.......los tuyos.

12. Esta comida es...*mejor*...(bueno)...*que*......la de ayer.

13. La ciudad de Buenos Aires es...*más*....(importante)...*que*.....Bogotá.

14. Aquel paisaje es....*más*...(bello)...*que*.....aquél. *landscape*

15. Este camino es...*más*......(estrecho) *narrower* ...*que*.....el de la finca.

16. El clima de La Habana es...*más*....(saludable) *healthy* ...*que*.....el de México.

17. La caña es...*más*....(dulce) *sweet* *dulce* ...*que*....la piña.

18. Esa rosa es.....*más*...(bonito) *bonita* ...*que*......este jazmín.

19. El auto de Martín está...*más*......(limpio)....*que*....el de Juan.

20. Hay animales...*más*.....(fiel) *faithful* ...*que*......otros.

21. Como pintor, Leonardo es...*mejor*...(bueno)...*que*.....Rafael.

22. El invierno es...*peor*...(malo)...*que*......el verano. *winter*

---

* *Bueno* and *malo* have special comparative forms. The comparative form of *bueno* is *mejor* (better). The comparative form of *malo* is *peor* (worse). Moreover, the word *más* is not used with these forms. (Examples: Esta revista es *mejor* que aquélla. El tiempo está hoy *peor* que ayer).

109

COMPARISON OF ADJECTIVES — *Superlative Degree*

The superlative degree of adjectives in Spanish is formed in the same way as the comparative degree, namely, by placing *más* before the adjective (see previous exercise). In the superlative degree, however, the definite article (*el, la, los* or *las*) is always used together with the adjective, preceding the word *más*.

Positive	*Comparative*
alto (*tall*)	más alto que (*taller than*)
bello (*beautiful*)	más bello que (*more beautiful than*)

Superlative

el más alto (*the tallest*)
el más bello (*the most beautiful*)
Juan es *el más alto de la clase.*
Esta es *la* calle *más ancha.*
Estos ejercicios son *los más difíciles* de todos.

In the blanks, supply the superlative form of the adjectives in parentheses. (Note that all adjectives appear here in masculine singular form. If another form is required, make the necessary changes in number and gender.)

1. Este paisaje es............(hermoso) del país.

(Example: Este paisaje es *el más hermoso* del país.)

2. Esta agua es............(frío) que hay.
3. Estos materiales son............(útil) que compramos.
4. Como mecánico, Pablo es............(malo)*.
5. Lucía, como estudiante va a ser............(bueno)*.
6. Este diccionario es............(práctico) de todos.
7. Tu empleado es............(activo) que he conocido.
8. El Everest es la montaña............(elevado) del mundo.
9. Estas láminas son............(lindo) de la colección.
10. Estos claveles son............(bellos) del jardín.
11. El tabaco cubano es............(bueno)* del mundo.
12. Esa casa es............(cómodo) de esta calle.
13. Aquellos son los muebles............(moderno) que he visto.
14. ....(feroz) animal de la selva es el tigre.
15. ....(grande) océano es el Pacífico.
16. Esta comida es............(malo)* que he probado.
17. María es la mujer............(elegante) en el baile.
18. Tu cuento es............(largo) que yo he oído.
19. Este café es............(caliente) que me han servido.
20. Carmen es la niña............(simpático) que hay en la casa.
21. Esa naranja es............(dulce) que he probado.
22. Esta ropa es............(caro) que hay en la tienda.

* *Malo* and *bueno* have the special forms *peor* and *mejor,* respectively. See footnote, page 109.

For further practice with the superlative degree of adjectives, change to plural form each of the nouns in italics. Then make the changes which are necessary in the adjective and article which accompany each noun. Follow example.

1. Trajeron el mejor *libro* de la biblioteca.

   (Example: Trajeron *los mejores libros* de la biblioteca.)

2. Visitamos ese país el peor *día* del mes.

3. No hagas el *ejercicio* más difícil de la lección.

4. Cristóbal escribió el mejor *artículo* del periódico.

5. Visitaremos el *lago* más grande del Canadá.

6. En esta semana vimos la mejor *comedia* del año.

7. Trabajaremos en el *salón* más fresco del edificio.

8. Ese es el *precio* más alto que he pagado.

9. Nadamos en el *río* más grande de la región.

10. Comimos en el *restaurante* más lujoso de la ciudad.

11. Fotografiamos la *ciudad* más grande de la América del Sur.

12. Lucía compró el *sombrero* más raro de la tienda.

13. Cervantes escribió la *novela* más interesante.

14. Describiremos el *estado* más rico de los Estados Unidos.

15. En esa tienda hice la mejor *compra* de zapatos de mi vida.

16. Visitaron el *museo* más importante de París.

17. Gregorio viajó durante el *mes* más frío del año.

18. Ellos residen siempre en el *barrio* más distinguido de la ciudad.

19. Esta es la mejor *medicina* de la farmacia.

20. Pasé allí el *día* mejor de mi vida.

21. Leímos la *página* más interesante del libro.

22. Llamó para el enfermo al *médico* más competente del país.

COMPARISON OF ADJECTIVES — *Continued*

As we have already learned, the comparative degree of adjectives in Spanish is followed by *que* (than)—See exercise, page 110.

> Tengo más libros *que* Juan.
> María cocina mejor *que* Elena.

In the superlative degree of adjectives, the preposition *de* is used.

> El es el estudiante más diligente *de* la clase.
> Estas montañas son las más altas *del* mundo.

In the blanks, supply *de* (*del*) or *que*, whichever is correct.

1. Ella es mucho más aplicada............María.

    (Example: Ella es mucho más aplicada *que* María.)

2. Tokio es la ciudad más grande............mundo.

3. El escribe mejor............tu padre.

4. Ella conoce mejor el idioma............el embajador.

5. Esa casa es más humilde............la de José.

6. Eres el amigo más fiel............yo tengo.

7. Juan vive ahora peor............el año pasado.

8. Ese fue el día más caluroso............la semana.

9. Este director es más atento............el anterior.

10. Esta es la lección más difícil............libro.

11. Tuve que esperar más............la vez anterior.

12. Son los ejercicios más fáciles............la lección.

13. El es el candidato más popular............todos.

14. Hoy me siento mejor............ayer.

15. Ernesto es más generoso............Enrique.

16. Esa es la mujer más fea............he visto.

17. Trae la ropa más limpia............nunca.

18. La encuentro más enferma............antes.

19. Siempre llega más temprano............ella.

20. Estas son las mejores............mes.

21. Mauricio es el muchacho más alegre............grupo.

22. Tengo más libros............una biblioteca pública.

COMPARISON OF ADVERBS

Adverbs are compared in the same way as adjectives, namely, by the use of *más* (see exercise, page 109). *Que* (than) usually follows the adverb. (Examples: *lentamente, más lentamente que; fácilmente, más fácilmente que*, etc.).

> Juan aprende *más rápidamente que* María.
> Ellos vinieron *más temprano que* nosotros.

The adverbs *bien* and *mal* have special comparative forms. The comparative form of *bien* is *mejor*; the comparative form of *mal* is *peor*. *Más* is not used with either of these forms (Examples: El trabaja *mejor que* su hermano. Ella habla francés *peor que* yo).

In the blanks, supply the comparative form of the adverbs in parentheses. Follow example.

1. Ellos practican el español. *mas* (frecuentemente) *que* nosotros.

   (Example: Ellos practican el español *más frecuentemente que* nosotros.)

2. Tú puedes bailar. *mas* (fácilmente) *que* ella.

3. Carlos escribe. *peor* (mal) *que* Andrés.

4. Lo recibieron. *mas* (atentamente) *que* nunca.

5. Eduardo empezó a trabajar. *mas* (temprano) *que* ayer.

6. Julia canta. *mejor* (bien) *que* la maestra.

7. Ellos estudian ahora. *mas* (intensamente) *que* el curso anterior.

8. El pobre anciano camina ahora. *mas* (despacio) *que* el año pasado.

9. Ella tocó el piano hoy. *mas* (cuidadosamente) *que* ayer.

10. Cruzó la calle. *mas* (rápidamente) *que* anteayer.

11. El lucha. *mas* (valientemente) *que* su enemigo.

12. Ellos jugaban hoy. *mas* (alegremente) *que* nunca.

13. Ahora los comprendo. *mas* (claramente) *que* antes.

14. La soprano cantó. *mas* (dulcemente) *que* en el acto anterior.

15. Se instaló. *mas* (cómodamente) *que* en la otra casa.

16. Raúl pinta. *mejor* (bien) *que* yo.

17. Esta flor huele. *peor* (mal) *que* ninguna otra.

18. Y salió. *mas* (violentamente) *que* otras veces.

19. El toca el violín. *peor* (mal) *que* usted.

20. Tú dormiste anoche. *mejor* (bien) *que* yo.

113

COMPARISON OF EQUALITY—*Adjectives and Adverbs*

In comparing two things of equal value, *tan* is placed before the adjective or adverb and *como* immediately after it. (The same idea is expressed in English with *as . . . as*).

> Juan es *tan* alto *como* Enrique.
> Chicago no es tan grande *como* Nueva York.
> El habla español *tan* bien *como* ella.

In the blanks, supply *tan . . . como* plus the indicated adjective or adverb. (Note that the adjectives in parentheses appear in singular masculine form. Therefore, make whatever changes in gender, number, or form are required in each sentence.) Follow example.

1. Aquellas muchachas no son....(alto)....éstas.

   (Example: Aquellas muchachas no son *tan altas como* éstas.)

2. Estas (láminas) son....*tan*......(bonito)....*como*..las otras.
3. Necesito una tela....*tan*..(ancho)..*como*..ésta.
4. Magdalena no es...*tan*..(diligente)...*como*..tú.
5. Julián no está..*tan*..(cansado)..*como*..Rafael.
6. Este pan está..*tan*...(bueno)...*como*..el de ayer.
7. Octavio no hizo el trabajo..*tan*..(fácil)..*como*..Eduardo.
8. Este paisaje no es..*tan*..(hermoso)..*como*..el de mi país.
9. Los hijos de Juana no son tan..........(estudioso)..*como*..los de María.
10. La película de anoche no fue..*tan*..(interesante)..*como*..la de hoy.
11. Los hijos son..*tan*...(inteligente)..*como*..los padres.
12. El Brasil no es..*tan*..(rico)..*como*..los Estados Unidos.
13. Ella no puede correr..*tan*...(rápido*)..*como*..el campeón.
14. Esta novela es..*tan*..(interesante)..*como*..las de Cervantes.
15. Estas fortalezas son..*tan*..(antiguo)..*como*..las de la Edad Media.
16. Mi abuela no es..*tan*..(viejo)..*como*..la tía de Carmen.
17. Los gatos no son..*tan*..(fiel)..*como*..los perros.
18. Estos pasteles no son..*tan*..(sabrosos)..*como*..los de (guayaba.)
19. Los estudiantes varones son..*tan*..(inteligente)..*como*..las hembras.
20. Tu butaca no es..*tan*..(cómodo)..*como*..la mía.

---

* *Rápido* is both adjective and adverb, and is more frequently used without the *mente* ending.

114

COMPARISON OF EQUALITY — *Nouns*

In comparing two things of equal value where a noun forms the basis of comparison, we put *tanto* before the noun and *como* after it. (The same idea is expressed in English with *as much . . . as* or *as many . . . as*). Observe that *tanto*, being an adjective, changes form to agree with the gender and number of the noun which it modifies.

> Yo tengo *tanto* dinero *como* (as much money as) él.
> El no tiene *tanta* ambición *como* su hermano.
> Había allí *tantos* muchachos *como* muchachas.

tanto, tanta
tantos, tantas

In the blanks, supply TANTO............COMO, plus the necessary noun. (Be sure to make *tanto* agree in gender and number with the noun which it modifies.)

1. Ella tiene *tantos* amigos *como* yo.

   (Example: Ella tiene *tantos* amigos *como* yo.)

2. En esa biblioteca no hay *tantos* libros *como* en la de mi pueblo.
3. En mi aula [classroom] estudian *tantos* alumnos *como* en la de Ernesto.
4. El doctor ya no fuma *tantos* cigarros *como* antes.
5. Esta sortija [ring] tiene *tanto* valor [worth] *como* la de Margarita.
6. Enriqueta gasta *tanto* dinero *como* su hermana Julia.
7. Rafael no ganó *tantos* méritos *como* su competidor.
8. Mi hijito comió *tantos* dulces *como* el suyo.
9. Ese estudiante no presta *tanta* atención [pay] *como* los demás [others].
10. Esos niños hacen *tanto* ruido *como* los de mi hermano.
11. Ella escribe *tantas* cartas en español *como* en inglés.
12. Yo estudio *tantas* horas *como* mis compañeros.
13. El profesor de Tomás tiene *tanto* tiempo libre *como* la profesora.
14. Hoy no se siente *tanto* frío *como* ayer.
15. En el mitin de anoche no había *tanto* público *como* en el de ayer.
16. Ella ya no nos visita con *tanta* frecuencia *como* antes.
17. No tiene *tanto* entusiasmo *como* antes.
18. El enfermo no duerme *tantas* horas *como* la semana pasada.
19. Yo tengo que escribir *tantas* composiciones *como* usted.
20. Ahora no tengo *tanto* trabajo *como* el mes pasado.

COMPARISON OF SUPERIORITY AND EQUALITY
Adjectives, Adverbs, Nouns — General Review

Choose the correct form in each of the following sentences.

1. Estas lecciones son más (difícil, difíciles) que las otras.

2. Yo tengo (tanto, tantos) dinero como mi hermano.

3. Esa casa es más (feo, fea) que la tuya.

4. Tus herramientas son tan (útil, útiles) como las mías.

5. Hay más alumnos (en, que) esta clase (que, de) en la otra.

6. Tengo los libros más interesantes (en, de) la biblioteca.

7. Ese lago es más grande (que, de) el del Norte.

8. Lucía no tiene (tanto, tanta) alegría con la noticia (que, como) yo.

9. Ellos son los (peor, peores) jugadores del club.

10. ¿Qué día (del, de, en) la semana es hoy?

11. Sergio es más (delgado, delgadas) que su primo Antonio.

12. Esta naranja no está (tan, tanto) dulce como la otra.

13. Tú tienes los (mejor, mejores) cuadros de asuntos marinos.

14. Estos son los muebles más modernos (en, de) la mueblería.

15. Ella es la niña más malcriada (de, en) la familia.

16. Don Pepe es el profesor más simpático (de, que) la escuela.

17. Ellos son los más (inteligente, inteligentes) de la familia.

18. Yo poseo la finca (más grande, más grandes) de la región.

19. Nosotros nunca gastamos (tanto, tantos) como ellos.

20. Ahora ganamos más (que, de) antes.

21. Samuel no escribe el español (tan, tanto) bien como Ricardo.

22. Recorrimos una distancia (de, que) más de diez kilómetros.

23. Hoy es el día más caluroso (en el, del) mes.

24. Esta es la lección más (larga, largo, largas) que he estudiado.

THE DEFINITE ARTICLE

The definite article is generally used in the same way in Spanish as it is in English. There are, however, certain uses in Spanish which differ from those in English:

a) Before nouns in a general sense, to denote a certain kind of thing or things. (Examples: *La* madera —i.e. *wood in general*— es útil. *El* vino estimula el apetito. El *agua* es transparente.)

b) With expressions of time (Examples: Es *la* una. Vinieron a *las* tres.) With the days of the week. (Examples: Van a llegar *el* miércoles. Vienen aquí los domingos.)

In the blanks, supply the necessary definite article where needed.

1. ....algodón tiene muchos usos en la industria textil.

2. ....vida de Juan es muy agitada.

3. No me agradan mucho...........nevadas.

4. ....seda es producida por un gusano.

5. ....ciencias estudian...........naturaleza.

6. El médico llegará a...........tres de la tarde.

7. El acto comenzará a...........una.

8. Yo empecé a trabajar...........lunes.

9. Siempre vamos a la playa...........domingos.

10. ....esperanza nunca debe faltar.

11. ....viernes tendremos exámenes.

12. ¿Qué día fue ayer?   Ayer fue...........sábado*.

13. Hazme el favor de decirme la hora.   Son...........tres.

14. Dicen que...............tiempo es oro.

15. ....mantequilla proviene de...........leche.

16. ....oro y...........plata son metales valiosos.

17. ....sábado te pagaré...........cuenta.

18. Hoy terminamos las clases a...........cuatro.

19. Asistiremos a misa a...........siete de la mañana.

20. Ella siempre pasea...........domingos.

21. ....días de la semana son siete.

22. ....paz se simboliza con una paloma.

---

* Note that no article is used with the days of the week after the various forms of the verb *ser*: Hoy *es miércoles*. Anteayer *fue lunes,* etc.

THE DEFINITE ARTICLE — *Continued*

Other uses of the definite article in Spanish which differ from English usage are the following:

a) The definite article is used in Spanish with names of languages. However, after *hablar, aprender, estudiar* and after the preposition *en*, the article is usually omitted (Examples: *El* español es fácil; *el* ruso es difícil. Hablan *español;* ahora quieren aprender *francés.* Siempre hablan en *inglés*).

b) The definite article is also used with the names of certain countries and a few cities in which the article seems to be a definite part of the name (Examples: *el* Perú, *el* Brasil, *la* Argentina, *el* Japón, *la* India, *La* Habana, *La* Paz, *el* Callao, *la* Florida, etc.).

In the blanks, supply the necessary definite article. Where no article is required in the sentence, simply leave blank.

1. En............Argentina está el río de............Plata.

   (Example: En *la* Argentina está el río de La Plata.)

2. ....capital de Cuba es............Habana.

3. En............Perú hay un puerto llamado............Callao.

4. ....Paz es la capital de Bolivia.

5. ....español es el idioma de Cervantes.

6. ....inglés es el idioma de Shakespeare.

7. ....monte Everest está en............India, en............Asia.

8. Pronto iremos a............México.

9. ....interesante ciudad de............Roma está en............Italia.

10. ....Cairo es la capital de............Egipto.

11. Nosotros vivimos en............Florida.

12. Me parece que............francés tiene una difícil pronunciación.

13. Ahora hay paz en............República Dominicana.

14. En la costa del Pacífico esta............Salvador.

15. ....Estados Unidos son ahora cincuenta estados.

16. En............Argentina la unidad de moneda es el peso.

17. La unidad de moneda en............Ecuador es el sucre.

18. En............Costa Rica se produce mucho café.

19. ....italiano es el idioma de las óperas.

20. Luisa siempre me habla en............portugués.

THE DEFINITE ARTICLE — *Continued*

In the last two exercises we have studied various uses of the definite article in Spanish which differ from those in English. The definite article is also used in Spanish:

a) before a proper noun modified by a title (except in direct address)—(Examples: *El* señor Gómez y *la* señora Ruiz vinieron juntos).

b) to avoid repetition of an earlier word in the sentence. In such cases the definite article is used alone and the noun which it modifies is dropped from the sentence (Examples: Este automóvil vale más que *el* del señor Gómez. Me gustan todas las novelas modernas excepto *las* de Hemingway.)

c) when referring to an action associated with parts of the body or clothing. (Examples: El niño no quiere lavarse *las* manos. Yo me pongo *los* guantes antes de salir.)

For further discussion and exercises covering this point, see pages 117 and 118.

In the blanks, supply the necessary definite article. Where no article is required, simply leave blank.

1. Ayer vi en la calle a............señora Andújar.

   (Example: Ayer vi en la calle a *la* señora Andújar.)

2. Juan, ¿cómo se siente............señor Fernández?
3. Esta máquina es mejor que............del señor Rodríguez.
4. Yo me lavo............manos varias veces al día.
5. Ella tenía............cara muy sucia.
6. ....dientes merecen cuidarse mucho.
7. Su nombre es............Fernando.
8. ¿Cómo le va,............señor García?
9. Soy socio de............hermanos Súarez.
10. ....señorita Rita es muy inteligente.
11. No me gustó tu sombrero, pero sí............de Juana.
12. Mi auto es más nuevo que............del señor Martínez.
13. Tú te debes limpiar con más frecuencia............zapatos.
14. Hoy me duele............cabeza.
15. Me gusta su traje, pero no............de su hermano Luis.
16. El nuevo vecino es............señor Alvarez.
17. Procuren no comerse............uñas.
18. Ella tiene bien arreglada............casa.
19. ....joven López es una buena profesora de piano.
20. ¿De dónde vino............señor Rafael Ortiz?
21. Voy a lavarme............cabeza con agua tibia.
22. ¿De quién es tía............señora Méndez?

CONOCER, PARECER, etc.

Verbs such as *conocer, parecer, producir* which end in *cer* or *cir* preceded by a vowel have *-zco* as the ending in the first person singular of the present tense indicative. The conjugations of *conocer* and *parecer* follow:

conocer				parecer		
yo conozco	nosotros conocemos			yo parezco	nosotros parecemos	
tú conoces	(vosotros conocéis)			tú pareces	(vosotros parecéis)	
usted } él, ella } conoce	ustedes } ellos } conocen			usted } él, ella } parece	ustedes } ellos } parecen	

Supply the correct present tense form of the verbs in parentheses.

1. Yo (conocer) bien a la señora López.

   (Example: Yo *conozco* bien a la señora López.)

2. Yo (parecerse)* a mi padre.

3. Ella (parecerse) mucho a su madre.

4. Julián dice que (conocer) a esos extranjeros.

5. Colombia (producir) el mejor café del mundo.

6. Ese animal raro (parecerse) al tigre.

7. Yo (conocer) muy bien esa especie de peces.

8. Nosotros (conocer) a todos los compañeros de la clase.

9. Pedro y Ramón no (parecer) hermanos.

10. Ellos no (conocer) a nadie en esa ciudad.

11. Tú sí (conocer) bien a la secretaria de Rafael.

12. Ella (parecerse) mucho a su tía Margarita.

13. Ustedes (conocer) muy bien todos los ríos del país.

14. Ellos (parecerse) mucho a los habitantes de cierta región del Africa.

15. La isla de Cuba (producir) mucha caña de azúcar.

16. El señor Martínez (conocer) muy bien el negocio de pieles.

17. Nosotros tenemos muchos parientes que no (conocer).

18. Ramona (parecerse) mucho a su mamá en los ojos.

19. La Argentina (producir) mucho ganado.

20. En mi fábrica yo (producir) varios artículos.

21. Yo (conocer) al autor de ese libro.

22. Ellos dicen que yo (parecer) italiano.

---

* *Parecer* means "seem" or "appear"; used reflexively (parecerse), it means "to resemble".

Other verbs belonging to the same group as *conocer* and *parecer* and having *-zco* as the ending in the first person singular of the present tense are *conducir, merecer, lucir, ofrecer, aparecer, crecer, traducir,* etc. (See previous exercise, page 120, for conjugations of *conocer* and *parecer*.) The present tense forms of *conducir, merecer* and *ofrecer* follow. (The remaining verbs of the group are, of course, conjugated in exactly the same way).

conducir	yo *conduzco*, tú *conduces*, usted *conduce*, él *conduce*, nosotros *conducimos*, (vosotros *conducís*), ustedes *conducen*, ellos *conducen*, etc.
merecer	yo *merezco*, tú *mereces*, usted *merece*, él *merece*, nosotros *merecemos*, (vosotros *merecéis*), ustedes *merecen*, ellos *merecen*, etc.
ofrecer	yo *ofrezco*, tú *ofreces*, usted *ofrece*, él *ofrece*, nosotros *ofrecemos*, (vosotros *ofrecéis*), ustedes *ofrecen*, ellos *ofrecen*, etc.

Supply the correct present tense form of the verb in parentheses.

1. Yo (conducir) muy bien este camión.

   (Example: Yo *conduzco* bien este camión.)

2. El perro (conducir) al pobre ciego por las calles.
3. Yo (lucir) mejor que tú, decía María a Juana.
4. La República de Venezuela (producir) mucho petróleo.
5. Ellos siempre (aparecer) a la hora del almuerzo.
6. Esas plantas (crecer) muy rápidamente.
7. Yo no (traducir) muy bien del inglés al español.
8. Me parece que yo (merecer) más respeto, señor Díaz.
9. Ese chofer (conducir) el ómnibus a mucha velocidad.
10. Ella no (merecer) que la maltraten.
11. La niñita (lucir) muy bien con ese sombrerito.
12. No (aparecer) mis libros por ninguna parte.
13. Yo le (ofrecer) mis servicios, señor Alvarez.
14. El buen estudiante siempre (merecer) las mejores notas.
15. Esta carretera (conducir) al estado de la Florida.
16. Ella no (conocer) a sus nuevos vecinos.
17. Los niños (crecer) rápidamente, dijo Don Juan.
18. Esa Academia (ofrecer) clases de español.
19. Yo no (merecer) más atención que los demás.
20. Ellos se (aparecer) cuando no los esperan.

CONOCER, SABER

Note that there are two verbs in Spanish, *conocer* and *saber*, which correspond to the English verb *to know*. A definite distinction in meaning and use is made between these two verbs in Spanish. *Saber* means to know something as the result of mental effort, study, or training. (Examples: El *sabe* bien su lección. Ella *sabe* nadar. Yo *sé* de memoria muchas poesías.) *Conocer* means to be acquainted with, to know someone or something through acquaintance or familiarity. (Examples: El *conoce* bien al señor Alvarez. Nosotros *conocemos* mucha gente en Santiago. Yo no *conozco* bien esta parte de la ciudad.)

In the blanks, supply the correct form of SABER or CONOCER that is required by the meaning of the particular sentence.

1. Juan no...*sabe*...sumar esos números.

   (Example: Juan no *sabe* sumar esos números.)

2. Ella no...*sabe*...las habitaciones de esa casa.

3. ¿...*Sabe*...usted resolver estos problemas de álgebra?

4. Yo no...*sé*...traducir ese párrafo.

5. ¿...*Conoce*...ella a su nuevo jefe?

6. Ese italiano...*sabe*...tocar muy bien el violín.

7. Ellos no...*saben*...a qué hora terminó la reunión.

8. Yo...*conozco*...a todos mis compañeros de clase.

9. Emilio...*sabe*...jugar al ajedrez muy bien.

10. Ustedes no...*conocen*...a nadie en esa ciudad.

11. Yo no...*sé*...cómo empezar el discurso.

12. Nadie...*sabe*...cuando terminará esta crisis.

13. Mariana...*conoce*...muy bien a esos artistas de California.

14. ¿...*Conocen*...ustedes dónde vive ahora Ernesto?

15. Hortensia...*sabe*...peinarse muy bien.

16. Esa viejita...*sabe*...a casi todo el mundo en el pueblo.

17. Nosotros...*sabemos*...patinar en el hielo.

18. Tu hermano...*sabe*...la geometría perfectamente.

19. Yo no...*conozco*...a nadie en esa oficina.

20. El señor Ortiz es diplomático y...*conoce*...muy bien todas las capitales del mundo.

21. Ya yo...*sé*...conjugar muchos verbos irregulares.

IMPERATIVE (COMMAND) FORM

Affirmative* familiar commands in the singular form *(tú)* are generally taken from third person singular of the present. Examples: *Habla* (from *él habla*); *Come* (from *él come*). There are eight frequently used exceptions:

(tener) - *ten*		(poner) - *pon*	
(saber) - *sabe*		(venir) - *ven*	
(hacer) - *haz*		(salir) - *sal*	
(ir) - *ve*		(decir) - *di*	

Commands of the formal type in Spanish involving persons normally addressed by use of the formal second person pronouns *usted* and *ustedes* are formed from the stem of the first person singular of the present tense verb. To this stem is added *e, en*, for verbs which end in *ar* (verbs of the first conjugation) and *a, an*, for verbs which end in *er* and *ir* (verbs of the second and third conjugations.)

ar → e, en
er y ir → a, an

1st person		Stem		
(Yo) hablo	*ar*	habl	*hable* (Ud.)	*hablen* (Uds.)
como	*er*	com	*coma* (Ud.)	*coman* (Uds.)
vivo	*ir*	viv	*viva* (Ud.)	*vivan* (Uds.)
pongo		pong	*ponga* (Ud.)	*pongan* (Uds.)
traigo		traig	*traiga* (Ud.)	*traigan* (Uds.)

Note that the polite command form is used as the plural of the familiar commands in Latin America. Example:

> *Singular: Habla* (tú) español en la clase.
> *Plural: Hablen* (Uds.) español en la clase.

Supply the singular imperative form of the verbs in parentheses.

1. (Leer-Ud.) los ejercicios en voz baja.
   (Example: *Lea* los ejercicios en voz baja.) *LEA*
2. (Esperar-tú) hasta que yo vuelva. *ESPERE*
3. (Poner-tú) los libros sobre mi escritorio. *PONGA*
4. (Comer-Ud.) esos dulces de fruta. *COMA*
5. (Vivir-Uds.) estos momentos de alegría. *VIVAN*
6. (Traer-tú) todos los paquetes del mercado. *TRAIGA*
7. (Ir-tú)* con los niños a la playa. *VAYA*
8. (Dar-tú)* esta carta a la señora Martínez. *DE'*
9. (Comprar-Uds.) las frutas en la frutería de la esquina. *COMPREN*
10. (Cerrar-Uds.) las ventanas porque va a llover. *CIERREN*
11. (Decir-tú) siempre la verdad. *DIGA*
12. (Tener-Ud.) mucho cuidado al bajar por la escalera. *TENGA*
13. (Permitir-Uds.) que los niños jueguen en el parque. *PERMITAN*
14. (Pedir-Uds.) los artículos necesarios. *PIDAN*
15. (Tomar-tú) el tren de las ocho de la noche. *TOME*
16. (Escribir-Ud.) la carta de recomendación. *ESCRIBA*
17. (Llevar-Uds.) todos estos libros para la biblioteca. *LLEVEN*
18. (Vivir-Ud.) en el campo y se sentirá mejor. *VIVA*

ar → e/en
er → a/an
ir → a/an

---
* The formal imperative form of *ir* is *vaya* (pl. *vayan*).
The formal imperative form of *dar* is *dé* (pl. *den*).

If direct object pronouns are used in a positive command, they are attached to the verb forming a single word:

> Abre la puerta.
> *Abrela.*
> Traiga los libros con usted.
> *Tráigalos* con usted.

(handwritten margin notes:) M F / S lo la / P los las

Supply the necessary pronoun which corresponds to the words in italics. Then add this pronoun to the verb to form a single-word, positive command.

1. Compre *los lápices* en la tienda.

   (Example: *Cómprelos* en la tienda.)

2. Venda *estas cortinas* a su vecina. *(handwritten: Véndolas)* *(notes: CURTAIN, neighbor)*

3. Lleva *estas cosas* a tu casa. *(handwritten: Llévalas)*

4. Eche *los papeles* en el cesto. *(handwritten: Échelos)* *(notes: THROW, basket)*

5. Limpie *los cristales.* *(handwritten: Límpielos)*

6. Espera a *la señorita* en la estación. *(handwritten: Espérala)* *(note: WAIT (FOR))*

7. Lave *esa ropa* en la lavadora nueva. *(handwritten: Lávela)*

8. Estudia *tus lecciones* con mucho cuidado. *(handwritten: Estúdialas)*

9. Pida *la llamada* por teléfono de larga distancia. *(handwritten: Pídala)*

10. Abra *la boca* para ver su dentadura. *(handwritten: Ábrala)* *(note: MOUTH)*

11. Traiga *el dinero* para pagar el alquiler. *(handwritten: Tráigalo)* *(note: PAY)*

12. Lea *los periódicos* todos los días. *(handwritten: Léalos)*

13. Revise *los resultados* para comprobar su exactitud. *(handwritten: Revíselos)* *(notes: CHECK, VERIFY, ACCURACY)*

14. Pon *las manos* sobre la mesa para examinarlas. *(handwritten: Pónlas)*

15. Preparen *los ejercicios* para el examen. *(handwritten: Prepárenlos)*

16. Oye *las noticias* por el radio. *(handwritten: Óyelas)*

17. Escriba *estas lecciones* en su cuaderno. *(handwritten: Escríbalas)*

18. Dibuje *las figuras* en la pared. *(handwritten: Dibújelas)* *(note: DRAW)*

19. Lleve *los perros* con usted. *(handwritten: Llévelos)*

20. Compra *las frutas* para los niños. *(handwritten: Cómpralas)*

21. Coma *la comida* sin pena. *(handwritten: Cómala)* *(note: PAIN (?))*

22. Termina *el trabajo* sin demora. *(handwritten: Termínalo)* *(notes: without, regret; without delay (?))*

IMPERATIVE (COMMAND) FORM — *Continued*

In the previous lesson (page 124) we learned that if a direct object pronoun is used in a positive command, it is attached to the verb, forming a single word. Similarly, in cases where two pronouns are used, one representing the direct object and the other representing the indirect object, both pronouns are attached. The indirect object pronoun, of course, precedes the direct object pronoun.

> Trae el café (a nosotros) ahora.
> *Tráenoslo* ahora.

> Lee el artículo en voz alta.
> *Léemelo* en voz alta.

> Manda esta carta (a ella) en seguida.
> *Mándasela* en seguida.

(For a full discussion of the position and use in sentences of direct and indirect object pronouns, see pages 51, 52, 53 and 68).

Substitute for the words in italics the correct direct object pronoun. Add this pronoun to the verb at the same time you add the indirect object pronoun corresponding to the words in parentheses. Follow example.

PERSON — me, te, se, nos, se
THING — lo, la, los, las

1. Traiga *el libro* (a mí)*. Example: *Tráigamelo.*
2. Lleve *estos periódicos* (a él) en seguida. LLÉVESELOS
3. Léeme *las poesías* (a mí) en voz alta. LÉEMELAS
4. Diga *los resultados* (a él). DÍGASELOS
5. Escriba *esa tarjeta* (a ella) ahora mismo. ESCRÍBASELA
6. Dé *esas cajas* (a ellos) en el almacén. DÉSELAS
7. Enseña *el alfabeto* (a él) en la clase. ENSÉÑASELO
8. Lave *su vestido* (a ella) de nuevo. LÁVESELO
9. Repita *su dirección* (a ellos) por teléfono. REPÍTASELA
10. Cuente *la anécdota* (a mí) otra vez. CUÉNTEMELA
11. Vende *la casa* (a él) por quince mil pesos. VÉNDESELA
12. Devuelva *esos muebles* (a ellos) para que los arreglen. DEVUÉLVASELOS
13. Trae *los refrescos* (a nosotros) en seguida. TRÁENOSLOS
14. Enseñe *los sombreros* (a ella) para que los reforme. ENSÉÑESELOS
15. Pinte *su automóvil* (a él) con pintura buena. PÍNTESELO
16. Compra *los víveres* (a nosotros) en la tienda de la esquina. CÓMPRANOSLOS
17. Abra *la puerta* (a ella) para que entre. ÁBRASELA
18. Diga *su nombre* (a él) para que lo inscriba. DÍGASELO

---

* The student should understand that the above sentences are somewhat artificial in form. The indirect object pronoun is artificially separated from the verb here and presented in prepositional form in parentheses. The purpose of the exercise is to give the student practice in changing this pronoun back to indirect object form and attaching it to the verb at the same time he attaches the direct object pronoun.

IMPERATIVE (COMMAND) FORM — *Continued*

In the previous two exercises we learned that if personal pronouns are used as the direct or indirect objects in a positive command, they are attached to the verb to form a single word (see pages 123-124). Observe, however, that if the command is negative, the pronouns occupy the usual place of all such object pronouns in the sentence and thus precede the verb.

Tómelo usted ahora.	Tráigame usted el libro.
No *lo* tome ahora.	No *me* traiga el libro.
Mándesela usted hoy.	Siéntese* usted aquí.
No *se la* mande hoy.	No *se* sienten aquí.

(Again, for a full discussion of the use and position of direct and indirect pronouns in sentences, see pages 51, 52, 53 and 68).

Change the following positive commands to negative form. In your answers, as shown in the example, include the word NO plus the necessary pronoun or pronouns and indicated verb.

1. *Hágalos* en la clase. Example: No *los* haga en la clase.
2. Póngaselos en el bolsillo. *No se los ponga en el bolsillo.*
3. Dígame la noticia ahora. *No me diga la noticia ahora.*
4. Lléveselo para la escuela. *No se lo lleve para la escuela.*
5. Ciérralas con llave. *No las cierra con llave.*
6. Quítese el sombrero al entrar. *No se quite el sombrero al en*
7. Mándale un telegrama ahora mismo. *No le manda un tg. ahora m*
8. Véndame los zapatos negros. *No me venda los zapatos negr*
9. Espérenme en la esquina de la iglesia. *No me esperen*
10. Piénselo antes de hacer el negocio. *No lo piense*
11. Tráigame los recibos del alquiler. *No me traiga*
12. Enciéndala ahora para mayor claridad. *No la encienda*
13. Píntelo de amarillo para que luzca mejor. *No lo pinte*
14. Repítale su nombre a los empleados nuevos. *No le repita*
15. Enséñaselos a ella en la casa. *No se los enseña*
16. Díganme lo que están pensando. *No me digan.*
17. Abranle la puerta a la criada. *No le abran la puerta*
18. Pónganselos sobre su cama. *No se los ponga*
19. Dale más dinero a tu señora. *No le da*
20. Llámenme más tarde. *No me llamen*

---

* Note that with reflexive verbs, in positive commands, the reflexive pronoun is attached to the verb in the same way as direct or indirect object pronouns. On the other hand, in negative commands the reflexive pronoun, like other pronouns, precedes the verb.

ADJECTIVES — *Special Forms*

We learned earlier (pages 6 and 7) that adjectives which terminate in a consonant have only one form in the singular for both masculine and feminine nouns (un libro *fácil*, una lección *fácil*). A few adjectives, however, which terminate in *an, on,* and *or* add the ending *a* to form the feminine (*haragán, haragana; trabajador, trabajadora,* etc.). Certain adjectives of nationality also add *a* in the feminine (un hombre *francés,* una mujer *francesa;* un pueblo *español,* una ciudad *española*).

Supply the correct form of the adjectives in parentheses.

1. Yo estoy estudiando la lengua (español).

   (Example: Yo estoy estudiando la lengua *española.*)

2. Tu hijita es muy (juguetón).

3. Esos son músicos (alemán).

4. Luisa es una persona (trabajador).

5. Aquella muchacha es muy (bonito).

6. Tu tía es una mujer demasiado (hablador).

7. Tengo un traje de tela (inglés).

8. Esos productos (inglés) son de buena calidad.

9. Hortensia es una persona (encantador).

10. He leído varias novelas (francés).

11. Todos esos radios nuevos son (japonés).

12. Compré una vajilla (chino).

13. La secretaria del club es una buena (organizador).

14. Carlos, tú conoces a esa vecina (burlón).

15. Ellos son amigos (leal).

16. María es mi compañera más (leal).

17. Pasé muchas situaciones (difícil).

18. Mis hijas son buenas (jugador) de tenis.

19. Esas artistas de ópera son (italiano).

20. Tu sobrina es una niña (haragán).

21. Esa fábrica es mi peor (competidor).

22. Se viste a la moda (escocés).

PRESENT PERFECT TENSE (El pasado perfecto)

The present perfect tense is formed with the present tense of the verb *haber* used as an auxiliary, and to this auxiliary is added the past participle of the main verb.

yo *he hablado	nosotros hemos hablado
tú has hablado	(vosotros habéis hablado)
usted } ha hablado él, ella }	usted } ellos } han hablado

Regular past participles in Spanish are formed as follows: If the infinitive ends in *ar* (verbs of the first conjugation), *ado* is added to the stem. If the infinitive ends in *er* or *ir* (verbs of the second and third conjugations), *ido* is added to the stem. (Examples: hablar, *hablado*; comer, *comido*; vivir, *vivido*, etc.) See page 134 for irregular past participles.

AR = ADO
IR y ER = IDO

Change the following verbs ~~form~~ from present tense to their equivalent present perfect tense form. Follow examples.

QUERER

1. Yo gano (*he ganado*)
2. El parte (*ha partido*)
3. Ella corre (*ha corrido*)
4. Usted viaja ...Ha viajado...
5. Nosotros damos Hemos dado
6. Ustedes aprenden Han aprendido
7. Juan vive Ha vivido
8. Ernesto va Ha tenido IDO
9. Ellas buscan Ha buscado
10. Nadie llama ...Ha llamado...
11. Alguien viaja ...Ha viajado...
12. Usted cierra ...Ha cerrado...
13. Los niños aprenden Han aprendido
14. Pedro sabe ...Ha sabido...
15. Ellos levantan Han levantado
16. Yo me peino He me peinado
17. El se cepilla Ha el cepillado
18. Ustedes regresan Han regresado
19. Tú te acuestas Has te acostado
20. Ellos cantan Han cantado

21. Tú compras Has comprado
22. Yo conozco He conocido
23. Ellos se visten Han visto
24. Usted sabe Ha sabido
25. Enrique prepara Ha prepar.
26. Luisa baila Ha bailado
27. Yo tengo He tenido
28. El sale Ha salido
29. Nosotros somos Hemos sid
30. Carmen está Ha estado
31. Ustedes insisten Han insistido
32. Pedro quiere Ha querido
33. Tú duermes Has dormido
34. Usted lee Ha leído
35. Ellas trabajan Han trabajado
36. El recibe Ha recibido
37. Yo empiezo He empezado
38. Catalina baila Ha bailado
39. Ellos copian Han copiado
40. Yo aprendo He aprendido

* Note that, as in English, the past participle remains unchanged in form when used with an auxiliary verb. English equivalents: I have *spoken*, you have *spoken*, he has *spoken*, etc.

Por ejemplo:
— me he peinado

PRESENT PERFECT TENSE — *Continued*

In Spanish, the present perfect describes the present of a finished action. We use the present perfect:

1. to indicate that a fact occured just prior to speaking about it. For example, a Spanish public speaker ends his speech with "he dicho" (I have said).
2. to describe an action which continues from the past to the present. For example: "España ha producido grandes hombres de armas y de letras. (Spain has produced great men of arms and letters).

Other examples: "Desde el principio del mundo (hasta hoy) el sol ha salido por el este". (Since the begining of the world —until now— the sun has arisen from the east).

Supply the correct present perfect tense form of the verb in parentheses.

1. María (regresar) a casa.

   (Example: María *ha regresado* a casa.)

2. El profesor nos (enseñar) a conversar en español. *HA ENSEÑADO*
3. Antonio (estar) ocupado todo el día. *HA ESTADO*
4. Ellos (recibir) muchas felicitaciones. *HAN RECIBIDO*
5. Nosotros (pedir) cinco pesos prestados. *HEMOS PEDIDO*
6. Ellos (vivir) siempre en el campo. *HAN VIVIDO*
7. Tú no (leer) bien ese artículo en el periódico. *HAS LEIDO*
8. Ernesto (vender) todas sus propiedades del campo. *HA VENDIDO*
9. Nosotros (viajado) por todos los estados del Atlántico. *HEMOS VIAJADO*
10. Tú no (conversar) con los nuevos vecinos. *HAS CONVERSADO*
11. Ellos (ir) a invitar a su profesor a la boda. *HAN IDO*
12. (terminar) las clases en esa escuela. *HAN TERMINADO*
13. ¿Quién (traer) esas malas noticias? *HA TRAIDO*
14. Yo no (conocer) aún a los tíos de Ricardo. *HE CONOCIDO*
15. Ellos (ser) siempre muy buenos alumnos. *HAN SIDO*
16. ¿(hablar) ustedes con el Director? *HAN HABLADO*
17. ¿(tratar) Uds. de comprar esa casa. *HAN TRATADO*
18. Ella (aprender) muy poco en esa clase. *HA APRENDIDO*
19. ¿Quién (partir) esta rama del árbol? *HA PARTIDO*
20. Carlos te (llamar) por teléfono desde Los Angeles. *HA LLAMADO*

---

* If a definite time in the past is referred to, then, of course, the preterit is used Examples: Yo *leí* ese libro *el año pasado*. Ellos *vendieron* su casa *ayer*.)

For practice in forming the present perfect tense, change the subject of each sentence below, substituting in its place the nine given subjects. Make all necessary changes. Follow example.

1. *Yo* nunca he comido en ese restaurante.

   (Example: *El* nunca ha comido en ese restaurante.)

   1) Usted *HA comido*   5) Ustedes *HAN*   7) Mariano *HA*
   2) Tú *HAS*   4) Ellos *HAN*   8) El señor García *HA*
   3) Nosotros *Hemos*   6) Mi hermano *HA*   9) Mis padres *HAN*

2. *Jorge* siempre ha regresado tarde.
   1) Yo *HE regresado*   4) Nosotras *HEMOS*   7) Pedro y Luis *HAN*
   2) Ella *HA*   5) Ellos *HAN*   8) La cocinera *HA*
   3) Usted *HA*   6) Tú *HAS*   9) Tomás *HA*

3. *El tren* ha llegado temprano hoy.
   1) Ellos *HAN llegado*   4) Yo *HE*   7) Los aviones *HAN*
   2) Tú *HAS*   5) Usted *HA*   8) El cartero *HA*
   3) Nosotros *HEMOS*   6) La profesora *HA*   9) Mi tío *HA*

4) *El abogado* ha estado enfermo.
   1) Los estudiantes *HAN*   4) Nosotros *HEMOS*   7) La señora López *HA*
   2) El médico *HA*   5) Ustedes *HAN*   8) Mi hija y yo *HEMOS*
   3) Los periodistas *HAN*   6) Yo *HE*   9) Martín *HA*

5. *La maestra* ha leído una interesante anécdota.
   1) Yo *he leído*   4) Ellos *HAN*   7) La abuela *HA*
   2) Usted *ha*   5) Nosotros *Hemos*   8) Los alumnos *HAN*
   3) El *ha*   6) Tú *HAS*   9) Mi prima *HA*

6. *Ella* nunca ha ido al hospital.
   1) Yo *he ido*   4) Eugenio *ha*   7) Los niños *han*
   2) Usted *ha*   5) Las secretarias *han*   8) Mi vecino *ha*
   3) El *ha*   6) Virginia Díaz *ha*   9) El señor Alvarez *ha*

7. *El estudiante* siempre ha venido en autobús.
   1) Yo *he venido*   4) La criada *ha*   7) La tía Juana *ha*
   2) Ella *ha*   5) El cobrador *ha*   8) Tú *has*
   3) Ustedes *han*   6) Nosotras *hemos*   9) Raúl Pérez *ha*

8. *Mi madre* se ha levantado a las seis de la mañana.
   1) Yo *he levantado*   4) El carpintero *ha*   7) Los lecheros *han*
   2) Ustedes *han*   5) Carmen e Inés *han*   8) El niñito *ha*
   3) Ellos *han*   6) Nosotros *hemos*   9) Mi tío Antonio *ha*

130

'or further practice with the present perfect tense, change the folowing verbs from first person singular to third person singular by hanging YO to EL. Follow example.

1. *Yo he estudiado* español en México.

   (Example: *El ha estudiado* español en México.)

2. Yo he estado ocupado toda la semana.

3. Yo lo he esperado en la oficina.

4. Yo he recibido tres telegramas de Pablo.

5. Yo he viajado por toda Europa.

6. Yo he sido un buen secretario del señor Martínez.

7. Yo he tenido muchas enfermedades.

8. Yo he leído todas las novelas de Julio Verne.

9. Yo he hablado con su jefe en la biblioteca.

10. Yo he vivido en Chile varios años.

11. Yo he ido a España tres veces.

12. Yo he tomado agua con mis comidas toda la vida.

13. Yo he bailado con todas las muchachas.

14. Yo he traído los paquetes del mercado.

15. Yo he preparado la cena sin ayuda alguna.

16. Yo he conocido a la señora Fernández por muchos años.

17. Yo he prometido mi ayuda a los niños huérfanos de la parroquia.

18. Yo he llamado por teléfono a Andrés.

19. Yo he aprendido muchas cosas esta semana.

20. Yo no he fumado esa clase de cigarrillos.

21. Yo siempre he tomado café después de la comida.

22. Yo ya he terminado este ejercicio.

NOTE: For further practice with this tense, repeat the above excercise orally, this time changing YO to NOSOTROS (*Nosotros hemos estudiado español en México*). Repeat, changing YO to TU (*Tú has estudiado español en México*). Repeat again, changing YO to USTEDES (*Ustedes han estudiado español en México*).

PRESENT PERFECT TENSE (*Use of HACE*)

We learned previously (page 129) that one of the uses of the present perfect tense in Spanish was to describe a past action which continues up to the present time. (Examples: Juan *ha estudiado* español durante tres meses. *Han vivido* aquí muchos años.) Note, however, that this same idea is also expressed very frequently in Spanish by the use of *hace** and the simple present tense:

> *Hace* tres meses que Juan *estudia* español.
>
> *Hace* muchos años que *viven* aquí.

Supply the correct present tense form of the verbs in parentheses. (Note that all sentences express actions which began in the past but continue up to the present time).

1. Hace más de un mes que ella (estar) ausente. *absent*

   (Example: *Hace* más de un mes que ella *está* enferma.)

2. *Hace* mucho tiempo que él no (recibir) cartas. *recibe* · recibe
3. *Hace* varios años que yo no (viajar) por Africa. *viajo*
4. *Hace* más de tres semanas que ella no (visitar) a su tía. *visita*
5. *Hace* tres años que usted (trabajar) en esa fábrica. *trabaja*
6. *Hace* tiempo que nosotros no (ver) a Julio González. *vemos*
7. *Hace* casi un año que ella (estar) ausente. *está*
8. *Hace* sólo un mes que Tomás (estudiar) español. *estudia*
9. *Hace* algunos días que yo no (visitar) a mi amigo Horacio. *visito*
10. *Hace* menos de dos horas que ellas (estar) en la tienda. *estan*
11. *Hace* tiempo que no (llover). *llueve*
12. *Hace* poco tiempo que Fermín (pintar) letreros. *signs pinta trabaja*
13. *Hace* casi un año que nosotros (trabajar) en la oficina de Antonio.
14. *Hace* mucho tiempo que yo no (ver) una buena película. *veo*
15. *Hace* una hora que María (hablar) por teléfono con su novio. *habl*
16. *Hace* un minuto que (dormir) el niñito. *duerme*
17. *Hace* varias horas que Raúl (cantar) en su cuarto. *canta*
18. *Hace* tiempo que ella no (recitar) en la escuela. *recita*
19. *Hace* tres años que él (tener) esa bicicleta. *tiene*
20. *Hace* solamente un mes que Jorge no (trabajar). *trabaja*
21. *Hace* algunas semanas que nosotros no (salir) de compras. *salim*

---

* *Hace*, when used in reference to time as in this exercise, acts as an impersonal verb, and its implicit subject is *ello* (it).

PAST PERFECT TENSE (Pretérito Pluscuamperfecto)

The past perfect tense is formed with the past tense form of *haber* (*habla*) used as an auxiliary, and the past participle of the main verb.

yo	había hablado	nosotros	habíamos hablado
tú	habías hablado	(vosotros	habíais hablado)
usted } él, ella }	había hablado	ustedes } ellos }	habían hablado

The past perfect tense is used in Spanish exactly as in English, to describe a past action which took place before another specified past action. Thus, the past perfect tense is always used together with a second verb in the preterit, either stated or implied. (Examples: Juan dijo que *había hablado* con ella. Yo vine a las dos, pero ellos ya *habían salido*.)

Supply the past perfect tense form of the verbs in parentheses. Follow example.

1. El alumno dijo que no (entender) bien la lección.

   (Example: El alumno dijo que no *había entendido* bien la lección.)

2. Julia llamó a Inés por teléfono pero (salir).
3. Juan le dijo que no lo (encontrar).
4. Ella nos (esperar) durante dos horas.
5. Yo me enteré que él (vivir) en Colombia tres años.
6. Julia dijo que ya (tomar) la leche.
7. El profesor sabía que nosotros (llegar) tarde a la clase.
8. María dijo que ya (cenar) en su casa.
9. Yo le informé que (hablar) con el gerente.
10. Ella no (ir) temprano porque tenía catarro.
11. Eduardo ya le (enviar) los paquetes por correo.
12. Los carteros (entregar) la correspondencia antes de llegar yo.
13. El profesor ya (explicar) la lección octava.
14. Ustedes no (lavar) los platos sucios del almuerzo.
15. Ellos (saber) los nombres de todos sus vecinos.
16. El socio de Enrique (comprar) los muebles de la oficina.
17. El no (avisar) que los niños estaban aquí.
18. Ernesto me dijo que (almorzar) con su padre en el hotel.
19. Ella ya (recibir) la mala noticia del accidente.
20. Nosotros ya (terminar) el ejercicio de pronunciación.

---

* Note here again that, as in English, the past participle remains unchanged when used with an auxiliary verb. English equivalent: *I had spoken, you had spoken, he had spoken,* etc.

133

IRREGULAR PAST PARTICIPLES

Note the following irregular past participles:

abierto	(abrir)	*escrito*	(escribir)	*puesto*	(poner)
cubierto	(cubrir)	*hecho*	(hacer)	*roto*	(romper)
dicho	(decir)	*muerto*	(morir)	*visto*	(ver)
				vuelto	(volver)

Note also that the past participles of *leer, creer, traer, oír* are regular but carry an accent: *leído, creído, traído, oído*. See list on p. 216.

Supply the correct past participle of the verbs in parentheses. Follow example.

1. Ella había (poner) los libros sobre el escritorio.   *puesto*

   (Example: Ella había *puesto* los libros sobre el escritorio.)

2. Los jóvenes no han (ver) las fotografías.   *visto*

3. Usted ya ha (leer) la nueva revista de deportes.   *leído*

4. Ella ha (traer) sus cuadernos de español.   *traído*

5. El había (decir) ya la verdad.   *dicho*

6. ¿Cuándo has (oír) la noticia de la guerra?   *oído*

7. El doctor no ha (creer) nada de lo que dijo el enfermo.   *creído*

8. Don Ramón no ha (volver) de su viaje a Panamá.   *vuelto*

9. ¿Qué ha (hacer) usted con el dinero que le di?   *hecho*

10. El gato ha (romper) las figuras de cristal.   *roto*

11. Ustedes no habían (volver) de sus vacaciones.   *vuelto*

12. Muchos soldados han (morir) en las dos guerras mundiales.   *muerto*

13. Ellos habían (cubrir) el hueco con ramas de árbol.   *cubierto*

14. Usted no ha (poner) los puntos sobre las íes.   *puesto*

15. Ella sí ha (escribir) bonitas poesías.   *escrito*

16. ¿Qué ha (decir) la madre de Margarita?   *dicho*

17. ¿Quién ha (ver) mi libro de español?   *visto*

18. ¿Por qué has (hacer) tan mal los ejercicios?   *hecho*

19. El cartero ha (traer) una carta certificada.   *traído*

20. El rey ha (morir).   *muerto*

21. ¿Quién ha (romper) mis lentes?   *roto*

22. ¿Dónde has (oír) esa noticia tan desagradable?   *oído*

PAST PARTICIPLES — *Review*

Supply the past participle of the following verbs.

1. cantar	(*cantado*)	25. reír	reido
2. partir	(*partido*)	26. dar	dado
3. escribir	(*escrito*)	27. llevar	llevado
4. decir	(*dicho*)	28. estar	estado
5. romper	roto	29. cubrir	cubierto
6. leer	leído	30. atender	atendido
7. ser	sido	31. prestar	prestado
8. estar	estado	32. ver	visto
9. poner	puesto	33. tener	tenido
10. coger	cogido	34. creer	creído
11. confundir	confundido	35. dirigir	dirigido
12. expresar	expresado	36. amar	amado
13. traer	traído	37. perder	perdido
14. morir	muerto	38. hablar	hablado
15. comer	comido	39. beber	bebido
16. empezar	empezado	40. gustar	gustado
17. vivir	vivido	41. hacer	hecho
18. conocer	conocido	42. saber	sabido
19. recibir	recibido	43. preparar	preparado
20. abrir	abierto	44. llamar	llamado
21. pintar	pintado	45. oler	olido
22. haber	habido	46. ir	ido
23. llover	llovido	47. nevar	nevado
24. atraer	atraído	48. terminar	terminado

PAST PARTICIPLES — *Continued*

Note carefully that, although past participles in Spanish do not change form when used together with the auxiliary verb *haber* to form the compound tenses, they change their endings if they are used alone as adjectives. In such cases, they must agree in number and gender with the nouns which they modify:

Botamos los platos *rotos*.
(We threw away the *broken* dishes.)

Los hombres *casados* viven más años que los solteros.
(*Married* men live longer than single men.)

Supply the correct <u>past participle</u> form of the verbs appearing in parentheses, used here as adjectives. Follow example.

1. La película (hacer) en Italia estuvo muy interesante. *hecha*

   (Example: La película *hecha* en Italia estuvo muy interesante.)

2. La silla estuvo (cubrir) de polvo. *CUBIERTA*

3. Es una herramienta (prestar). *prestada*

4. El libro quedó bien (imprimir). *Impreso,*

5. Todas las ventanas están (abrir). *abridas. ABIERTAS*

6. Compré un par de zapatos (coser) a mano. *cosidos*

7. Ella tenía los ojos (cerrar). *cerrados*

8. El autor de esos libros es poco (conocer). *conocido* *rotas*

9. Nuestro equipo terminó el juego con dos cabezas (romper) y tres brazos (partir). *partidos*

10. Vamos a botar todos los juguetes (romper). *rotos*

11. Tu contestación estuvo bien (decir). *dicha* *la*

12. El aula quedó bien (adornar) para la celebración. *adornado.*

13. Los muebles están (cubrir) de polvo. *CUBIERTOS*

14. Esa obra esta muy bien (traducir). *TRADUCIDA*

15. El soldado (herir) llegó al hospital . *HERIDO*

16. Ya tengo el trabajo (terminar). *TERMINADO*

17. El banco estuvo recién (pintar) y me manché. *PINTADO*

18. El tiempo (perder) no se puede recuperar. *PERDIDO*

19. Juan es la persona (indicar) para ese trabajo. *INDICADA*

20. Mandé a hacer unas tarjetas (imprimir) con letra gótica. *IMPRESAS*

21. La señora García tiene su casa bien (arreglar). *ARREGLADA*

22. Todo eso ocurrió el mes (pasar). *PASADO*

136

Passive Voice (LA VOZ PASIVA)

The passive voice in Spanish is used and formed like the passive voice in English*. The verb *ser* (to be) is used as the auxiliary verb, and to this auxiliary is added the past participle of the main verb:

(Present)	La correspondencia *es entregada* (por el cartero).
(Past)	La correspondencia *fue entregada*...
(Future)	La correspondencia *será entregada*...
(Pres. Perf.)	La correspondencia *ha sido entregada*... etc.

Note that in the passive voice the past participle must agree with the subject in gender and number. (Examples: El paquete fue *entregado* ayer. Los dos paquetes fueron *entregados* ayer. La carta fue *escrita* por Juan).

In the following passive voice sentences, supply the correct past participle form of the verbs given in parentheses.

1. Su primer libro fue (publicar) en 1945.

(Example: Su primer libro fue *publicado* en 1945.)

2. La nueva revista será (publicar) la próxima semana.
3. Los embajadores serán (recibir) por el Presidente.
4. La carta fue (escribir) por la secretaria de Bernardo.
5. Ellos han sido (invitar) para la cena de Navidad.
6. Mariana es (felicitar) por todos sus condiscípulos.
7. El ingeniero González ha sido (nombrar) jefe de la nueva obra.
8. Su discurso fue (aplaudir) por el público.
9. Las Novelas Ejemplares de Cervantes fueron (escribir) en el siglo XVI.
10. Esas obras teatrales serán (representar) el año que viene.
11. Los bultos postales serán (enviar) enseguida.
12. El buen estudiante es (admirar) por todos.
13. La fortaleza fue (atacar) por los soldados enemigos.
14. El asesino será (sentenciar) a la pena de muerte.
15. La ciudad de San Agustín en la Florida fue (fundar) en 1565.
16. Muchos hombres de ciencia han sido (premiar) con el premio Nobel.
17. Una exquisita comida ha sido (preparar) por el cocinero.
18. La reina es (recibir) por el emperador.

---

* The student should understand the difference between the terms *active voice* and *passive voice*. In the active voice the subject of the sentence performs the action. (*El cartero entregó la carta*). In the passive voice the subject of the sentence is acted upon, that is, becomes the receiver of the action. (*La carta fue entregada por el cartero*.)

137

The present tense of the passive voice is used less frequently than in English. One would rarely say, for example, "Las lecciones son preparadas diariamente". One would say instead, "Preparan las lecciones diariamente", or the reflexive form might be used, "Se preparan las lecciones diariamente".

The past tense (preterite) form of the passive voice has somewhat more extensive use, although here again it should be kept in mind that, in general, the passive voice is used less often in Spanish than in English. The form of the past tense (preterite) of the passive voice follows:

yo	fui recibido(a)*	nosotros	fuimos recibidos(as)
tú	fuiste recibido(a)	(vosotros	fuisteis recibidos(as))
usted } el, ella }	fue recibido(a)	ustedes } ellos }	fueron recibidos(as)

OBJET ACTED UPON   *FORMA SER*   *PAST PARTICIPLE*   *POR*   *INITIATOR OF ACCION*

Change the verbs of the following past tense (preterite) sentences to passive voice. *(IN LIBRETA #3) (8/29)*

·1. El *escribió* ese libro hace muchos años.

(Example: Ese libro *fue escrito* por él hace muchos años.)

2. Cristóbal Colón *descubrió* el Nuevo Mundo en 1492.
3. Ellos *admiraron* a la joven pianista.
4. Enrique *cerró* la puerta de su automóvil.
5. *Hicieron* los ejercicios por la mañana.
6. Ese pintor *pintó* las habitaciones del hotel.
7. *Hicieron* esos barcos en Inglaterra.
8. El alcalde *recibió* a los turistas en su oficina.
9. *Pusieron* las cortinas azules en las ventanas.
10. *Enviaste* la correspondencia por avión.
11. El arquitecto Díaz *planeó* el túnel.
12. *Sentenciaron* al criminal a cadena perpetua.
13. *Castigaron* a los estudiantes desaplicados.
14. El policía *multó* al chofer por estacionamiento ilegal.
15. *Recogieron* los papeles que estaban en el suelo.
16. Ellas te *escucharon* con mucha atención.
17. El profesor *escribió* una oración en la pizarra.
18. Los niños *rompieron* el espejo del armario.   *ROTO*

---

* Note that the tense is formed regularly: the past tense (preterite) form of *ser* is used as the auxiliary verb, and to this auxiliary is added the past participle of the main verb (see page 137). The form of the past participle, furthermore, agrees in gender and number with the subject of the sentence.

NO INITIATOR DE ACCION

The future tense forms of the passive voice* follow. (Note here again that the tense is formed regularly: the future tense of *ser* is used as the auxiliary verb, and to this auxiliary is added the past participle of the main verb (see page 137).

yo	seré recibido (a)	nosotros	seremos recibidos (as)
tú	serás recibido (a)	(vosotros	seréis recibidos (as))
usted } él, ella }	será recibido (a)	ustedes } ellos }	serán recibidos (as)

Change the verbs of the following future tense sentences to passive voice.

1. Virginia *preparará* la comida.

   (Example: La comida *será preparada* por Virginia.)

2. Ricardo *publicará* un libro de poesías.
3. Tú lo *invitarás* a él a la fiesta.
4. El profesor *examinará* a los nuevos alumnos.
5. Mañana *entregarán* los premios a los triunfadores.
6. Esos actores *representarán* una obra de García Lorca el sábado.
7. *Anunciarán* el estado del tiempo en la Florida.
8. Rosa y Carlos *traerán* a sus amigos en el auto.
9. El próximo mes *inaugurarán* el nuevo edificio de la escuela.
10. Rafael *enviará* las cartas por correo aéreo.
11. Ellos *terminarán* el trabajo por la noche.
12. Mi tía *escribirá* una novela de misterio.
13. Los pintores *pondrán* un letrero en la fachada.
14. Los empleados *usarán* las nuevas máquinas de calcular.
15. *Obsequiarán* a los invitados con dulces y helados.
16. Los médicos *llamarán* a las enfermeras.
17. El cajero *contará* el dinero recibido.
18. Pronto *usarán* los artículos pedidos.
19. El señor Pérez *enviará* las medicinas a su hermano.

---

* Again it should be kept in mind that in general, the passive voice is used less often in Spanish than in English (see page 138). Especially in everyday conversation, whenever there is a possibility of choice between an active and a passive form, the tendency in Spanish is to use the active rather than the passive form. Thus, instead of saying, as might be said in English, "*El paquete será entregado mañana — The package will be delivered tomorrow,*" the Spanish speaking person would tend to say "*Entregarán* el paquete mañana" or even "*Entregan* el paquete mañana."

The present perfect tense *pretérito perfecto* of the passive voice is formed regularly: the present perfect tense form of *ser* is used as the auxiliary verb, and to this auxiliary is added the past participle of the main verb (see page 137). (For explanation concerning use of the passive voice in Spanish see exercise page 138, also footnote page 139.)

yo	he sido recibido (a)	nosotros	hemos sido recibido (as)
tú	has sido recibido (a)	(vosotros	habéis sido recibidos (as))
usted} él, ella}	ha sido recibido (a)	ustedes} ellos}	han sido recibidos (as)

Change the verbs of the following present perfect tense sentences to passive form. (in libreta #3)(8/29)

1. Mis tíos *han vendido* su casa.

   (Example: Su casa *ha sido vendida* por mis tíos.)

2. Nosotros *hemos firmado* el contrato.

3. Toda la sociedad *ha admirado* a su director.

4. Los empleados *han dicho* muchas cosas buenas acerca del secretario.

5. *Han entregado* los recibos de la compra.

6. *Hemos escrito* algunos artículos periodísticos.

7. La enfermera *ha llevado* al herido a la cama.

8. *Han matriculado* al niño en una escuela elemental.

9. Ya *he aprobado* las solicitudes de empleo.

10. *Han capturado* a muchos prisioneros fugados.

11. No *han encontrado* todavía la nueva dirección de Carlos.

12. Nosotras *hemos recibido* buenas ofertas de empleo.

13. No *han vacunado* a los extranjeros.

14. El fuego *ha destruido* la iglesia.

15. Ellas *han comprado* un nuevo carro.

16. *Han anunciado* la llegada del avión.

17. *Hemos lavado* muy bien esas camisas.

18. *Han traducido* la Biblia a muchos idiomas.

19. Ella *ha vendido* sus libros usados.

20. *Hemos terminado* los ejercicios.

Reflexive Verbs as a Substitute for the Passive Voice

We have previously had some practice with the use of reflexive verbs in Spanish as substitutes for the passive voice (see pages 138-139). The student should be particularly alert to this usage in Spanish. The reflexive form is commonly used in this way, especially in the present tense, whenever the subject of the sentence is an inanimate thing or when the agent who performs the action is unimportant or not indicated. The verb is singular or plural according to the subject, which usually follows the verb.

Se venden periódicos en esa tienda. (3ᵈ PERSON)
Aquí *se habla* español.

Supply the correct present tense reflexive form of the verbs in parentheses.

1. No (venderse) carne en esa tienda.

   (Example: No *se vende* carne en esa tienda.) Se vende

2. (Necesitarse) una taquígrafa. se necesita

3. ¿Cómo (decirse) "sugar" en español? se dice

4. ¿Dónde (lavarse) la ropa en este edificio? se lava

5. No (permitirse) estacionarse en esta zona. Se permite

6. ¿A qué hora (abrirse) la farmacia? se abre

7. Frecuentemente (verse) muchos niños en el parque. se ven

8. Aquí (oírse) mucho ruido de motores. se oye

9. El idioma español (hablarse) mucho en la Florida, Texas y California. se habla

10. No (poderse) perder el tiempo en cosas sin importancia. se puede

11. En Cuba (producirse) mucho azúcar. se produce

12. En la China (comerse) mucho arroz. se come

13. En Brasil (hablarse) el portugués. se habla

14. Según las últimas noticias (esperarse) un ciclón. se espera

15. Todavía no (saberse) nada sobre las causas del incendio. Se sabe

16. (Decirse) que hubo un naufragio en el océano Pacífico. se dice

17. En los Estados Unidos (tomarse) mucha leche. se toma

18. En ese hotel (poderse) alquilar una buena habitación. se puede

19. (Venderse) terrenos a plazos en la playa. se venden

20. (Hacerse) alteraciones en esa sastrería. se hacen

21. No (poderse) engañar tan fácilmente a ese ciego. se puede

22. (Terminarse) pronto estos ejercicios. se terminan

PRESENT PARTICIPLES (El Gerundio)

Present participles are used in Spanish in much the same way as in English: 1) as adjectives to modify some noun or pronoun: *Hablando* francamente, yo no tengo ningún interés en ir allí —(*Speaking* frankly, I have no interest in going there.) 2) to form the so-called progressive tenses: El *está trabajando* en Nueva York ahora—(He *is working* in New York now.) We shall study these various usages in succeeding lessons.

Present participles are formed by adding -*ando* to the stem of *ar* verbs and -*iendo* to the stems of *er* and *ir* verbs. (In all constructions the form of the present participle remains invariable.)

hablar — *hablando*   comer — *comiendo*   vivir — *viviendo*

Note: contrary to English, the present participle is called *gerundio* in Spanish.

In the blanks, supply the present participle form of the indicated verbs.

1.	copiar	(*copiando*)	23.	escribir	....
2.	beber	(*bebiendo*)	24.	llamar	....
3.	partir	(*partiendo*)	25.	saber	....
4.	patinar	....	26.	atacar	....
5.	nevar	....	27.	admirar	....
6.	usar	....	28.	crecer	....
7.	salir	....	29.	servir	....
8.	perder	....	30.	volar	....
9.	nadar	....	31.	abrir	....
10.	cerrar	....	32.	dar	....
11.	recibir	....	33.	asistir	....
12.	pegar	....	34.	comprar	....
13.	vender	....	35.	necesitar	....
14.	levantarse	....	36.	poner	....
15.	firmar	....	37.	echar	....
16.	llover	....	38.	tocar	....
17.	trabajar	....	39.	descansar	....
18.	conocer	....	40.	querer	....
19.	andar	....	41.	lavarse	....
20.	limpiar	....	42.	llevar	....
21.	traducir	....	43.	producir	....
22.	indicar	....	44.	terminar	....

Progressive Form

The progressive tenses in Spanish are formed by use of the auxiliary verb *estar*. To this auxiliary is added the present participle (el gerundio) of the main verb. The present progressive tense is conjugated thus:

yo	estoy hablando		nosotros	estamos hablando
tú	estás hablando		(vosotros	estáis hablando)
usted} él, ella}	está hablando		usted} el, ella}	están hablando

The present progressive tense in Spanish is used, as in English, to express an action which goes on now or at the present moment. (Examples: Juan *está hablando* con su padre ahora. ¿Qué *están haciendo* ellos en el cuarto?).

Supply the present tense progressive form of the verbs in parentheses.

1. Ahora Carlos (hacer) su tarea.

   (Example: Ahora Carlos *está haciendo* su tarea.)

2. Los estudiantes (aprender) ahora más que antes.
3. Ella (hablar) por teléfono en este momento.
4. ¿(estudiar) tu hermana francés o inglés?
5. ¿Dónde (vivir) sus padres ahora?
6. Mi profesor (explicar) ahora la lección de hoy.
7. Precisamente, en este momento él (ensayar) una pieza de piano.
8. Nosotras (hacer) los vestidos para el baile.
9. La población de los Estados Unidos siempre (crecer).
10. Manuel no (escuchar) lo que dice su amigo Juan.
11. La señora de la casa (limpiar) los muebles en este momento.
12. Me parece que alguien (tocar) a la puerta.
13. ¿Por qué (llorar) tanto esa pobre mujer?
14. Los muchachos (jugar) ahora a la pelota en el parque.
15. El poeta (omitir) muchos versos de ese poema.
16. Alguien (llamar) por teléfono de larga distancia.
17. Creo que (empezar) a nevar nuevamente.
18. Tu amiga (esperar) en la esquina a su tía María.
19. Observa como el aeroplano (aterrizar) en el aeropuerto.
20. ¿Dónde (trabajar) tu padre en estos días?
21. El estudiante (acabar) el ejercicio de gramática.

PRESENT PARTICIPLES (El Gerundio) — *Continued*

In a previous exercise (page 142), we studied the formation of present participles in Spanish. Note, now, the following irregular present participles:

a) Present participles of vowel changing verbs of the third conjugation* have irregular stems. They use the same stem as the third person singular and plural of the preterite (sentir, *sintiendo;* servir *sirviendo;* dormir, *durmiendo.*

b) The present participles of *creer, caer, leer, oír* and *traer* are slightly irregular since the normal letter *i* of the participal ending must change to *y* between two vowels (creer, *creyendo;* caer, *cayendo;* leer, *leyendo;* oír, *oyendo;* traer, *trayendo*).

c) The present participles of these verbs must be learned separately since their irregularities follow no particular rule: poder, *pudiendo;* decir, *diciendo;* ir, *yendo;* venir, *viniendo.*

Supply the correct present participial form of the verbs in parentheses.

1. Juan está (decir) la verdad.

   (Example: Juan está *diciendo* la verdad.)

2. Ellos están (oír) las noticias por el radio.
3. Olimpia está (leer) la lección de geografía.
4. El cartero está (traer) la correspondencia.
5. Las manzanas se están (caer) del árbol.
6. El herido se está (morir) en el hospital.
7. Las muchachas se están (divertir) mucho en el baile.
8. Yo creo que el testigo está (mentir) en su declaración.
9. El profesor está (repetir) la lección de gramática.
10. Yo me estoy (reír) de sus chistes.
11. La joven bañista está (pedir) auxilio.
12. Yo no me estoy (sentir) bien del estómago.
13. Tu hermana se está (vestir) delante del espejo.
14. No hagas ruido, el niño está (dormir).
15. Yo estoy (ir) a clases nocturnas todos los días.
16. Ella está (decir) cosas muy interesantes.
17. Los fuertes vientos están (venir) del norte.
18. No creo lo que estoy (oír).
19. Ellos siempre están (pedir) dinero prestado.
20. Tu tía siempre está (ir) y (venir).

---

* For a discussion of vowel changing verbs of the third conjugation, see pages 83, 84, 85, 86, 87, 88, 89, 90. Such verbs include, in addition to those named above, *divertirse, preferir, mentir, morir, pedir, repetir, reír, vestir, despedir.*

PRESENT PARTICIPLES (*Used As Adjectives*) — *Continued*

As already indicated (page 142), present participles are often used as adjectives in Spanish, in the same way as in English, to modify some noun or pronoun.

Hablando francamente, yo no tengo ningún interés en ir allí.
No *teniendo* nada que hacer, fuimos al cine.

Supply the present participial forms of the verbs in parentheses:

1. (Terminar) el ejercicio se lo entregué al profesor.

   (Example: *Terminando* el ejercicio se lo entregué al profesor.)

2. (Llegar) la policía, los ladrones huyeron.

3. (Hablar) solamente en español, el alumno practicará más.

4. (Pasar) por el parque oímos un ruido enorme.

5. (Decir) la última palabra, se apagó la luz.

6. (Correr) la cortina, tendremos más claridad.

7. (Tener) más tiempo, podremos terminar el trabajo hoy.

8. (Abrir) las ventanas, sentiremos más fresco.

9. (Escribir) claro ellos lo entenderán mejor.

10. (Tratar) de comprobar los resultados, se demoró una hora.

11. (Ser) la más bonita, Lucía obtuvo el primer premio.

12. (Caminar) tan despacio, no llegaremos nunca.

13. No (poder) visitar a mis tíos, los llamé por teléfono.

14. (Llegar) tarde no encontraremos asientos desocupados.

15. (Estar) distraído no aprenderás nada.

16. Si estás (hablar) tan deprisa no te entenderán.

17. (Escribir) las oraciones, cometí tres errores.

18. (Decir) la verdad, se logra un mejor éxito.

19. (Terminar) la lectura del cuento me quedé dormido.

20. (Ser) extranjero no pudo obtener el empleo oficial.

21. (Saltar) de ese modo te vas a caer.

22. (Estudiando) tan poco obtendrás muy malas calificaciones.

23. (Saber) las direcciones, no me perderé.

24. (Cantar y bailar) pasamos una noche muy divertida.

145

PAST PROGRESSIVE TENSE

The past progressive tense is formed regularly (see page 143); that is, the past imperfect of *estar* is used as the auxiliary verb, and to this auxiliary is added the present participle (el gerundio) of the main verb.

yo	estaba hablando *	nosotros	estábamos hablando
tú	estabas hablando	(vosotros	estabais hablando)
usted} él, ella}	estaba hablando	ustedes} ellos}	estaban hablando

The past progressive tense is used, exactly as in English, to describe a past action which was going on or continuing at some particular point in past time. Very often this particular point in past time is designated by a second verb in the simple past. (Examples: Cuando llegaron, Juan *estaba leyendo* el periódico. *Estaba lloviendo* cuando yo me levanté esta mañana.)

Supply the past progressive tense form of the verbs in parentheses.

1. Ellos (estudiar) cuando nosotros llegamos.

   (Example: Ellos *estaban estudiando* cuando nosotros llegamos.)

2. Los estudiantes (ver) la televisión en el momento que entró Tomás.
3. Ella (buscar) su cartera cuando llegó su hermana Rosa.
4. Cuando salimos anoche (llover) muy fuerte.
5. Cuando llamé a Rita ella (dormir) profundamente.
6. Berta (escribir) una carta cuando llegó su amiga Luisa.
7. En el momento que él (decir) los resultados, lo interrumpieron.
8. Ellas (vivir) en esa quinta cuando eran jóvenes.
9. Los niños (desayunar) cuando llegó el autobús escolar.
10. El profesor (calificar) los trabajos del examen cuando llegó Pedro.
11. Hasta muy tarde ellos (discutir) la nueva ley.
12. Los jugadores (ganar) mucho dinero cuando llegó la policía.
13. Tú perdiste mucho peso cuando (trabajar) doce horas.
14. Ella siempre (viajar) cuando su esposo tenía vacaciones.
15. El (residir) en Nueva York cuando terminó la guerra.
16. Los niños (escuchar) a la maestra cuando sonó el timbre.
17. Julio (comer) su almuerzo cuando lo llamaron por teléfono.
18. ¿Qué (hacer) el niño en la calle cuando empezó a llover?
19. ¿Dónde (trabajando) Antonio en aquellos tiempos?

---

* English equivalent: *I was talking, you were talking, he was talking,* etc.

Note that the past progressive tense, which is used to describe an action which was going on or continuing at some particular point in past time (see page 147), duplicates in Spanish one of the uses of the past imperfect tense previously studied (see pages 92, 93, 94, 95, 96, 97). For example, we may say "Cuando Juan llegó, yo *preparaba* mis lecciones" or "Cuando Juan llegó, yo *estaba preparando* mis lecciones." Both forms, of course, are correct, and both are used. The progressive tense form, however, seems the more common.

Change the verbs in italics from past imperfect to past progressive tense form. (Keep in mind that the meaning remains the same in both cases.)

1. Los alumnos *estudiaban* en el aula cuando yo llegué.

   (Example: Los alumnos *estaban estudiando* en el aula cuando yo llegué.)

2. Los muchachos *jugaban* al tenis cuando empezó a llover.

3. *Llovía* fuertemente cuando estaba amaneciendo.

4. La enfermera *dormía* profundamente cuando entró el doctor.

5. *Comíamos* en el restaurante cuando empezó a nevar.

6. Me di cuenta de que ella *ocultaba* algo cuando me acerqué.

7. Tu hermana *hablaba* con Carmen en el momento que llegué.

8. Ellos *discutían* acaloradamente cuando llegó el policía.

9. ¿Qué *hacían* los niños en la cocina cuando llegó la cocinera?

10. El profesor *pasaba* lista cuando sonó la campana.

11. El hombre sordo no *entendía* lo que le decían.

12. Mientras *trabajaba* en Caracas, se casó con Juanita.

13. Mientras el *pintaba,* se cayó de la escalera.

14. *Tronaba* mucho durante toda la noche.

15. Ellos *trataban* de abrir la puerta.

16. Rafael *copiaba* los nombres de sus compañeros.

17. El choque ocurrió mientras ellos *iban* hacia Miami.

18. Mientras usted se vestía, ella *regresaba* de la escuela.

19. Yo *terminaba* de comer cuando nos visitó Enrique.

20. Isabel *lavaba* la ropa en la lavadora cuando se fue la electricidad.

FUTURE AND PRESENT PERFECT PROGRESSIVE TENSES

We have already studied the formation of the present progressive and past progressive tenses (pages 143-147). Other tenses of *estar* used as an auxiliary verb may be employed together with a present participle to express a continuing action in the future (future progressive tense), a continuing action in present perfect time (present perfect progressive tense), etc. These latter tenses are not so widely used as the present progressive or past progressive tenses, but they exist and, as in English, serve to express the particular action indicated.

> Si llegamos a las seis, ellos *estarán comiendo.*
> (If we arrive at six o'clock, they will be eating.)
>
> El *ha estado trabajando* muy bien últimamente.
> (He has been working very well recently.)

Supply the future progressive tense form of the verbs in parentheses.

1. Si vamos allá ahora, ellos (mirar) la televisión.

   (Example: Si vamos allá ahora, ellos *estarán mirando* la televisión.)

2. No la llames ahora porque ella (estudiar) sus lecciones.
3. Dentro de tres horas (volar) sobre el Océano Atlántico.
4. Esas vecinas (hablar) toda la tarde sin cansarse.
5. El obrero (trabajar) hasta las nueve de la noche.
6. El ahora (buscar) trabajo por todos los talleres.
7. Ella (preparar) las maletas para el viaje al Japón.
8. No la llames ahora porque (dictar) las cartas a la taquígrafa.
9. Yo creo que ellos se (divertir) mucho en el teatro.

Supply the present perfect progressive tense form of the verbs in parentheses.

1. El doctor (trabajar) durante todo el día.

   (Example: El doctor *ha estado trabajando* durante todo el día.)

2. Nosotros (hablar) más de dos horas en la oficina.
3. Tus amigas (conversar) sobre el viaje a Colombia.
4. El (buscar) por todas partes sus espejuelos perdidos.
5. La enferma (dormir) durante ocho horas.
6. El pelotero (jugar) en el estadio por la mañana.
7. Ellas (ver) las películas muchas veces.
8. Mis amigos (esperar) a la maestra en el portal.
9. Ella (escribir) varias cartas durante la noche.

PRESENT PARTICIPLES—WITH PRONOUN OBJECTS

In the progressive tenses formed with *estar* and the present participle of the main verb (see pages 143, 147), the pronoun objects, indirect and direct, may either precede the verb or be attached to the present participle. Both forms are equally correct and frequently used.

> El *nos* estaba dando el regalo.
> El estaba *dándonos** el regalo.
>
> El *nos lo* estaba *dando*.
> El estaba *dándonoslo*.

Note that whenever both the indirect and direct pronouns are used, the indirect object pronouns me, (te), se**, nos, se** les always precede the direct object pronouns lo (s), la (s). Examples: *comprándosela, partiéndoselo, viéndoselos*, etc. (See pages 68 to 72.)

For practice with the two forms described above, shift the object pronouns from their present position before the verb and attach them to the present participle. Use two pronouns wherever possible.

1. Ella *me* estaba prestando el dinero.

   (Example: Ella estaba *prestándomelo*.)

2. María *lo* está escribiendo con mucho cuidado.
3. Octavio *nos* está diciendo la verdad.
4. Tú *lo* estabas leyendo en alta voz.
5. Tomás *le* está escribiendo en español.
6. Los niños *la* están llamando por teléfono.
7. Ricardo *me* estaba recomendando esa medicina.
8. Ella *se* estaba vistiendo ahora mismo.
9. El presidente *los* estaba esperando en su oficina.
10. Ana *nos* estaba invitando para ir al teatro.
11. Ese alumno desaplicado *le* está dando mucho trabajo al maestro.
12. Usted *la* ha estado escuchando durante una hora.
13. El empleado *nos* estaba explicando el motivo de su ausencia.
14. La profesora *les* estaba enseñando la conjugación.
15. La enfermera *les* estaba inyectando la vacuna, en el brazo.
16. En nuestro país *nos* estaban enseñando inglés.
17. Ella *le* estaba poniendo muy poca atención a su discurso.
18. Yo *la* he estado esperando todo el día.
19. Mi amigo *me* estaba dando un consejo.
20. Ella *nos* estaba rogando que le ayudáramos.
21. Luis *les* estaba contestando la pregunta muy bien.
22. Yo *les* estoy terminando el trabajo.

---

* All present participles with attached object pronouns are accented.
** Se is used in place of le, les before lo, la, los, las to avoid cacophony.

In the previous exercise (page 149), we learned that in the progressive tenses, a personal object used as direct or indirect object of a verb may either precede the verb or be attached to the present participle. (Example: El *nos* estaba mirando con mucho interés — El estaba *mirándonos* con mucho interés.) In the present exercise, to gain further practice with these forms, remove the pronoun objects from the present participle to which they are attached and place them in conventional position before the verb.

1. Ella estaba *enseñándomelo.*

   (Example: Ella *me lo* estaba *enseñando.*)

2. Yo estaba *escribiéndole* las oraciones en la pizarra.

3. La vecina estaba *mirándome* desde el balcón.

4. Mis primos están *explicándole* las lecciones con María.

5. El director está *firmándosela.*

6. María esta *visitándolos* en su casa.

7. Ellos estarán *aprendiéndolo* en el taller.

8. No están *vendiéndolos* muy caros.

9. Juana estaba *recitándomelo* con mucho gusto.

10. Esos problemas están *preocupándole* a Inés.

11. Están *enviándoselos* desde la Argentina.

12. Yo creo que ellas no están *escribiéndolas* bien.

13. ¿Dónde estaban *curándolo?*

14. ¿Quiénes estarán *esperándolo?*

15. ¿Quién está *copiándonoslo?*

16. ¿Quién estaba *invitándome* al paseo?

17. Los gatos están *rompiéndolos* en la cocina.

18. Ella esaba *echándola* en el buzón.

19. Tú estabas *escuchándome* muy atentamente.

20. Allí estaban *edificándolo* el mes pasado.

21. El niño está *pidiéndoselo* a Pedro.

22. Los alumnos están *leyéndolo* con gran interés.

23. Yo voy a *entregárselo* a María.

150

PARA — POR

The prepositions *para* and *por*, although both correspond in meaning to the English "for" and 'by" have distinctive uses in Spanish. These must be studied carefully.

Para is generally used to express: a) use (una taza *para* café), b) purpose or motive (Este libro es *para* Juan. Vinieron aquí *para* aprender español.) c) destination (Salieron ayer *para* Madrid. El regalo es *para Miguel.*)

Por is used variously with the idea of *through, by* or *per.* (El ladrón entró *por* la ventana. Cogí al niño *por* la mano. Viene aquí dos veces *por* semana.) As previously studied, *por* is also used to indicate the agent in the passive voice (Este libro fue escrito *por* él).

In the blanks, supply PARA or POR, whichever is correct.

1. El avión partió ahora................Río de Janeiro.

2. Mi padre trajo dulces................los niños.

3. Vamos a enviar esos paquetes................correo aéreo.

4. Ella se quedó en la biblioteca................copiar.

5. El robo fue cometido................un chino.

6. Ellos saldrán mañana................Chicago.

7. Recibimos las flores................la tarde.

8. Esa historia fue escrita................Sebastián.

9. Compraremos varias sillas................el comedor.

10. Ernesto fue elegido................todos sus compañeros.

11. Ella sólo vino................comer con nosotros.

12. Tuvimos que escribir................solicitar el catálogo.

13. Ese bello cuadro fue pintado................Velázquez.

14. La novela *Don Quijote de la Mancha* fue escrita................Cervantes.

15. Trajeron estos regalos................tu hermana Julia.

16. El concierto fue ejecutado................un pianista francés.

17. Ella escribió esta tarjeta................mí.

18. Mis primos tienen clases cuatro veces................semana.

19. He venido solamente................saludarte.

20. Estas cortinas son................las ventanas del cuarto.

21. Compramos pintura................las puertas.

22. Margarita condujo al ciego................la mano.

23. Este ejercicio está hecho................mí.

PARA — POR *Continued*

In the previous exercise (page 151), we studied the general distinctions in usage between *para* and *por*. Note, in additon, the following somewhat idiomatic uses of *para*.

> Estoy listo *para* salir. (I am ready to leave.)
> No sirve *para nada.* (It is good for nothing.)
> Estudia *para* médico. (He is studying to be a doctor.)
> Es pequeño *para* su edad. (He is small for his age.)

Also note the following rather idiomatic uses of *por*.

> *Por* la mañana (tarde, noche) (in the morning, afternoon, evening)
> *Por* lo general (in general)
> *Por* eso (also *por* lo tanto, *por* consiguiente) (therefore, accordingly)
> Lo compré *por* un peso (I bought it for one dollar)

In the blanks, supply PARA or POR, whichever is correct.

1. Ellos vendrán hoy................la noche.
2. Tomás nunca está en su casa................la tarde.
3. Ella tiene................lo menos treinta años de edad.
4. ....lo general, Ricardo trabaja tres veces................semana.
5. Ya estaba preparado................el viaje cuando me llamaron............teléfono.
6. Tomás estudia mucho y................eso progresa tanto.
7. Tu auto no sirve................nada.
8. Dice Gloria que no le agrada viajar................tren.
9. Andrés quiere estudiar................médico.
10. Tu amiga compró este reloj................quince pesos.
11. Ese espectáculo no es propio................su edad.
12. ....eso yo creo que lo mejor es renunciar.
13. El jovencito fue castigado................desobedecer al maestro.
14. Me dieron esta medicina................el catarro.
15. Esa niñita habla muy bien................su edad.
16. Hicimos el viaje solamente................saludarlo.
17. El come demasiado................eso está tan gordo.
18. Ella nunca va a la iglesia................la noche.
19. A Virginia le gusta ir al cine................la tarde.
20. Ella,................lo general compra en la tienda de Antonio.
21. Tu sobrino quiere estudiar................aviador.
22. Yo siempre estoy listo................pasear.

Verbs Ending in UIR **(Present Tense Forms)**

In verbs ending in *uir* (*incluir, huir, destruir, construir, contribuir*) the letter *i* is introduced in the present tense before all endings except those which begin with *i*. Typical conjugation of two verbs of this group, *incluir* and *huir*, follow. (The remaining verbs of the group are conjugated in the same way.)

yo	inclu*yo*	nosotros	incluimos
tú	inclu*yes*	(vosotros	incluís)
usted él, ella}	inclu*ye*	ustedes ellos}	inclu*yen*

yo	hu*yo*	nosotros	huimos
tú	hu*yes*	(vosotros	huís)
usted él, ella}	hu*ye*	ustedes ellos}	hu*yen*

Supply the correct present tense form of the verbs in parentheses.

1. Yo (incluir) esta carta entre las tuyas.

   (Example: Yo *incluyo* esta carta entre las tuyas.)

2. Ellos (contribuir) siempre a los ciegos.
3. Nosotros (huir) de las malas compañías.
4. Tú siempre (concluir) sus tareas temprano.
5. No me (incluir) en la lista de los asistentes.
6. Los incendios (destruir) rápidamente las casas de madera.
7. El niñito (huir) del perro grande.
8. El nuevo ingeniero (construir) el puente sobre el río.
9. Ella nos (incluir) entre sus mejores amigos.
10. Las clases (concluir) la próxima semana.
11. El cobarde siempre (huir) cuando lo atacan.
12. Los valientes nunca (huir) ante el peligro.
13. Ellos no (incluir) sus nombres porque son extranjeros.
14. Las bombas nucleares (destruir) ciudades enteras.
15. El nuevo gobierno (construir) buenas carreteras.
16. Algunos insectos(destruir) las plantas del huerto.
17. La señora Hernández siempre (contribuir) a la iglesia.
18. El señor Fernández siempre (concluir) su discurso dando las gracias.
19. Ella nunca me (incluir) en la lista de invitados de honor.
20. Tú no (contribuir) nunca a nada.
21. Si tú (contribuir) yo (construir) la casa.

Verbs Ending in **UIR** *(Past Tense Form)*

In the previous exercise (page 153), we studied the present tense forms of the verbs endings in *uir (incluir, destruir, construir, concluir, contribuir.)* Note, further, that in the past tense (preterite) of these verbs, the letter *y* is also introduced before all endings which do not begin with *i**. Conjugations in the past tense (preterite) of the typical verbs *incluir* and *huir* of this group follow.

yo	incluí		nosotros	incluimos
tú	incluiste		(vosotros	incluisteis)
usted			ustedes	
él, ella	} incluyó		ellos	} incluyeron

yo	huí		nosotros	huimos
tú	huiste		(vosotros	huisteis)
usted			ustedes	
él, ella	} huyó		ellos	} huyeron

Supply the correct past tense (preterite) form of the verbs in parentheses.

1. Ellos no (incluir) esos gastos de viaje.

   (Example: Ellos no *incluyeron* esos gastos de viaje.)

2. El arquitecto (construir) el edificio del museo.
3. El ladrón (huir) cuando oyó el timbre de alarma.
4. Ella no (destruir) las cartas de su hermana.
5. Rafael (concluir) el trabajo muy pronto.
6. Nosotros (concluir) nuestros estudios por hoy.
7. Usted no (incluir) mi nombre en esa lista.
8. Ellos (huir) de Rusia por el comunismo.
9. Un fuerte tornado (destruir) muchas casas.
10. El explorador (concluir) su excursión por la América del Sur.
11. Tú (contribuir) para la Cruz Roja.
12. Ellos sí (contribuir) para auxiliar a las víctimas del terremoto.
13. En el choque, el automóvil se (destruir) por completo.
14. Yo (huir) cuando vi el león suelto.
15. Ya García (concluir) su período presidencial.
16. Los Estados Unidos (construir) el canal de Panamá.
17. El ciclón (destruir) los puentes sobre los cayos de la Florida.
18. Los obreros (reconstruir) los puentes destruídos.
19. Nosotros (contribuir) con nuestro esfuerzo para evitar la guerra.
20. Ya ella (concluir) su biografía de Bolívar.

---

* The letter *y* is also introduced in the present participle of verbs in *uir* (*huyendo, incluyendo, destruyendo,* etc.).

Spelling Changes in Verbs Ending in **GAR**

The pronunciation of *g* in Spanish is always hard before *a* and *o** (paga, cargo); it is soft before *i* and *e* (región, coger). Consequently, in verbs ending in *gar* (*pagar, llegar, entregar, jugar, juzgar,* etc.), the letter *u* introduced after *g* in the first person singular of the past tense (preterite). Although voiceless, the *u* of the *gue* ending is needed to retain the hard sound of *g*.**

	Preterite	*Command Form*
pagar —	*pagué*, pagaste, pagó, pagamos, pagaron	*pague* (Ud.)
llegar —	*llegué*, llegaste, llegó, llegamos, llegaron	*llegue* (Ud.)

Supply the correct past tense (preterite) form of the verbs in parentheses.

1. Yo (pagar) la cuenta de la tienda. *pagué*

   (Example: Yo *pagué* la cuenta de la tienda.)

2. Mis compañeros (jugar) al ajedrez con Don Pepe. *jugaron*
3. Tú (llegar) tarde a las clases de francés. *llegaste*
4. Ayer yo (regar) las flores de mi jardín. *regué*
5. La cocinera (fregar) muy bien los platos. *fregó*
6. Yo no (investigar) las causas del asesinato. *investigué*
7. Yo (juzgar) que ya era demasiado tarde. *juzgué*
8. El tren no (llegar) a la hora señalada. *llegó*
9. ¿Sabe Ud. cuánto yo (pagar) a Carlos por esa bicicleta? *pagué*
10. ¿Cuándo (llegar) el cartero con la correspondencia? *llegó*
11. Nuestro club de peloteros (jugar) muy bien ayer. *jugó*
12. Usted (pagar) mucho dinero por esos muebles. *pagó*
13. Ya yo (entregar) mis ejercicios completos al profesor. *entregué*
14. Ellos todavía no (pagar) el alquiler de la casa. *pagaron*
15. Yo (llegar) a tiempo a mi clase de música. *llegué*
16. El sábado (entregar) los papeles al abogado. *entregué*
17. El (pagar) pero yo no (pagar). *pagó, pagué*
18. Yo (llegar) demasiado tarde. *llegué*
19. Yo (jugar) al tenis con él. *jugué*

---

* The *g* is also pronounced hard before *u* sound, such as *gustar, guardar, guante,* etc.
** Note that in this and succeeding exercises covering spelling changes in various verbs, all of the verbs are completely regular; there are no basic changes of stem, ending, or pronunciation. The slight spelling changes which occur are made simply to keep the pronunciation consistent.

Spelling changes in verbs ending in CAR - Preterite

The pronunciation of c in Spanish is always hard before a and o (vaca, poco); it is soft before i and e (reciente, hacer). Consequently, in verbs ending in car (sacar, tocar, buscar, colocar, embarcar, etc.) the final c of the stem is changed to qu in the first person singular of the past tense (preterite) in order to retain the hard sound of the c. (Without this change, the c would become soft before the e ending of the first person singular of this tense.) Note that the u of que or qui is not pronounced.*

Preterite	Command Form
sacar — saqué, sacaste, sacó, sacamos, sacaron	saque (Ud.)
tocar —toqué, tocaste, tocó, tocamos, tocaron	toque (Ud.)

Supply the correct past tense (preterite) form of the verbs in parentheses.

1. Yo (sacar) las manos del bolsillo. _saqué_

(Example: Yo *saqué* las manos del bolsillo.)

2. Ellos (sacar) el dinero de la caja fuerte. _sacaron_
3. Yo (sacar) los libros de la gaveta del escritorio. _saqué_
4. Ellos (tocar) el agua de la piscina. _tocaron_
5. Yo (tocar) la frente del enfermo. _toqué_
6. ¿Qué (tocar) ella en el piano? _tocó_
7. (Tocar) usted el timbre, por favor. _tocó (toque)_
8. Yo me (embarcar) en una lancha de motor. _embarqué_
9. Los Martínez se (embarcar) en el vapor Florida. _embarcaron_
10. Yo le (indicar) al chofer la dirección de mi casa. _indiqué_
11. Nosotros (sacar) la cuenta sin errores. _sacamos_
12. Yo me (refrescar) con una limonada. _refresqué_
13. Ellos (brincar) por la cerca de piedra. _brincaron_
14. Anoche yo me (dislocar) el brazo izquierdo. _disloqué_
15. Fui a pescar al lago, pero no (pescar) nada. _pesqué_
16. Catalina (roncar) mucho durante la noche. _roncó_
17. Creo que anoche yo no (roncar). _ronqué_
18. El presidente (colocar) la primera piedra. _coloco_
19. Mi amigo Juan se (sacar) la lotería. _sacó_
20. La señora González (tocar) muy bien el violín en el concierto. _tocó_

---

* See footnote, page 155.

Spelling changes in verbs ending in **GER** and **GIR** · **Present Tense**

Note that verbs ending in GER and GIR (*coger, escoger, recoger, dirigir, corregir, exigir*, etc.) change the final *g* of their stem to *j* in the first person singular of the present tense, in order to retain the original soft sound of the *g*. Here again, the reason in that *g* is always hard in Spanish before *a* and *o**, and soft before *i* and *e* (see page 155). Without this change, the *g* would become hard before the *o* ending of the first person singular of this tense.**

Present Tense	*Command Form*
coger — co*j*o, coges, coge, cogemos, cogen	co*j*a (Ud.)
dirigir — diri*j*o, diriges, dirige, dirigimos, dirigen	diri*j*a (Ud.)

Similarly, the verbs *seguir* and *distinguir* have the forms *sigo* and *distingo* in the first person singular of the present tense. The final *u* of the stem is dropped because *g* is always hard before *o* and thus the *u* not necessary.

Present Tense	*Command Form*
distinguir — distin*go*, distingues, distingue, distinguimos, distinguen	distin*ga* (Ud.)
seguir — si*go*, sigues, sigue, seguimos, siguen	si*ga* (Ud.)

Supply the correct present tense forms of the verbs in parentheses.

1. Yo (coger) al niño de la mano.

    (Example: Yo *cojo* al niño de la mano.)

2. Nosotros siempre (escoger) las frutas con cuidado.
3. Ella (escoger) los libros del mostrador.
4. Yo no (seguir) esa dirección tan confusa.
5. Sus niños frecuentemente (coger) catarro.
6. Yo (recoger) los papeles que están por el suelo.
7. No (distinguir) nada sin los lentes.
8. Yo (dirigir) el departamento de ventas.
9. El policía (dirigir) el tránsito.
10. ¿Por qué no (corregir) los errores de acentuación?
11. Yo (corregir) mis defectos de pronunciación.
12. Ellos (exigir) muchas obligaciones.
13. Yo no (exigir) mucho a mis amigos.
14. Yo siempre (recoger) mi correspondencia.
15. Yo me (dirigir) a mi casa después de clases.
16. Yo (seguir) estudiando en mi casa con mi libro.
17. Yo no (distinguir) la diferencia entre esos colores.
18. ¿Quién (escoger) las telas para hacer los vestidos?
19. ¿Cómo (seguir) Enrique con su resfriado?
20. Ellas (seguir) estudiando en esa Academia de Idiomas.

---

* G is also hard before *u* but does not occur in any verb ending.
** See footnote page 155.

Spelling changes in verbs ending in ZAR - Preterite

The letter z is not usually used in Spanish before i or e; the letter c is used instead. Consequently, the final z of the stem of verbs ending in zar (empezar, comenzar, alcanzar, gozar, enlazar, etc.) changes to c before the regular ending e of the first person singular of the past tense (preterite).

Supply the correct past tense (preterite) form of the verbs in parentheses.

1. Yo (comenzar) a trabajar a los veinte años de edad. _Comencé_

   (Example: Yo comencé a trabajar a los veinte años de edad.)

2. Ellos (empezar) sus clases de historia a las dos de la tarde. _empazaro_
3. Yo no (utilizar) mis herramientas para arreglarlo. _utilicé_
4. Los soldados (avanzar) cuando recibieron la orden del capitán.
5. El sueldo de este mes no me (alcanzar) para pagar mis gastos. _avanzaron_ _alcanzó_
6. Los aviadores (utilizar) el radar para volar de noche. _utilizaron_
7. El buque (avanzar) poco durante la tempestad. _avanzó_
8. Yo (comenzar) mis clases de español el año pasado. _comencé_
9. Nosotros (utilizar) todos los recursos para curarlo. _utilizamos_
10. Yo (gozar) en el parque zoológico con los niños. _gocé_
11. Nosotros (empezar) a trabajar a las ocho. _empezamos_
12. La señora (comenzar) su limpieza temprano. _comenzó_
13. Ellos (avanzar) todo lo posible. _avanzaron_
14. Ella me (lanzar) una piedra desde el techo. _lanzó_
15. Yo (abrazar) a mi madre cuando la ví. _abracé_
16. Los esposos se (abrazar) cuando se despidieron. _abrazaron_
17. Yo (cruzar) el río en bote. _crucé_
18. Los soldados (lanzar) varias granadas de mano. _lanzaron_
19. Yo (utilizar) todos los papeles que estaban en la gaveta. _utilicé_
20. Yo (comenzar) mi ejercicio temprano y ya lo terminé. _comencé_

POSSESSIVE ADJECTIVES

The possessive adjectives *mi, tu, su, nuestro,* etc., studied previously* are really shortened forms of the following:

mío (a), míos (as)	nuestro (a), nuestros (as)
tuyo (a), tuyos (as)	vuestro(a), vuestros(as)
suyo (a), suyos (as)	suyo (a), suyos (as)

While *mi, tu, su, nuestro,* etc., always precede the noun they modify, the above forms are used after the noun. They are slightly more emphatic; thus they are equivalent to the English *of mine, of yours,* etc. (Examples: El es un amigo *mío* de Caracas — He is a friend *of mine* from Caracas).

More importantly, the above forms are used alone after the verbs *ser* as predicate adjectives. Note carefully, however, that when so used they must agree in number and gender with the subject of the sentence.

> Estos libros no son *míos.*
> Esta pluma es *suya.*

Substitute the appropriate predicate adjective for the words in italics. Follow example.

1. Este sombrero es *mi sombrero.*

   (Example: Este sombrero es *mío.*)

2. ¿Es suyo este paraguas? No, no es *su paraguas.*
3. ¿Es tuya esta camisa? No, no es *mi camisa.*
4. Aquellas cartas son *sus cartas.*
5. Esa casa es *nuestra casa.*
6. Esos zapatos son *nuestros zapatos.*
7. Este paquete es *tu paquete.*
8. Esta corbata no es *mi corbata.*
9. Yo creo que este cuaderno es *mi cuaderno.*
10. Aquellos papeles son *sus papeles.*
11. Aquel libro es *mi libro.*
12. Aquellos muebles son *nuestros muebles.*
13. Estas son *nuestras butacas.*
14. Parece que esos dos perros son *sus perros.*
15. ¿Es este abrigo *su abrigo,* señor Díaz?
16. Este abrigo no es *mi abrigo,* es de Fernández.
17. ¿Cree usted que esta casa es *su casa?*
18. Me parece que ésta no es *su oficina.*
19. Ellos creen que son *de ellos.*
20. Este trabajo es *mi trabajo.*

---

* See pages 28 and 29.

POSSESSIVE PRONOUNS

Note that the same possessive adjectives studied in the last exercise (*mío, tuyo* *suyo*, etc.) are used together with the corresponding definite article *el, la los, la* to form possessive pronouns: *el mío, la mía, los míos, las mías* (mine); *el tuyo el suyo, la suya, los suyos, las suyas* (yours, his, hers, theirs); *el nuestro, la nues- tra, los nuestros, las nuestras* (ours).

> Este lápiz es mejor que *el mío.*
> Sus amigas son más fieles que *las mías.*
> Mis libros están aquí. ¿Dónde están *los suyos?*

Note here again that the form of the possessive pronoun in Spanish is determined by the number and gender of the thing to which the possessive pronoun refers, and not simply by the possessor as in English.

Substitute the corresponding possessive pronoun in place of the words in italics. Follow example.

1. Ella desea comprar *mi automóvil.*

   (Example: Ella desea comprar *el mío.*)

2. Aquí están sus libros. ¿Dónde están *mis hermanos?*
3. Ellos se llevaron *nuestro automóvil.*
4. ¿Dónde vive *su familia* (de usted)?
5. ¿Dónde vive *tu amigo?*
6. Yo quiero ver *sus libros* (de ellos).
7. Déme *su mano* y yo le doy *mi mano* también.
8. *Mi padre* tiene más dinero que *su padre.*
9. *Su sombrero* (de usted) es más grande que *mi sombrero.*
10. Esa escuela es mejor que *mi escuela.*
11. Aquellas son *mis tarjetas* postales.
12. Aquellos son *mis zapatos* nuevos y estos son *mis zapatos* viejos.
13. María, ¿éstas son *sus medias* de seda?
14. Dice Juana que éstas son *nuestras invitaciones.*
15. Yo creo, Julio, que ésta es *tu camisa* y no *mi camisa.*
16. Yo deseo saber dónde viven *sus hermanos* (de ella).
17. Aquella casa verde es *nuestra casa.*
18. *Su cartera* (de usted) es de piel muy fina pero *mi cartera* es de plástico.
19. *Mi automóvil* es más moderno que *su automóvil.*
20. Dame *mi dinero*, Daniel.

Since *el tuyo, el suyo, la suya*, etc., may mean *yours, his, hers, theirs* (see page 160), ambiguity is avoided when necessary by substituting the appropriate definite article together with *de usted, de él, de ella, de ellos*, etc.

Tengo la dirección de él, pero no la *suya*.

or

Tengo la dirección de él, pero no la *de usted*.

Me gustan más los zapatos de usted que los *suyos*.

or

Me gustan más los zapatos de usted que los *de él*.

Substitute the word in italics for the corresponding definite article and the preposition *de*. Follow example.

1. El desayuno de Enrique y el *suyo* están servidos (Luis).

   (Example: El desayuno de Enrique y *el de Luis* están servidos.)

2. Este es el libro de Antonio, pero no el *suyo* (Tomás).

3. Esta casa es más fresca que la *suya* (ellos).

4. Me gusta más el auto suyo que el *suyo* (Alfredo).

5. ¿Dónde estará la sombrilla de María? ¿Y la (Mariana).

6. ¿Quién cogió los lápices de usted?   ¿Y los *suyos*? (Enrique).

7. No tenemos la dirección de Antonio ni la *suya* (Raúl).

8. Su sortija es muy bonita, pero la *suya* (ella) no me gusta.

9. Los alumnos del profesor Fernández y los *suyos* (usted) están aquí.

10. Mi reloj y el *suyo* son de oro (tu tío).

11. Conocemos a la hermana de Inés, pero no a la *suya* (Virginia).

12. Esta Biblia es muy antigua como la *suya* (Ministro González).

13. Nuestras medias son negras y las *suyas* (él) son blancas.

14. Recibí la contestación de Antonio, pero no la *suya* (mi hermano).

15. Aquéllas son mis libretas, y éstas las *suyas* (Juan y Alberto).

16. Creo que estos documentos son *suyos* (usted).

17. Mi perro es más inteligente que el *suyo* (María).

18. Aquí está su cartera y ésta es la *suya* (mamá).

19. Tus ojos son azules, pero los *suyos* (Olimpia) son verdes.

20. Mi casa es azul y la *suya* (ellos) es blanca.

Conditional form (EL MODO POTENCIAL)

The conditional form in Spanish is similar in its formation to the future tense in that the entire infinitive of the verb is used as the stem. This applies to verbs of all three conjugations. To this stem is added the endings *ía, ías, íamos, íais, ían.* (Compare with formation of the future tense — pages 99-104).

yo	hablaría*		nosotros	hablaríamos
tú	hablarías		(vosotros	hablaríais)
usted él, ella }	hablaría		ustedes ellos }	hablarían

(English equivalent: I would talk, you would talk, he would talk, etc.)

Change the following present tense verbs to future tense and to conditional form. Follow example.

Present Tense	Future Tense	Conditional Form
1. yo escribo	(escribiré)	(escribiría)
2. tú hablas	....	....
3. él conoce	....	....
4. usted trabaja	....	....
5. ella repite	....	....
6. Tomás llega	....	....
7. nosotros estudiamos	....	....
8. ustedes traducen	....	....
9. ellos escogen	....	....
10. ella se acuesta	....	....
11. el cartero llega	....	....
12. la niña lee	....	....
13. los criados limpian	....	....
14. el auto corre	....	....
15. usted pinta	....	....
16. nosotros gustamos	....	....
17. los profesores dictan	....	....
18. tú pides	....	....
19. yo prometo	....	....
20. ellos cantan	....	....
21. nosotros terminamos	....	....
22. ellos aprenden	....	....

---

* As will be studied in detail in subsequent lessons, these forms are used in so called conditional sentences (Si yo lo conociera, yo *hablaría* con él — *If I knew him, I would speak with him*) and in indirect discourse (El dijo que *hablaría* con ella — *He said he would speak with her*).

USE OF CONDITONAL FORM

The conditional form is used like its equivalent in English:

1) It is used together with the subjunctive mood in the so-called answer clause of true conditional sentences (Si yo fuera (*subjunctive*) usted, yo no le *hablaría*. If I were you, I wouldn't speak to him.) We shall study this use of the conditional later when we study subjunctive forms.

2) The conditional is also used in indirect speech. Thus, if the main verb of a sentence is in the past tense, the second verb, denoting future action or intention in the past, is put into conditional form.

> Juan dice que hablará con ella.
> Juan dijo que *hablaría* con ella. (John said that he *would speak* with her.)
> Ella promete que lo traerá pronto.
> Ella prometió que lo *traería* pronto. (She promised that she *would bring* it soon.)

Supply the correct conditional form of the verbs in parentheses.

1. Ellos dijeron que (comprar) un libro de español.

   (Example: Ellos dijeron que *comprarían* un libro de español.)

2. Juan les prometió que los (invitar) al almuerzo.

3. Ella me dijo que (estudiar) francés el año próximo.

4. Jorge y Mariana nos dijeron que les (gustar) pasear en automóvil con nosotros.

5. El creyó que Rafael (cumplir) su promesa.

6. Sebastián me anunció que (viajar) al Canadá.

7. El profesor me dijo que (repetir) la lección octava.

8. Los médicos dijeron que (curar) muy pronto al herido.

9. Ella insistió en que (volver) por la noche.

10. El inquilino me prometió que (pagar) mañana.

11. Antonio me ofreció que (tratar) el asunto con el jefe.

12. Yo creí que (ir) a trabajar mañana.

13. Ella estaba segura que Jaime (comprar) la joya.

14. El ingeniero calculó que (costar) mucho dinero la obra.

15. El secretario nos informó que los certificados (estar) listos pronto.

16. Carmen repitió varias veces que no (estudiar) más en esa escuela.

17. Mi vecino me dijo que me (prestar) unos discos de canciones.

18. Ellos nos prometieron que (rebajar) los precios.

19. Tú sabías que ella no le (permitir) usar su automóvil.

20. Alejandro me dijo que Juan (llamar) por teléfono a Raúl.

21. El maestro me prometió que me (explicar) de nuevo la lección.

In the previous exercise (page 163), we learned that the conditional form is often used in indirect speech where the first verb of the sentence is in the past tense and the second verb, indicating future action or intention in the past, is put into conditional form (El dijo que *hablaría* con ella. Ella prometió que lo *traería* pronto).

For further practice with the conditional form used in this way in indirect speech, change the first verb of each of the following sentences to simple past tense (preterite). Then change the second verb to conditional form. Follow example.

1. Ellos *dicen* que los *visitarán* mañana.

   (Example: Ellos *dijeron* que los *visitarían* mañana.)

2. Yo le *prometo* que *iré* el jueves próximo.

3. José *dice* que lo *llamará* por la noche.

4. Ella *piensa* que la función *será* un éxito extraordinario.

5. Nosotros *insistimos* en que *compraremos* el piano.

6. El radio *dice* que no *transmitirá* mañana.

7. Juan me *asegura* que me *comprará* mi automóvil.

8. *Dicen* que nos *encontrarán* en el teatro.

9. El director *aclara* que no *renunciará*.

10. Tomás *cree* que ella lo *invitará* al baile.

11. Alfredo *dice* que él *trabajará* más.

12. Los carteros *dicen* que no *repartirán* los sábados.

13. El barbero *anuncia* que *rebajará* el precio del corte de pelo.

14. Carolina *cree* que Domingo la *llevará* al baile.

15. Yo *pienso* que la maestra nos *perdonará* la falta de asistencia.

16. Nosotros *prometemos* que *pintaremos* la casa de Luisa.

17. Me *aseguran* que me *colocarán* en esa oficina.

18. Ricardo *dice* que *estará* en casa por la noche.

19. Nostros *insistimos* en que no *prestaremos* nuestras maletas.

20. Yo me *imagino* que ellos *vendrán* el viernes.

21. Ernesto *afirma* que ellos *ayudarán* en la obra.

22. Yo *aseguro* que *terminaré* este ejercicio enseguida.

CONDITIONAL FORM (*Irregular verbs*)

Note that the same verbs which were irregular in the future tense* are irregular in the conditional form (*potencial*).

Note, further, that the irregularities are identical in both cases: that is, the same alteration which takes place in the stem of each of these verbs in the future tense also occurs in the conditional form.

haber	— *habría*, etc.	salir	— *saldría*, etc.	decir	— *diría*, etc.
poder	— *podría*, etc.	tener	— *tendría*, etc.	hacer	— *haría*, etc.
saber	— *sabría*, etc.	valer	— *valdría*, etc.	querer	— *querría*, etc.
caber	— *cabría*, etc.	venir	— *vendría*, etc.	poner	— *pondría*, etc.

Change the following present tense verbs to the future tense and to conditional form. (See similar exercise covering regular verbs, page 163).

Present Tense	Future Tense	Conditional Form
1. yo vengo	(vendré)	(vendría)
2. ellos salen		
3. usted tiene		
4. nosotros sabemos		
5. el y ella valen		
6. el policía viene		
7. nadie puede		
8. Julio dice		
9. ustedes quieren		
10. Elena hace		
11. yo pongo		
12. hay dinero		
13. hace tiempo		
14. el profesor dice		
15. las maestras saben		
16. María quiere		
17. nosotros venimos		
18. yo hago		
19. yo he		
20. ellos salen		
21. el niño no puede		
22. la carta cabe		
23. yo quepo		
24. yo sé		

* For future tense forms of irregular verbs, see pages 101-104. Also see appendix for reference to future tense and conditional form of both regular and irregular verbs.

Supply the conditional form (*potencial*) of the verbs in parentheses. (See similar exercise, plus explanation covering regular verbs, page 164.) Follow example.

1. Ella dijo que no (hacer) la carta.

   (Example: Ella dijo que no *haría* la carta.)

2. Ellos no pensaron que el avión (llegar) tarde.

3. Enrique me prometió que (poner) dinero en el negocio.

4. Usted me dijo que no lo (hacer) demasiado caro.

5. Supongo que no (haber) muchas personas en el mitin.

6. Yo creo que él (poder) hacer muy bien ese ejercicio.

7. Fernando sabía que ella (querer) asistir al paseo en lancha.

8. Dijeron que el tren (salir) a las ocho de la mañana.

9. Tú te imaginaste que él (venir) a visitar a Margarita.

10. No creí que Raúl le (decir) la verdad del suceso.

11. Ellos dijeron que (hacer) el trabajo por la noche.

12. Yo creí que ella (saber) recitar mejor.

13. Nosotros suponíamos que ese negocio (fracasar).

14. Ernesto dijo que mañana no (haber) clases en la escuela.

15. Usted prometió que (volver) a cooperar con nosotros.

16. ¿Dijo ella que (comprar) medicinas en la farmacia?

17. Tú no creías que ella (tener) que trabajar en una fábrica.

18. Me informó que (ir) en ómnibus al campo.

19. ¿(Cambiar) él de idea si lo aconsejaran?

20. ¿Prometió que (llevar) a los niños al parque zoológico?

21. Yo pensé que Pedro ya (haber) terminado su novela.

22. Yo pensé que (terminar) su discurso más temprano.

23. Le dije a Tomás que no (hacer) tal cosa.

24. Carmen esperaba que ellos no (venir) a esa hora.

Change the first verb of each of the following sentences to past tense (preterite); then change the second verb to conditional form (potencial). (See similar exercise, plus explanation covering regular verbs, page 165.) Follow example.

1. Me informaron que *vendrá* temprano.

   (Example: Me *informaron* que *vendría* temprano.)

2. Ellos *dicen* que *pondrán* más dinero en el negocio.

3. Yo *creo* que Juan *hará* el ejercicio temprano.

4. Nos *prometen* que *podrán* escribir las cartas enseguida.

5. El maestro *dice* que *sabremos* suficiente español.

6. Yo *aseguro* que todos esos libros *cabrán* en la caja.

7. Las vecinas *dicen* que no *recibirán* al extranjero.

8. Yo *creo* que ella *pondrá* más cuidado en su trabajo.

9. Me *imagino* que *habrá* poca asistencia a la conferencia.

10. Ella *promete* que nos *dirá* su secreto.

11. Nadie quiere *informarme* cuándo *vendrá* Benjamín.

12. Ellos me *prometen* que la casa *valdrá* mucho en poco tiempo.

13. Ricardo *dice* que no *podrá* hacer tanto esfuerzo.

14. Ellos *creen* que no *tendremos* dificultades en el viaje.

15. Yo *supongo* que ella *dirá* todo lo que sucedió.

16. ¿*Aseguran* ellos que el director *vendrá* mañana?

17. ¿*Sabe* usted si él *saldrá* a esa hora?

18. Alguien *dice* que no *tendré* que ir.

19. El médico no *cree* que el enfermo *querrá* curarse.

20. *Creo* que Domingo *vendrá* en el tren de las cinco de la tarde.

21. El jefe *dice* que *habrá* mucho trabajo mañana.

22. Nosotros le *prometemos* a usted que *saldremos* bien en el examen.

23. Me *informan* que María se *casará* el día treinta de este mes.

24. Yo *creo* que él *hará* esos ejercicios sin ayuda alguna.

The subjunctive mood has many varied uses in Spanish* and it must be studied carefully. The present tense of the subjunctive mood is formed as follows: the stem of all regular verbs and most irregular verbs is derived from the *first person singular, present tense,* of the indicative mood**. To this stem is added, for -*ar* ending verbs (first conjugation), the following endings: *e, es, e, emos, éis, en*. The conjugation of the typical first conjugation verb *hablar* in the present tense of the subjunctive mood is as follows:

yo	hable	nosotros	hablemos
tú	hables	(vosotros	habléis)
usted él, ella }	hable	ustedes ellos }	hablen

Supply the corresponding subjunctive form of the following present indicative -*ar* ending verbs.

Indicative	Subjunct.	Indicative	Subjunct.
1. yo pregunto	(pregunte)	21. yo mando	....
2. él compra	(compre)	22. él saluda	....
3. usted toma	....	23. ella roba	....
4. nosotros miramos	....	24. usted necesita	....
5. ella pregunta	....	25. ellas pintan	....
6. ellos cuentan	....	26. ellos hablan	....
7. ellas llaman	....	27. ustedes cambian	....
8. yo hablo	....	28. nosotros enseñamos	....
9. ella escucha	....	29. ella explica	....
10. ustedes pagan	....	30. yo mando	....
11. ellos se lavan	....	31. ellos gastan	....
12. yo copio	....	32. alguien llega	....
13. usted escucha	....	33. nadie mira	....
14. nosotros estudiamos	....	34. ellos pasan	....
15. ella se levanta	....	35. usted se enferma	....
16. tú esperas	....	36. ellas contestan	....
17. yo recuerdo	....	37. él se cansa	....
18. nadie paga	....	38. yo me peino	....
19. nosotros empezamos	....	39. él canta	....
20. usted vende	....	40. yo termino	....

* Some of the uses of the subjunctive in Spanish are as follows: a) after verbs of wish or command (El *quiere* que usted le *hable* en español). b) after verbs of emotion (Me *alegro* que usted *hable* español). c) after impersonal expressions of necessity and opinion (Es *necesario* que usted *hable* español). d) after expressions of doubt (*Dudo* que él *hable* español), etc. These and other uses of the subjunctive will be studied in detail in subsequent lessons.

** Note that this formation is the same as that of the imperative (command) form already studied (page 123).

As already studied, first conjugation verbs in *ar* form the subjunctive by adding the endings *e, es, e, emos, éis, en;* furthermore, the stem of all regular verbs and most irregular verbs in the present tense of the subjunctive mood is derived from the *first person singular, present tense,* indicative mood. (See previous exercise, page 168. Also read footnote on the same page concerning use of the subjunctive mood in Spanish.)

To form the subjunctive, present tense, of verbs ending in *er* and *ir* (ie. second and third conjugation verbs), we add the following endings to the stem: *a, as, a, amos, áis, an.* The conjugations of the typical second and third conjugation verbs *comer* and *vivir,* in the present tense of the subjunctive mood, are as follows:

yo	com*a*		nosotros	com*amos*
tú	com*as*		(vosotros	com*áis*)
usted } él, ella }	com*a*		ustedes } ellos }	com*an*

yo	viv*a*		nosotros	viv*amos*
tú	viv*as*		(vosotros	viv*áis*)
usted } él, ella }	viv*a*		ustedes } ellos }	viv*an*

In the blanks supply the corresponding subjunctive form of the following present tense verbs of the second and third conjugations.

Indicative	Subjunct.	Indicative	Subjunct.
1. yo aprendo	(aprenda)	19. él vive	....
2. él reparte	....	20. ella sube	....
3. usted insiste	....	21. yo descubro	....
4. yo leo	....	22. nosotros tememos	....
5. nosotros metemos	....	23. yo escojo	....
6. ella debe	....	24. él asiste	....
7. tú coges	....	25. ellos beben	....
8. usted comete	....	26. ellas venden	....
9. yo escribo	....	27. nadie teme	....
10. él responde	....	28. yo parto	....
11. ellos abren	....	29. ellos sirven	....
12. tú comes	....	30. tú recibes	....
13. alguien se aburre	....	31. yo cubro	....
14. yo permito	....	32. ella prohibe	....
15. usted insiste	....	33. usted prefiere	....
16. nosotros debemos	....	34. ella recoge	....
17. nadie asiste	....	35. usted se sorprende	....
18. yo protejo	....	36. yo cubro	....

As studied previously, the stem of all regular verbs and most irregular verbs* in the present tense of the subjunctive mood is derived from the *first person singular, present tense,* of the indicative mood. Note the following typical subjunctive forms of various irregular verbs, all of which derive their stems exactly according to the rule from the first person singular, present tense, of the indicative mood. Note, further, that the endings are regular for all of these verbs.

	Stem:		*Subjunctive Forms:*
hacer	(yo hago)	*hag*	*hag*a, *hag*as, *hag*a, *hag*amos, (*hag*áis), *hag*an
poner	(yo pongo)	*pong*	*pong*a, *pong*as, *pong*a, *pong*amos, (*pong*áis), *pong*an
traer	(yo traigo)	*traig*	*traig*a, *traig*as, *traig*a, *traig*amos, traig*áis), *traig*an
tener	(yo tengo)	*teng*	*teng*a, *teng*as, *teng*a, *teng*amos, (*teng*áis), *teng*an

Supply the corresponding subjunctive form of the following present tense verbs. Follow examples.

1.	yo puedo	(pueda)	21.	él hace	(haga)
2.	él pierde	(pierda)	22.	usted tiene	(tenga)
3.	ella quiere	....	23.	tú vuelves	....
4.	usted oye	....	24.	nosotros salimos	....
5.	nosotros venimos	....	25.	ella dice	....
6.	tú ves	....	26.	tú te sientes	....
7.	yo hago	....	27.	ellos cierran	....
8.	nadie muere	....	28.	yo pongo	....
9.	todo sirve	....	29.	alguien vuelve	....
10.	ellas traducen	....	30.	yo traigo	....
11.	ustedes quieren	....	31.	nosotros tenemos	....
12.	ella merece	....	32.	usted conoce	....
13.	yo ofrezco	....	33.	ellas almuerzan	....
14.	nosotras decimos	....	34.	tú sales	....
15.	nadie tiene	....	35.	ustedes se caen	....
16.	ellos vuelven	....	36.	él pone	....
17.	tú entiendes	....	37.	ellos sienten	....
18.	alguien pierde	....	38.	nosotras oímos	....
19.	yo sueño	....	39.	yo cuento	....
20.	él cierra	....	40.	usted ofrece	....

* Only the following five verbs have slightly distinctive forms in the present tense of the subjunctive mood: *dar, estar, ir, saber, ser.* These forms will be studied separately in later lessons (pages **174-175**).

USE OF SUBJUNCTIVE *after verbs of Wish and Command*

In general, the subjunctive mood is used only in subordinate clauses introduced by the conjunction *que*. As the word *subjunctive* itself suggests (from the Latin *subjoined*), the subjunctive always depends upon another verb and denotes, *not a fact,* but a wish, an uncertainty, an expression of emotion, etc.

The first use of the subjunctive we shall study is that of following verbs of wish or command (*querer, desear, pedir, exigir, insistir preferir, etc.*) when the main verb and the subordinate verb have different subjects.

> El quiere que Juan *haga** ese trabajo.
> Exigen que yo *firme* el contrato hoy.
> Ella insiste en que usted *espere* aquí.

Choose the correct form.

1. El Director exige que (compramos, compremos) la enciclopedia.

2. Yo quiero que él (leo, lea) estos versos de Darío.

3. Ellos insisten en que ella (asista, asiste) a la recepción.

4. Usted desea que su señora (compre, compra) los vestidos.

5. Carlos quiere que tú (estudie, estudies) en su casa.

6. Nosotros exigimos que (salen, salgan) de la piscina.

7. Yo espero que ellas (traigan, traen) los cuadernos de ejercicios.

8. El aspira a que su amigo (sale, salga) electo en las próximas elecciones.

9. Lo que más yo deseo es que me (pagan, paguen) lo que me deben.

10. Mi jefe insiste en que me (examino, examine) el médico.

11. El policía exige que usted (paga, pague) la multa.

12. Ella quiere que le (escribamos, escribimos) una tarjeta postal.

13. Yo deseo que ella se (mejora, mejore) cuanto antes.

14. Alguien dice que ustedes no (salgan, salen) ahora porque es peligroso.

15. Yo deseo que la guerra se (termina, termine) pronto.

---

* Note: The English student may grasp the idea of the subjunctive more easily if he recalls that although the infinitive is more commonly used in such constructions in English (He wants John *to do* that work), there remains a small group of verbs (*demand, insist, recommend, wish,* etc.) after which the subjunctive is still required. Thus, one says: John insists that she *wait* (not *waits*). Henry demands that she *be* (not *is*) there. She wishes that her sister *were* (not *is*) here. These are pure subjunctive uses, similar to Spanish. The main fact to remember is that, while in English the subjunctive has only limited use after these few verbs, in Spanish the subjunctive is used after all verbs of wish or command, as well as in many other comparable constructions.

SUBJUNCTIVE AFTER VERBS OF WISH AND COMMAND
Continued

Supply the correct subjunctive form of the verbs in parentheses. (See previous exercise, page 171, for an explanation of this use of the subjunctive—also see footnote at bottom of same page.) Follow example.

1. Yo deseo que mis hijos (estudiar) en la Universidad.

   (Example: Yo deseo que mis hijos *estudien* en la Universidad.)

2. El quiere que María (venir) a visitarnos mañana.

3. Ella no permite que ustedes (jugar) en el jardín.

4. Nosotros insistimos en que el nos (pagar) la cuenta.

5. Mi profesor insiste en que yo (traducir) ese párrafo al francés.

6. Samuel quiere que el médico (asistir) a su hermano enfermo.

7. Dígale al secretario que (estar) aquí por la tarde.

8. El dice que no quiere que su novia (ponerse) ese vestido.

9. El reglamento prohibe que uno (faltar) a los exámenes finales.

10. Ella prefiere que la (trasladar) a otra oficina.

11. Hágame el favor de decirle a Tomás que no (gritar) tanto.

12. La ley exige que (pagar) los impuestos.

13. Nosotros deseamos que nos (traer) el desayuno al cuarto.

14. El director no permite que (fumar) en la escuela.

15. El cartero quiere que le (abrir) la puerta de la oficina.

16. La cocinera espera que le (aumentar) el sueldo.

17. Nosotras preferimos que nos (llevar) en automóvil.

18. Ustedes desean que yo (cantar) en el concierto.

19. Ellas no permiten que las (molestar) tantas veces.

20. Dígale a su amigo que me (esperar) en la esquina.

21. El me recomienda que no (aceptar) ese empleo.

22. Ellos le aconsejaron que (visitar) a un médico.

23. Yo sugiero que (caminar) despacio.

24. Todos deseamos que este trabajo (resultar) bien.

SUBJUNCTIVE AFTER VERBS OF WISH AND COMMAND
Continued

We have already learned that one of the principal uses of the subjunctive in Spanish is after verbs of wish and command when the main verb and the subordinate verb have different subjects (see pages 171-172). Naturally, if the sentence contains only one subject, there is no need to use the subjunctive; then, as in English, a simple infinitive is used.

> Yo quiero *salir* temprano.
> María quiere *esperar* aquí.

Note, however, that when a subordinate clause with a different subject from that of the main verb of the sentence is introduced, the subjunctive must be used.

> Yo quiero que *usted salga* temprano.
> María quiere que *ellos esperen* aquí.

For further practice in using subjunctive forms, substitute a subjunctive clause with USTED as a subject for each of the infinitives in the following sentences.

1. El quiere *empezar* más temprano.

    (Example: El quiere que *usted empiece* más temprano.)

2. Ella prefiere *comprar* una sortija de oro.
3. Yo deseo *decir* la noticia antes que ella.
4. ¿Prefiere él *venir* más temprano?
5. Ustedes desean *salir* a las ocho de la noche.
6. Nosotros deseamos *regresar* por la tarde.
7. Eduardo prefiere *volver* la semana próxima.
8. Los padres quieren *hacer* un viaje a España.
9. Ella insiste en *regresar* hoy mismo.
10. Yo quiero *ayudar* en esa obra.
11. Nosotras deseamos *trabajar* en el campo.
12. Pedro no quiere *tener* ninguna responsabilidad.
13. El aspira a *sacar* muy buenas notas en el examen de Español.
14. Yo prefiero *esperar* a que escampe.
15. Ellas insisten en *vender* su casa junto al lago.
16. Luis y Julio desean *vivir* en el hotel.
17. Ellas no quieren *visitar* a su vecina Margarita.
18. Nosotros aconsejamos *observarlo* con detenimiento.

NOTE: For further practice with these same subjunctive forms, repeat the above exercises, this time using USTEDES in place of USTED as the subject clause (1. Yo quiero que *ustedes empiecen* más temprano.) Repeat again using JUAN instead of USTED as subject. (Yo quiero que *Juan empiece* más temprano.)

Subjunctive mood (*irregular verbs* **IR** *and* **DAR**)

Note that the verbs *ir* and *dar* are irregular in the present tense of the subjunctive mood. Their conjugations follow:

ir

yo	*vaya**	nosotros	*vayamos*
tú	*vayas*	(vosotros	*vayáis*)
usted } él, ella }	*vaya*	ustedes } ellos }	*vayan*

dar

yo	*dé**	nosotros	*demos*
tú	*des*	(vosotros	*déis*)
usted } él, ella }	*dé*	ustedes } ellos }	*den*

In the blanks, supply the correct present tense subjunctive form of IR.

1. El desea que ella.....................con Jaime a la conferencia.

   (Example: El desea que ella *vaya* con Jaime a la conferencia.)

2. Usted no quiere que yo.....................a la iglesia ahora.
3. Yo siento que María.....................tan desarreglada a la fiesta.
4. Ellos prefieren que nosotros.....................bien temprano.
5. Rafael espera que ustedes.....................a saludar a Ramón.
6. Sólo deseo que ella.....................al concierto conmigo.
7. A mí no me agrada que usted.....................sin saco.
8. Mi madre insiste en que yo.....................a ver al médico.
9. Yo quiero que los niños.....................a la playa por la mañana.
10. Nosotros esperamos que él.....................a comprar las medicinas.
11. Mariana no quiere que usted.....................a cenar esta noche.

In the blanks, supply the correct present tense subjunctive form of DAR.

1. Ella quiere que mi padre me.....................dinero para el viaje.

   (Example: Ella quiere que mi padre me *dé* dinero para el viaje.)

2. Yo espero que usted.....................su opinión en este caso.
3. Jorge desea que nosotros.....................las contestaciones enseguida.
4. Pedro y Pablo quieren que yo.....................mi permiso para salir.
5. A mí no me gusta que nadie.....................quejas de mi trabajo.
6. Esperamos que el jefe nos.....................unas vacaciones.
7. Tomás desea que ustedes.....................buenos consejos a su hijo.
8. El médico quiere que le.....................la medicina al enfermo.
9. Mi maestra prefiere que nosotros.....................respuestas claras.
10. Ellos no quieren que yo.....................mi voto a Carlos.
11. Yo sí quiero que usted.....................las gracias al público.

---

* Observe that these forms are the same as those used in the imperative (command) form previously studied (see footnote page 123).

In addition to *ir* and *dar* (page 174), there are only three other verbs which are irregular in the present tense of the subjunctive mood: *ser, estar,* and *saber.* The conjugations in the present tense, subjunctive mood, of these three verbs follow.

ser

yo	sea		nosotros	seamos
tú	seas		(vosotros	seáis)
usted } él, ella }	sea		ustedes } ellos }	sean

estar

yo	esté		nosotros	estemos
tú	estés		(vosotros	estéis)
usted } él, ella }	esté		ustedes } ellos }	estén

saber

yo	sepa		nosotros	sepamos
tú	sepas		(vosotros	sepáis)
usted } él, ella }	sepa		ustedes } ellos }	sepan

Supply the present tense subjunctive form of the verbs in parentheses.

1. Yo quiero que ella (ser) mi compañera.

   (Example: Yo quiero que ella *sea* mi compañera.)

2. Esperemos a que la escuela (estar) abierta.
3. Ella desea que tú (saber) la noticia cuanto antes.
4. Roberto prefiere que Tomás (saber) la verdad de lo ocurrido.
5. Usted se opone a que ellos (ser) soldados.
6. Ella quiere que nosotras (ser) enfermeras de ese hospital.
7. Sara se empeña en que su hijo (ser) sacerdote.
8. Yo deseo que Rosita (estar) con nosotros en la reunión.
9. Espera a que nosotros (estar) desocupados.
10. El no desea que nadie (saber) cuanto costó la casa.
11. Cuando nosotros (saber) hablar español iremos a España.
12. Todos deseamos que Carmen (ser) la secretaria del club.
13. Es necesario que ellos (ser) protegidos por la policía.
14. Esperemos a que tú (estar) bien de salud.
15. Mercedes no quiere que ellos (saber) su edad.
16. Es necesario que todos (ser) atentos con la nueva secretaria.
17. Cuando nosotros (estar) cansados dejaremos de trabajar.
18. El padre de Horacio quiere que su hijo (ser) ingeniero.
19. Yo insisto en que él (estar) estudiando toda la tarde.
20. El profesor desea que nosotros (saber) bien la lección.

For further practice with the irregular verbs previously studied (pages 174-175), substitute a subjunctive clause beginning with QUE for the italicized infinitive in each of the following sentences. Use USTED as the subject of this clause. (See similar exercise, plus explanation, covering verbs of regular formation — page 173.) Follow example.

1. Yo quiero *estar* con mi amigo Luis.

    (Example: Yo quiero que *usted esté* con mi amigo Luis.)

2. Ella desea *saber* dónde vive Eduardo.

3. Nosotros deseamos *ir* allá hoy.

4. El prefiere *dar* dinero para la fiesta.

5. Nosotros queremos *ser* los primeros en llegar.

6. Aspiramos a *dar* consejos a los adolescentes.

7. Ellos quieren *estar* fuertes para la competencia.

8. Yo no aspiro a *ser* tesorero de la compañía.

9. Todos deseamos *ir* a viajar por la América del Sur.

10. Trataremos de *estar* bien temprano en la clase.

11. Ellos sí quieren *ir* ahora a la biblioteca.

12. Todos preferimos *saber* las instrucciones enseguida.

13. Deseo *darle* las gracias a su mamá por sus atenciones.

14. Ella prefiere *ir* acompañada a la playa.

15. Los policías desean *saber* lo que tienen que hacer.

16. Ella aspira a *ser* buena amiga suya.

17. Ellos insisten en *ir* en bicicleta al campo.

18. Luis y Pedro desean *saber* dónde vive él.

19. Yo insisto en *darle* la información a Pablo.

NOTE: For further practice with these same subjunctive forms, repeat the above exercise, this time using JUAN in place of USTED as the subject of the subjunctive clause (1. Yo quiero que *Juan esté* con mi amigo Luis.) Repeat, using TU in place of USTED. (Yo quiero que *tú estés* con mi amigo Luis.) Repeat again using JUAN Y SU HERMANO instead of USTED as subject (Yo quiero que *Juan y su hermano estén* con mi amigo Luis), etc.

SUBJUNCTIVE AFTER VERBS OF EMOTION

The subjunctive mood is used in Spanish after all verbs of emotion, such as *sentir, alegrarse, lamentar, temer, extrañarse, sorprenderse*, etc. (Remember here again, however, that the verb in the subjunctive clause must have a subject of its own; if there is only one subject in the sentence, then an infinitive is used—see exercise, page 174).

Yo siento mucho que ella *esté* enferma hoy.
El tiene miedo que ella *diga* la verdad.
but
El tiene miedo de *decir* la verdad.

Supply the present tense subjunctive form of the verbs in parentheses.

1. Me alegra mucho que mi hijo (traducir) bien el español.

   (Example: Me alegra mucho que mi hijo *traduzca* bien el español.)

2. Lamento bastante que ella (tener) que ingresar en el hospital.

3. Me sorprende que tu hermano (ser) mi rival.

4. A Andrés le extraña bastante que tú no (hablar) inglés.

5. Ellos temen que alguien los (reconocer) en la calle.

6. El siente mucho que tú (perder) tanto tiempo.

7. No me extraña lo que ellos (decir).

8. Se sienten contentos de que ella (estar) aquí con nosotros.

9. Nos extraña que ella no (saber) cantar y bailar.

10. Tememos que él (comprar) otro automóvil de uso.

11. Estoy satisfecho de que él (tener) buenos profesores.

12. ¿Cree usted que él (ser) tan pobre?

13. Ellos temen que Antonio (olvidar) todo lo aprendido.

14. Nos preocupa bastante que tú (estar) tan nervioso.

15. Juan siente mucho que su hermano (ir) solo en el viaje.

16. Nos alegramos de que Enrique (sacar) buenas notas en el examen.

17. A ellas les sorprende que él no (saber) ni escribir ni leer.

18. Creo que le preocupa que su hija (tener) que ir tan lejos.

19. Yo temo que Benjamín no (saber) convencer a sus socios.

20. Es lamentable que Ramona no (poder) curarse totalmente.

21. Yo siento que mi trabajo no (estar) mejor hecho.

SUBJUNCTIVE AFTER CERTAIN IMPERSONAL PHRASES

The subjunctive is used in Spanish after certain impersonal phrases expressing necessity, opinion, emotion, etc. (*es necesario que, es imposible que, es importante que, es sorprendente que, es lástima que, no importa que,* etc.)

> *Es importante que* usted vaya allí enseguida.
> *Es probable que* vengan por avión.
> *No importa que* ella tenga que trabajar.

Supply the present tense subjunctive form of the verbs in parentheses.

1. No importa que él (llegar) tarde hoy.

   (Example: No importa que él *llegue* tarde hoy.)

2. No es necesario que ella (ir) a trabajar de noche.

3. Es preciso que tu hermano (decir) la verdad.

4. Es imposible que él no (saber) traducir esa carta.

5. Es muy importante que Enrique (cobrar) hoy.

6. Es muy probable que (llover) esta noche.

7. No importa que tú (perder) ese dinero.

8. Es una lástima que Luisa (ir) con ese vestido tan feo.

9. Es muy seguro que usted (tener) buen éxito en la gestión.

10. Es indispensable que la madre (dar) su permiso.

11. Creo importante que ellos (renunciar) inmediatamente.

12. Es justo que se le (pagar) un sueldo más alto.

13. Me parece necesario que tú (dar) tu opinión.

14. Opino que el abogado no (poder) defenderlo.

15. Opinamos que los médicos sí (saber) la causa de su enfermedad.

16. Es preciso que Ernesto (asistir) a las clases el sábado.

17. No es probable que el cartero (venir) tan tarde.

18. Creo muy importante que María (aconsejar) a su hijo.

19. No importa que (costar) tanto si es bueno.

20. Es imposible que él (ir) mañana al trabajo.

21. Opino que Tomás (excusarse) por sus incorrecciones.

22. Es mejor que (terminar) ya este ejercicio.

SUBJUNCTIVE AFTER EXPRESSIONS OF DOUBT OR UNCERTAINTY

The subjunctive is used in Spanish after expressions which indicate some doubt or uncertainty in the mind of the speaker (*dudo que, niego que, no creo que,* etc.).

> *Dudo que haya* otra como ella.
> *No creo que tengan* mucho dinero.

Note, however, that if no doubt is expressed and a mere statement of fact is made, then the subjunctive is not needed. (Examples: Creo que *tienen* dinero. No hay duda que lo *harán* pronto).

Supply the present tense subjunctive form of the verbs in parentheses.

1. Yo no creo que usted (poder) subir tan alto.

   (Example: Yo no creo que usted *pueda* subir tan alto.)

2. El duda que ellos (ir) a la playa en invierno.
3. Ellos niegan que él (ser) extranjero.
4. Ella espera que él (pensar) ofrecerle un empleo.
5. Nosotros creemos que no (haber) espacio para uno más.
6. El duda que (necesitar) ayuda inmediatamente.
7. Mis amigos no creen que (tener) que volver enseguida.
8. Esperamos que tú (poder) hacer ese trabajo correctamente.
9. Yo no creo que Ramón y Octavio (tener) suficiente dinero.
10. Temo que la criada (estar) disgustada.
11. Yo niego que él (saber) quién es el autor del robo.
12. Dudo que usted (tener) tiempo suficiente para llegar a las seis.
13. No creemos que tú (necesitar) nuestros consejos.
14. Su padre cree que él (decidir) pronto si se casa o no.
15. Usted duda que Fernando (poder) resolver el problema.
16. La policía no cree que el ladrón (estar) escondido allí.
17. Es difícil que ellos (quedarse) tan tranquilos.
18. No creo que ese nuevo profesor (ser) muy exigente.
19. Esperamos que el cartero (venir) a las ocho.
20. El chofer niega que él (ser) el culpable del choque.

SUBJUNCTIVE IN ADVERBIAL CLAUSES

The subjunctive is used in Spanish in adverbial clases introduced by certain conjunctions expressing future condition or event, purpose or result, concession or supposition. The principal conjunctions used in this way are: a) *cuando, antes que, hasta que, tan pronto como, mientras*; b) *para que, a fin de que, de manera que, sin que*; c) *aunque, menos que, con tal que**.

> Yo le preguntaré *cuando* él *venga*.
> Iremos *tan pronto como llegue* Juan.
> Le doy este libro *para que lo lea*.
> Iremos al campo mañana *a menos que haga* mal tiempo.

Supply the present tense subjunctive form of the verbs in parentheses.

1. Yo espero aquí hasta que (salir) el avión.

   (Example: Yo espero aquí hasta que *salga* el avión.)

2. Vamos a invitar a Antonio antes que (ir) para el trabajo.
3. Iremos a visitarlo aunque (ser) de noche.
4. Estaremos preocupados hasta que se (saber) el resultado de su gestión.
5. Con tal que (repasar) bien las lecciones, quedarán bien en el examen.
6. El no puede llevarse el auto a menos que lo (pagar).
7. Actuaré tan pronto (recibir) la orden.
8. Para que lo (saber) bien debe estudiarlo bien.
9. Le presté mi paraguas a fin de que no se (mojar).
10. Mientras no te (portar) bien no te daré permiso para jugar.
11. Le daré todos los datos de manera que no se (equivocar).
12. Los llamaremos por teléfono tan pronto como (saber) la noticia.
13. No podré ir hasta que (dejar) de llover.
14. Pensamos ir al campo a menos que (llover).
15. Ellos nos ayudan siempre que (ser) algo importante.
16. Pagaré mi cuenta tan pronto (recibir) mi sueldo.
17. Le daré su recado cuando lo (ver).
18. Trataremos de aprovecharlo aunque no (servir).

---

* The reason for using the subjunctive in Spanish after the various conjunctions mentioned is that a future or hypothetical situation which has not yet become a factual one is indicated; therefore, a subjunctive rather than an indicative form is called for. If, of course, a definite situation or accomplished fact is indicated, then, as in English, the indicative mood is used.

SUBJUNCTIVE IN ADJECTIVE CLAUSES

The subjunctive is used in Spanish in all adjective clauses where the relative pronoun *que* has a negative antecedent or where the antecedent represents some indefinite or hypothetical person or thing.

> No hay *nadie* aquí que *sepa* español.
> No tengo *ningún* libro de gramática que *sirva.*
> Necesitamos un hombre (any man—as yet an indefinite
> and unknown person) que *sepa* arreglar máquinas.
> Buscan a una secretaria que *hable** español.

Supply the present tense subjunctive form of the verbs in parentheses.

1. No conozco a nadie que (saber) más español que él.

   (Example: No conozco a nadie que *sepa* más español que él.)

2. Solicito una secretaria que (ser) bilingüe.
3. Ella necesita una cocinera que (poder) hacer dulces y postres.
4. Compraremos una quinta que (dar) al lago.
5. Buscaremos un atlas que (dar) más datos sobre Australia.
6. No hay nadie en la clase que (recitar) mejor que Luisa.
7. Enséñeme un radio que (ser) barato.
8. ¿Tiene usted alguna herramienta que (poder) servir para arreglar esto?
9. Nos conviene un piloto que (conocer) bien ese país.
10. ¿Tienen ustedes a alguien que (traducir) bien al alemán?
11. Busco un ingeniero que (ser) experto en la construcción de túneles.
12. Necesitamos una profesora que (dar) clases de taquigrafía.
13. Usted no tiene en venta ningún automóvil que (tener) cuatro puertas.
14. No hay ninguna en el baile que (lucir) tan bien como Ramona.
15. Se solicitan dos agentes que (hablar) el portugués.
16. Preferimos un chofer que (tener) experiencia.
17. Todavía no hemos encontrado a nadie que (comprar) la casa vieja.
18. No tenemos ningún amigo que (estudiar) en el extranjero.

---

* Here again, if the antecedent represents not an unknown, indefinite, and hypothetical person, but someone who is already definite and known, then the subjunctive is no longer called for and the indicative may be used. (Example: Por fin él ha encontrado una secretaria que *habla* español.)

Supply the subjunctive form of the verbs in parentheses. (All uses of the subjunctive mood studied up to the present time are reviewed here.) Follow example:

1. Espero que el trabajo (ser) bien pagado.

   (Example: Espero que el trabajo *sea* bien pagado.)

2. Ella duda mucho que ellos (tener) suficiente dinero para el negocio.

3. Es posible que las competencias de este año (ser) mejores.

4. Escríbame cuando (llegar) a Buenos Aires.

5. No creo que ella (hablar) correctamente el francés.

6. Deseo que ustedes se (sentir) felices y satisfechos.

7. Es necesario que lo (entender) perfectamente.

8. Iremos con tal que (hacer) buen tiempo.

9. Le daremos un empleo cuando (saber) bien el inglés.

10. Antonio no quiere que su hijo (perder) el tiempo jugando.

11. El señor Hernández duda que ella (quedarse) aquí para siempre.

12. Voy a esperar a que (venir) el cartero.

13. Es probable que el viejo campesino (ocultar) su dinero en su colchón.

14. Nos extraña mucho que no (manden) los paquetes.

15. Pídale que (traer) las medicinas lo más pronto posible.

16. No conocemos a nadie que (poder) arreglar este auto europeo.

17. Esperamos que el viaje a la India (ser) instructivo e interesante.

18. No tenemos ningún libro que (trate) sobre biología.

19. Dígaselo con delicadeza, de manera que no se (ofender).

20. Tan pronto como (llegar) el señor Martínez, le avisaré.

21. No le entregues la mercancía a menos que (pagar) por adelantado.

22. Le traje esta carta para que la (traducir) al español.

23. Marina quiere que su hija (aprender) a bailar y a cantar.

24. Saldré de vacaciones aunque (llover), (tronar) o (relampaguear).

For further practice with subjunctive forms, substitute a subjunctive clause beginning with QUE for the infinitive in each of the following sentences. Use USTED as the subject of this clause.

1. María teme (leer) la carta.

   (Example: María teme *que usted lea* la carta.)

2. Orlando prefiere (saber) el idioma antes de ir a ese país.

3. Es necesario (llegar) allá enseguida.

4. Procuraremos terminarlo antes de (salir).

5. Siento muchísimo (estar) tan ocupado.

6. Regina se alegra (poder) tomar sus vacaciones.

7. El quiere (explicarles) bien la lección quinta.

8. Deseamos mucho (descansar) unos cuantos minutos.

9. Creo que es imposible (ir) ahora mismo a la estación.

10. Josefa insiste en (llevar) a su casa.

11. Yo deseo (cambiar) esas monedas de oro por billetes.

12. Ricardo debe (tomar) parte en el juego de pelota.

13. Prometo terminarlo antes de (salir).

14. Lavaré los platos después de (despedir) de la visita.

15. Quiero (ganar) mucho dinero.

16. Es imposible (componer) ese aparato sin herramientas apropiadas.

17. Es conveniente (dar) buenos consejos.

18. Yo deseo (llevar) a su casa en automóvil.

19. Me sorprende mucho (saber) que no tenemos fondos para pagar.

20. Todos sentimos no (poder) asistir al baile.

21. Es necesario (comprar) más provisiones para la excursión.

NOTE: For further practice with these same subjunctive forms, repeat the above exercise, this time using JOSE instead of USTED as the subject of the subjunctive clause (1. María teme *que José lea* la carta.) Repeat again, this time using USTEDES as the subject of the subjunctive clause (1. María teme *que ustedes lean* la carta.)

PRESENT PERFECT SUBJUNCTIVE

The present perfect subjunctive is formed from the present subjuntive of *haber* and the past participle of the main verb.

yo	haya hablado	nosotros	hayamos hablado
tú	hayas hablado	(vosotros	hayáis hablado)
usted } el, ella }	haya hablado	ustedes } ellos }	hayan hablado

The present perfect subjunctive has somewhat limited usage, but is used occasionally instead of the present subjunctive to express present perfect time; that is, to indicate an action which took place at an indefinite point in past time (See use of present perfect tense —page 129).

Yo siento mucho que ellos *hayan salido* (have left).
Es posible que usted *haya perdido* (have lost) su libro.

Supply the present perfect subjunctive form of the verbs in parentheses.

1. Yo no creo que ella (poder) terminar la tarea.

   (Example: Yo no creo que ella *haya podido* terminar la tarea.)

2. Es posible que ellas (llegar) ya a Bogotá.
3. Sentimos que él (perderse) en el desierto.
4. Probablemente la policía (encontrar) al ladrón de las joyas.
5. Dudo que tú (ver) esa película extranjera.
6. Es una lástima que el señor Blanco no (ganar) en el concurso.
7. Tememos que el avión (extraviarse) en la selva.
8. Nos alegramos que Raúl (salir) bien en el examen.
9. Ustedes no creen que la tía (curarse) tan pronto.
10. Siento muchísimo que su primo (enfermarse) nuevamente.
11. ¿Será posible que tú (equivocarse) tantas veces?
12. Es probable que la cocinera no (venir) todavía.
13. Me extraña mucho que tu hermana no (regresar) de su trabajo.
14. Ellos no creen que Jacinto (comprar) un avión.
15. Dudo mucho que él (estar) en esa ciudad tan lejana.
16. Sentiremos bastante que doña Juana no (recibir) noticias de su nieto.
17. Ella no cree que Andresito (comerse) toda la comida.
18. Posiblemente el ratón (caer) en la ratonera.
19. ¿Piensa usted que Rogelio (salir) para Montevideo?
20. Nosotros tememos que la señora López (perder) el tren.
21. Es probable que ellos (llegar) en el tren de las seis.

184

IMPERFECT SUBJUNCTIVE

The imperfect subjunctive has many important uses in Spanish. It is used in all subjunctive clauses where the main verb of the sentence is in the past tense. (Insistieron en que yo *hablara* en español). It is used in certain conditional sentences (Si yo *hablara* bien español, haría un viaje a México). We shall study uses in subsequent lessons.

The imperfect subjunctive is formed as follows: The stem for all verbs is derived from the third person plural of the indicative preterite. To this stem, for verbs of the first conjugation ending in *ar*, these endings are added: *ara**, *aras*, *ara*, *áramos*, (*arais*), *aran*. The conjugation in the imperfect subjunctive of the typical first conjugation verb *hablar* follows:

yo	habl*ara**	nosotros	habl*áramos*
tú	habl*aras*	(vosotros	habl*arais*)
usted } él, ella }	habl*ara*	ustedes } ellos }	habl*aran*

Change the following verbs from present subjunctive to imperfect subjunctive form. Follow example.

	Pres. Subj.	Imperf. Subj.		Pres. Subj.	Imperf. Subj.
1.	(que) yo compre	(comprara)	19.	(que) ella piense	....
2.	(que) él mire	(mirara)	20.	(que) nosotros enseñemos	......
3.	(que) ella salude	....	21.	(que) usted robe	....
4.	(que) ellos canten	....	22.	(que) tú pintes	....
5.	(que) usted hable	....	23.	(que) el escuche	....
6.	(que) tú llames	....	24.	(que) ella mande	....
7.	(que) nosotros copiemos	....	25.	(que) ellos empiecen	....
8.	(que) usted acabe	....	26.	(que) ustedes gasten	....
9.	(que) Juan salude	....	27.	(que) José se peine	....
10.	(que) ella escuche	....	28.	(que) Inés piense	....
11.	(que) yo busque	....	29.	(que) tú pagues	....
12.	(que) Mario mire	....	30.	(que) nadie regale	....
13.	(que) alguien tome	....	31.	(que) yo necesite	....
14.	(que) ellos paguen	....	32.	(que) usted cobre	....
15.	(que) nosotras trabajemos	......	33.	(que) nosotros descansemos	....
16.	(que) él se levante	....	34.	(que) ella se acueste	....
17.	(que) ustedes ganen	....	35.	(que) yo cambie	....
18.	(que) tú te canses	....	36.	(que) yo termine	....

* There is a second set of endings which may also be used with verbs of the first conjugation to form the imperfect subjunctive, namely: *ase, ases, ase, ásemos, (aseis), asen*. These endings, however, are rather literary in form and thus are seldom heard today in everyday conversation — especially in Latin America. Under these circumstances it seems more practical for the students to concentrate, for the time being at least, on the single set of endings given above.

185

In the previous exercise (page 185), we learned that, with verbs of the first conjugation, we form the imperfect subjunctive by adding these endings to the stem: *ara, aras, ara,áramos, (arais), aran*. We also learned that the stem for all verbs of this tense is derived from the third person plural of the preterite.

For verbs ending in *er* and *ir* (i.e. second and third conjugation verbs), we form the imperfect subjunctive by adding the following endings to the stem: *iera, ieras, iera, iéramos, (ierais), ieran**. The conjugations, in the imperfect subjunctive, of the typical second and third conjugation verbs *comer* and *vivir* follow:

Imp. Subj.

yo comiera   nosotros comiéramos
tú comieras (vosotros comierais)
usted, él, ella} comiera   ustedes, ellos} comieran

Imp. Subj.

yo viviera   nosotros viviéramos
tú vivieras (vosotros vivierais)
usted, él, ella} viviera   ustedes, ellos} vivieran

Change the following verbs from present subjunctive to imperfect subjunctive form.

Pres. Subj. | Imp. Subj.

1. (que) yo tema (temiera)
2. (que) él asista (asistiera)
3. (que) usted suba ....
4. (que) nosotros partamos ....
5. (que) ustedes metan ....
6. (que) yo coja ....
7. (que) él abra ....
8. (que) ellos cubran ....
9. (que) ustedes partan ....
10. (que) tú subas ....
11. (que) yo me aburra ....
12. (que) usted deba ....
13. (que) José venda ....
14. (que) ellos cometan ....
15. (que) yo descubra ....
16. (que) usted viva ....
17. (que) tú temas ....
18. (que) María beba ....
19. (que) yo admita ....
20. (que) él cometa ....
21. (que) ella viva ....
22. (que) usted coma ....
23. (que) él descubra ....
24. (que) él prefiera ....
25. (que) tú recojas ....
26. (que) nosotros abramos ....
27. (que) usted escriba ....
28. (que) yo reparta ....
29. (que) ustedes vendan ....
30. (que) él aprenda ....
31. (que) nosotras creamos ....
32. (que) Luis reciba ....
33. (que) él insista ....
34. (que) ella rompa ....
35. (que) tú debas ....
36. (que) usted escriba ....
37. (que) ellos corran ....
38. (que) Luis repita ....
39. (que) tú vendas ....
40. (que) yo prefiera ....

* Again, there is a second or optional set of endings which may be added to verbs of the second and third conjugations to form the imperfect subjunctive, namely: *iese, ieses, iese, iésemos,(ieseis), iesen*. These endings, like the second set of endings to be added to first conjugation verbs, have limited use today; thus it seems advisable, for the present at least, for the student to concentrate upon the single set of endings given above. (See footnote at bottom of previous page.)

IMPERFECT SUBJUNCTIVE — *Continued*

As we have already learned, the stem for all verbs in the imperfect subjunctive tense is derived from the third person plural of the preterite (see pages 185-186). Note the following typical forms of so-called irregular verbs, all of which remain completely regular in this tense. They derive their stems, exactly according to the rule, from the third person plural of the preterite. Their endings are also regular.

Prete. Indic.,	*Imperfect Subjunctive*
3rd pers. pl. *Stem*	

hacer hicieron *hic-hic*iera, *hic*ieras, *hic*iera, *hic*iéramos, (*hic*ierais), *hic*ieran
poner pusieron *pus-pus*iera, *pus*ieras, *pus*iera, *pus*iéramos, (*pus*ierais), *pus*ieran
tener tuvieron *tuv-tuv*iera, *tuv*ieras, *tuv*iera, *tuv*iéramos, (*tuv*ierais), *tuv*ieran
saber supieron *sup-sup*iera, *sup*ieras, *sup*iera, *sup*iéramos, (*sup*ierais), *sup*ieran

---

Change the following verbs from present subjunctive to imperfect subjunctive form.

Pres. Subj.	*Imperf. Subj.*		*Pres. Subj.*	*Imperf. Subj.*
1. (que) yo ponga	(*pusiera*)	18.	(que) yo haga	....
2. (que) él sienta	(*sintiera*)	19.	(que) tú oigas	....
3. (que) usted sepa	....	20.	(que) él venga	....
4. (que) ustedes digan*	....	21.	(que) ellos vayan	....
5. (que) nosotros hagamos	....	22.	(que) usted dé*	....
6. (que) tú pongas	....	23.	(que) él sea*	....
7. (que) ella vaya*	....	24.	(que) yo esté*	....
8. (que) usted pierda	....	25.	(que) ellas sientan	....
9. (que) él vea	....	26.	(que) nosotras salgamos	....
10. (que) ellos traigan	....	27.	(que) tú mueras	....
11. (que) tú traduzcas	....	28.	(que) ellos oigan	....
12. (que) usted quiera	....	29.	(que) nosotros demos	....
13. (que) Enrique ofrezca	....	30.	(que) yo caiga	....
14. (que) ella esté	....	31.	(que) ella tenga	....
15. (que) nosotros vayamos	....	32.	(que) ustedes sean	....
16. (que) tú digas	....	33.	(que) Raúl ofrezca	....
17. (que) Tomás merezca	....	34.	(que) yo traduzca	....

* In the imperfect subjunctive, DECIR has the forms: *dijera, dijeras, dijera, dijéramos,* (*dijerais*), *dijeran.* IR and SER are conjugated: *fuera, fueras, fuera, fuéramos,* (*fuerais*), *fueran.* DAR and ESTAR, though terminating in *ar,* follow the same irregularities they have in the preterite and thus add the usual endings *iera, ieras, iera,* etc. DAR is thus conjugated *diera, dieras, diera,* etc. ESTAR is conjugated *estuviera, estuvieras, estuviera, estuviéramos,* (*estuvierais*), *estuvieran.*

USE OF IMPERFECT SUBJUNCTIVE

The imperfect subjunctive is used in the same way as the present subjunctive, namely, after verbs of emotion and desire, impersonal expressions, certain conjunctions, negative antecedents, etc. However, while the present subjunctive is used when the principal verb is in the present (or future) tense, the imperfect subjunctive is used:

1) When the main verb is in the present indicative, but the second verb refers to an action in the *past*. Example: Yo *dudo* que Fernando *dejara* ayer los libros abandonados. (I doubt that Ferdinan abandoned his books yesterday).

2) Whenever the main verb is in the past time (the preterite, the past imperfect tense, or the conditional). Examples:

Fue necesario que él *tomara* parte en la discusión.
(It was necessary that he take part in the discussion.)

Insistieron en que Juan *comiera* con ellos.
(They insisted that John eat with them.)

Temíamos que ella no *llegara* a tiempo.
(We feared that she might not arrive on time.)

Supply the required IMPERFECT SUBJUNCTIVE form of the verbs in parentheses. Follow example.

1. Juan temía que ellos (decir) una mentira.

   (Example: Juan temía que ellos *dijeran* una mentira.)

2. Yo le pedí que (escribir) una carta a su tía.
3. Nosotros queríamos que nuestro hijo (ser) arquitecto.
4. Ella dudaba que él (saber) tanta historia.
5. Usted preferiría que su hijo (estudiar) varios idiomas.
6. Ustedes me prohibieron que (hablar) en voz alta.
7. El me aconsejó que (invitar) al jefe de ese departamento.
8. Desearíamos que ellas (asistir) a la boda de Hortensia.
9. Isabel le ordenó a Samuel que (abandonar) la habitación.
10. No permitían que (pisar) el césped del jardín.
11. Era dudoso que el señor Ramírez (pagar) esa cuenta atrasada.
12. Mi prima insistió en que yo le (prestar) mi automóvil.
13. Sebastián me recomendó que (descansar) durante dos semanas.
14. Ellas no querían que (irse) tan temprano.
15. No esperaba que ella (aceptar) ese empleo.
16. Preferiríamos que ustedes (volver) el próximo viernes.
17. Yo le rogué a Rafael que no lo (despedir).
18. Exigieron que todos los estudiantes (asistir) a las conferencias.
19. Ella me dijo que (pedir) auxilio a los bomberos.
20. Todos dudaban que él (poder) ganar la carrera de obstáculos.
21. Alguien quiso que yo (pagar) los vidrios rotos.
22. Mis tíos deseaban que ella (almorzar) con ellos.

Supply either the PRESENT SUBJUNCTIVE form or the IMPER-FECT SUBJUNCTIVE form of the verbs in parentheses—whichever is correct. (Remember that the present subjunctive is used when the main verb of the sentence is in the present or future tense; the imperfect subjunctive is used when the main verb is in the preterite or the past imperfect tense—see previous exercise page 188.) Follow examples.

1. Yo insisto en que (estudiar) las lecciones.

   (Example: Yo insisto en que *estudien* las lecciones.)

2. Llevé mi traje al sastre para que (coser) las roturas.

   (Example: Llevé mi traje al sastre para que *cosiera* las roturas.)

3. Yo dudo que Fernando (dejar) sus libros abandonados.

4. Ellas no querían que nadie (saber) la noticia.

5. Es necesario que Jorge (pedir) permiso para ausentarse.

6. Ellos no permitieron que la profesora (pagar) el almuerzo.

7. Domingo y Julieta dicen que (hacer) pronto las compras.

8. Ellos temían que él no (ir) a la asamblea.

9. Se dudaba mucho que el enfermo (mejorar) enseguida.

10. Ellos exigen que (conocer) bien el idioma español.

11. Lo mandó a esa academia para que (aprender) el inglés.

12. No quisieron que Carlos (mencionar) su nacionalidad.

13. Leonardo duda que su hijo (poder) aprobar esa asignatura.

14. Considero justo que nosotros le (pagar) por las horas extra.

15. Es necesario que usted (obtener) más experiencia como profesor.

16. Se solicita una cocinera que (dormir) en la casa.

17. Temíamos que Josefina (extraviarse) en ese barrio.

18. Mi hermano dijo que lo (sustituir) en su empleo.

19. Es muy importante que (curar) a ese caballo de carrera.

20. María no quiere que (venderse) la casa de su abuelo.

21. Ellos insisten en que la secretaria (escribir) taquigrafía.

22. El alpinista duda que ese joven (llegar) hasta la cima de la montaña.

For further practice with the imperfect subjunctive form, change the main verb of each of the following sentences to past time (preterite or past imperfect tense). Then make the required corresponding change in the verb of the subordinate clause from present subjunctive to imperfect subjunctive. Follow examples.

1. Yo me *alegro* que ella *vaya* con Ramón.

   (Example: Yo me *alegré* que ella *fuera* con Ramón.)

2. El *quiere* que Luis *venga* inmediatamente.

   (Example: El *quería* que Luis *viniera* inmediatamente.)

3. *Necesito* una bicicleta que *valga* cuarenta pesos.

4. Yo *prefiero* un médico que *cobre* barato.

5. Ellos me *exigen* que *pague* en oro.

6. *Es* probable que tu hermano *esté* ocupado.

7. Nos *extraña* mucho que usted *sea* tan viejo.

8. Yo *dudo* que la policía *capture* al ladrón.

9. *Vamos* a la playa para que se *bañen* los niños.

10. No *hay* un empleado en esa oficina que *sepa* mecanografía.

11. Ellos *quieren* que Isabel *pinte* la silla.

12. No *exigimos* que el tesorero nos *pague* ahora mismo.

13. *Es* muy necesario que usted *haga* calistenia.

14. Antonio y Antonia *prefieren* que Ricardo *cante*.

15. *Vamos* al campo para que ella *vea* los lindos paisajes.

16. *Es* muy probable que el barco *llegue* esta tarde a las seis.

17. Si *hay* alguien que *pueda* ayudarnos en este problema.

18. No *deseamos* que el doctor *trabaje* de noche.

19. Ya *es* hora de que usted *comience* a estudiar español.

20. Me *alegra* saber que ella *termine* sus estudios este año.

21. *Preferimos* que *canten* nuestro himno nacional.

22. *Tememos* que ustedes se *cansen* demasiado con este ejercicio.

In the following sentences, choose correctly between use of the present subjunctive or the imperfect subjunctive form.

1. Yo prefiero que ella (estudie, estudiara) una carrera.

   (Example: Yo prefiero que ella *estudie* una carrera.)

2. Ricardo me dijo que (copie, copiara) esta lección.

   (Example: Ricardo me dijo que *copiara* esta lección.)

3. El no quiere que nadie (escriba, escribiera) en su cuaderno.

4. Jaime dudaba que tú (estes, estuvieras) enfermo.

5. Alberto y Carmen insisten en que yo (pase, pasara) mis vacaciones aquí.

6. Fuimos para que ellos (vean, vieran) los cuadros.

7. Yo sí quiero que usted (hable, hablara) en la convención.

8. Tomás tiene miedo que Pedro no (pague, pagara) la cuenta.

9. Nos sorprendió mucho que Octavio no (asista, asistiera) al baile.

10. Ella desea que tú le (ayudes, ayudaras) en la mudanza.

11. Sentimos mucho que usted no (vaya, fuera) ayer a la excursión.

12. No creo que ellos ahora (dejen, dejaran) a su amigo solo.

13. Me alegré que él (ingrese, ingresara) en la Universidad.

14. Usted me pidió que (escoja, escogiera) entre el grande y el pequeño.

15. Nosotros insistimos ahora en que (vendan, vendieran) la finca.

16. Nos dirigimos entonces a la estación para que (entreguen, entregaran) el baúl.

17. Rogelio me suplicó ayer que yo (acompañe, acompañara) a su hijito.

18. No permitimos ahora que nadie (grite, gritara) en el salón.

19. Me sorprende mucho que tú ahora no la (saludes, saludaras).

20. Fernando me dijo ayer que (traduzca, tradujera) esta carta.

21. Ella va para que le (examinen, examinaran) la vista.

22. Yo quiero que usted (cambie, cambiara) de opinión.

191

CONDITIONAL SENTENCES (*Future-Possible Conditions*)

A conditional sentence is a sentence consisting of two clases, a dependent claus beginning with *if* and a main clause or answer to the *if clause*. (Example: *Si* Jua viene, traerá los discos.—If John comes, he will bring the records.)
Conditional sentences are of three classes: 1. *Future-possible* conditions. 2. Pr sent-unreal conditions. 3. *Past-unreal* conditions.

We will first consider future-possible conditions. A *future- possible* condition one which indicates a simple future action which may or may not take place. Th type of condition offers no difficulty. In Spanish, as in English, the present tens is used in the *if clause,* and the future tense is used in the main or answer claus

> Si Juan *viene, traerá* los discos.
> Si *tengo* tiempo mañana, *iré* a la playa.

Supply the necessary present tense required in the *if clause* of eac of the following future-possible conditions. Follow example.

1. Si él (querer), vendrá temprano al trabajo.

   (Example: Si él *quiere,* vendrá temprano al trabajo.)

2. Si yo (tener) dinero, te compraré la bicicleta.

3. Si no (hacer) mucho calor, trabajaremos en el campo.

4. Si Tomás (estar) en la casa, conversaremos con él.

5. Si Guillermo (desear) unas vacaciones, se las daremos.

6. Si ella (preferir) ir al cine, la llevaremos.

7. Si tu abuela (llamar) por teléfono, le darás el recado.

8. Si ustedes (querer) un refresco, se lo serviremos.

9. Si el tiempo (ser) corto, iremos enseguida.

10. Si (dejar) de llover pronto, iremos de paseo.

11. Si tu hermana (llegar) enseguida, la invitarás a la comida.

12. Si (hacer) mucho frío, te pondrás el abrigo.

13. Si (hacer) calor, iremos a bañarnos a la playa.

14. Si te (encontrar) con Horacio, le darás mis saludos.

15. Si el maestro (estar) en la biblioteca, le entregarás el libro.

16. Si usted (preferir) un periódico, podrá cogerlo.

17. Si Carolina (poder), ella lo complacerá.

18. Si Carlos (estudiar) mucho más, seguramente saldrá bien en el examer

19. Si yo (terminar) este ejercicio pronto, podré hacer el siguiente.

In the last exercise (page 192), we learned that a future-possible condition is one in which a simple future action may or may not take place; moreover, the present tense is used in the *if clause* of such a condition, and the future tense in the main or answer clause. In the sentences below, supply the necessary future tense required in the main or answer clause of each of the following future-possible conditons. Follow example.

1. Si compro hoy la bicicleta, (poder) pasear por el parque.

    (Example: Si compro hoy la bicicleta, *podré* pasear por el parque.)

2. Si vendo mi reloj, (comprar) un radio portátil.

3. Si me encuentro con Elena, le (dar) tu recado.

4. Si voy a la ciudad, te (traer) un bonito regalo.

5. Si aprendo a conducir (ir) en auto a la Florida.

6. Si me invitan al almuerzo, les (llevar) un regalo.

7. Si tus hermanos vienen, los (invitar) a la cena.

8. Si ustedes quieren, (poder) convencer al vendedor.

9. Si me aprueban en el examen, mis padres se (alegrar).

10. Si hace buen tiempo, (visitar) a tu hermana Luisa.

11. Si usted espera un momento, lo (recibir) enseguida.

12. Si enviamos ahora la carta, (llegar) mañana.

13. Si no llueve hoy, (jugar) al tenis en el casino.

14. Si la guerra termina pronto, (empezar) un nuevo negocio.

15. Si ellos aceptan las condiciones, (comenzar) la fabricación.

16. Si usted se apura, (alcanzar) el tren.

17. Si hallo mi perro, te (avisar) por teléfono.

18. Si consigo trabajo, (comprar) un automóvil de uso.

19. Si traduces bien ese libro, te (pagar) quinientos pesos.

20. Si quieres, la (llevar) al parque de diversiones.

21. Si don Ramón me presta el dinero, (ampliar) mi negocio.

22. Si mi jefe me autoriza, (viajar) por la América del Sur.

193

PRESENT-UNREAL CONDITIONS

The next type of conditional statement which we must study is the so-called *present-unreal condition.* (See page 192 for explanation of the three general types of conditional statements).

A *present-unreal* condition is one which, while referring in general to present time, indicates some unreal or contrary-to-fact situation. In such conditions, the imperfect subjunctive is used in the *if clause* and the conditional is used in the main or answer clause.

Si Juan *tuviera** un automóvil, *pasaría* sus vacaciones en el campo.
(If John had an automobile, he would spend his vacations in the country.)
Si María *supiera** nadar, *iría* a la playa todos los días.
(If Mary knew how to swim, she would go to the beach every day.)

Supply the imperfect subjunctive form of the verb in parentheses as required in the *if clause* of all such present-unreal conditions. Follow example.

1. Si él (poder) ayudarle, lo haría gustosamente.

   (Example: Si él *pudiera* ayudarle, lo haría gustosamente.)

2. Si yo (saber) bien el español, podría traducir esa novela.
3. Si ella (estudiar) más, obtendría mejores calificaciones.
4. Si usted (tener) tiempo, podría terminar esas traducciones.
5. Si el doctor (querer), ganaría más dinero en la nueva clínica.
6. Si ella no (tener) miedo, subiría por esa escalera de cuerda.
7. Si el señor Rodríguez (poder), él resolvería el problema.
8. Si mi jefe me (autoriza), yo acompañaría a Alfredo.
9. Si los soldados (combatir) con más fervor, ganarían la batalla.
10. Si el profesor (explicar) mejor, entenderíamos bien la lección.
11. Si yo (saber) francés, iría a París este verano.
12. Si Manuel (triunfar), ella se pondría muy contenta.
13. Si el jefe me (aumentar) el sueldo, iría con más frecuencia al cine.
14. Si ella (sentirse) mejor, podría asistir a las clases.
15. Si la señora de Hernández me (invitar), yo iría a su fiesta.
16. Si yo (tener) más tiempo, viajaría hasta Filipinas.

---

* Note as mentioned above, that in these sentences there is indicated a hypothetical situation which is "unreal" or contrary to fact. Thus: Juan NO TIENE un automóvil ahora; pero—si él *tuviera* un automóvil, *pasaría* sus vacaciones en el campo. María NO SABE nadar; pero—si ella *supiera* nadar, *iría* a la playa todos los días.

194

In the previous exercise (page 194), we learned that a present-unreal condition is one which indicates some unreal or contrary-to-fact situation; moreover, in such conditions, the imperfect subjunctive is used in the *if clause* and the conditional is used in the main or answer clause. In the sentences below, supply the conditional form of the verbs in parentheses as required in the main or answer clause of all such present-unreal conditional statements.

1. Si yo tuviera buena salud, (trabajar) intensamente.

   (Example: Si yo tuviera buena salud, *trabajaría* intensamente.)

2. Si él no fuera tan haragán, (ganar) más dinero.

3. Si ellos vivieran más cerca, los (visitar) con más frecuencia.

4. Si Roberto fuera mi amigo, yo le (prestar) los cien pesos.

5. Si ustedes supieran la verdad, no (estar) tan contentos.

6. Si no tuviera que trabajar tanto, (ir) con ustedes al teatro.

7. Si tu hermana Manuela supiera coser, me (arreglar) estos pantalones.

8. Si ese hotel fuera más barato, él se (mudar) allá.

9. Si su mamá le diera permiso, ella (asistir) al baile de carnaval.

10. Si yo fuera rey, (dar) una gran fiesta en mi palacio.

11. Si hiciera buen tiempo, él (concurrir) a las carreras de caballos.

12. Si usted supiera español, ya (estar) empleado en ese banco.

13. Si hubiera menos ruido, usted (poder) oír mejor la sinfonía.

14. Si hiciera mucho frío, (patinar) en el hielo.

15. Si supiéramos su dirección, la (visitar) esta noche.

16. Si Rolando fuera más joven, (entrar) en la marina.

17. Si yo supiera tocar el piano, te (acompañar) en tu canción.

18. Si esa máquina no fuera tan vieja, Rogelio la (comprar) en seguida.

19. Si usted lo conociera mejor, no le (ayudar) tanto.

20. Si ella tuviera teléfono, la (llamar) para invitarla a pasear.

The sentences below are all present-unreal conditions, each indicating a situation which is unreal or contrary-to-fact. (See explanation of present-unreal conditions, page 194, also footnote on same page.) In these sentences, supply the required imperfect subjunctive form of the verb in the *if clause;* also supply the required conditional (Potencial) form of the verb in the main or answer clause. Follow example.

1. Si ellos (tener) más dinero, (comprar) la casa.

   (Example: Si ellos *tuvieran* más dinero, *comprarían* la casa.)

2. Si yo (estar) en la escuela ahora, (consultar) el mapa de Europa.

3. Si usted (manejar) con cuidado, no (tener) accidentes.

4. Si ella (asistir) a las clases con puntualidad, (aprender) más.

5. Si tú te (interesar) más por el estudio, (obtener) mejores notas.

6. Si usted (ser) mecánico, (arreglar) ese automóvil.

7. Si Ana (saber) el italiano, (entender) mejor la ópera.

8. Si Guillermo y Lorenzo (tomar) el avión ahora (llegar) muy pronto.

9. Si usted (salir) temprano, (poder) asistir al primer acto de la obra.

10. Si esta casa (ser) más barata, yo (poder) comprarla.

11. Si él (tener) más tiempo libre, (hacer) ese trabajo extra.

12. Si no (estar) lloviendo, (acompañar) a su hermana a su casa.

13. Si tú (repasar) las lecciones, (contestar) mejor a sus preguntas.

14. Si ustedes (trabajar) con más interés, (ganar) más dinero.

15. Si Josefa (ser) maestra, (enseñar) a sus sobrinos.

16. Si a usted le (gustar) la música, (asistir) a los conciertos.

17. Si tú (ser) rico, (viajar) alrededor del mundo.

18. Si nosotros (pensar) más, (hacer) menos disparates.

19. Si tú (querer) acompañarme, te lo (agradecer) muchísimo.

20. Si el maestro (hablar) más alto, lo (oír) mejor.

196

The sentences below are all stated in *future-possible** conditional form. By making the necessary changes in the verbs, convert each of these sentences to *present-unreal* conditional form. (That is, change the verb of the *if clause* of each sentence to imperfect subjunctive form; change the verb of the main or answer clause to conditional (Potencial) form.) Follow example.

1. Si ellos me *pagan* mañana, *pagaré* la cuenta.

   (Example: Si ellos me *pagaran* mañana, *pagaría* la cuenta.)

2. Si él *tiene* tiempo, *visitará* a su tía.

3. Si Felipe *llega* hoy, *iremos* a saludarlo.

4. Si yo *trabajo* más, *ganaré* más.

5. Si la profesora *sabe* bien el español, lo *enseñará* bien.

6. Si tú te *apuras, llegarás* a tiempo.

7. Si nosotros *estamos* desocupados, *recibiremos* al señor Pérez.

8. Si ellas *escriben* bien el inglés, *conseguirán* trabajo.

9. Si yo *ahorro* más dinero, *podré* comprar pronto la enciclopedia.

10. Si usted *espera* un momento, lo *atenderé* en seguida.

11. Si Jaime *canta* bien, lo *contratarán* para la televisión.

12. Si tú te *cansas, tendrás* que descansar.

13. Si la cocinera *cocina* bien, la *contrataremos*.

14. Si él *paga* el alquiler, no *tendremos* que mudarnos.

15. Si *llueve* mucho, *iremos* en ómnibus.

16. Si Roberto se *matricula* ahora, *empezará* el curso en seguida.

17. Si él *quiere,* podrá *ayudarnos*.

18. Si Sebastián *resuelve* los problemas, *sacará* buena nota.

19. Si yo *tengo* ganas, *asistiré* a la conferencia del profesor Díaz.

20. Si *pagan* la multa, no *irán* a la cárcel.

---

* For explanation of future-possible conditions, see page 192; for present-unreal condition, see page 194, also footnote on same page.

PAST-UNREAL CONDITIONS
Formation of Past Perfect Subjunctive

The third and last type of conditional statement to be studied is the *past-unreal* condition. The *past-unreal* condition refers to past time, but otherwise functions in the same way as a present-unreal condition. In past-unreal condition, the past perfect subjunctive (*Pretérito Pluscuamperfecto*) is used in the *if clause*, and the perfect conditional (*Potencial Perfecto*) is used in the main or answer clause. (Example: Si usted *hubiera hablado* con Juan, él le *habría ayudado* —If you had talked with John, he would have helped you.)

Since, however, we are not yet acquainted with either the past perfect subjunctive of the perfect conditional, we must first study each of these forms before attempting any practice with past-unreal conditions. The imperfect subjunctive of *haber* is used as the auxiliary verb, and to the auxiliary is added the past participle of the main verb.

yo	hubiera hablado*	nosotros	hubiéramos hablado
tú	hubieras hablado	(vosotros	hubierais hablado)
usted } él, ella }	hubiera hablado	ustedes } ellos }	hubieran hablado

(English equivalent: (*if*) *I had talked*, (*if*) *you had talked*, etc.)

Change the following verbs from IMPERFECT SUBJUNCTIVE to PAST PERFECT SUBJUNCTIVE form. Follow examples.

Imperf. Subj.	*Past Perf. Subj.*	*Imperf. Subj.*	*Past Perf. Subj.*
1. (si) ella fuera	(hubiera sido)	19. (si) tú salieras	....
2. (si) él gustara	....	20. (si) usted cogiera	....
3. (si) yo cambiara	....	21. (si) yo regresara	....
4. (si) usted fumara	....	22. (si) usted buscara	....
5. (si) yo supiera	....	23. (si) él conociera	....
6. (si) ellos fueran	....	24. (si) ellos salieran	....
7. (si) él preparara	....	25. (si) tú dijeras	....
8. (si) usted pasara	....	26. (si) usted trabajara	....
9. (si) tú visitaras	....	27. (si) ella insistiera	....
10. (si) yo escribiera	....	28. (si) yo aprendiera	....
11. (si) usted viviera	....	29. (si) nosotros tuviéramos	....
12. (si) nosotros trajéramos	....	30. (si) ellos fueran	....
13. (si) él pasara	....	31. (si) tú hablaras	....
14. (si) yo cometiera	....	32. (si) yo me levantara	....
15. (si) tú te acostaras	....	33. (si) usted se sentara	....
16. (si) usted aceptara	....	34. (si) ella hiciera	....
17. (si) nosotros pusiéramos	....	35. (si) ellos trajeran	....
18. (si) lloviera	....	36. (si) nevara	....

* The optional set of endings *iese, ieses, iese, iésemos, (ieseis), iesen* may also be used here with the imperfect subjunctive of *haber*, but again it seems simpler and more practical for the student to concentrate upon the single set of *iera* endings (see footnote, page 187).

PAST-UNREAL CONDITIONS
Formation of Perfect Conditional

In the last exercise we studied the formation of the past perfect subjunctive, which is used in the *if clause* of all past-unreal conditions. We must next study the formation of the perfect conditional, which is used in the main or answer clause of past-unreal conditions (see previous exercise, page 198).

The perfect conditional is formed as follows: the present conditional form of *haber* is used as the auxiliary verb, and to this auxiliary is added the past participle of the main verb.

yo	habría comido	nosotros	habríamos comido
tú	habrías comido	(vosotros	habríais comido)
usted él, ella }	habría comido	ustedes ellos }	habrían comido

(English equivalent: *I would have eaten, you would have eaten,* etc.)

Change the following verbs from present conditional to perfect conditional form. Follow example.

Pres. Cond.	*Perf. Cond.*	*Pres. Cond.*	*Perf. Cond.*
1. yo tomaría	(habría tomado)	21. yo abriría	....
2. él iría	(habría ido)	22. ella buscaría	....
3. ella sabría	....	23. usted daría	....
4. nosotros haríamos	....	24. tú vendrías	....
5. ellos escribirían	....	25. nosotros iríamos	....
6. yo esperaría	....	26. yo prepararía	....
7. tú comerías	....	27. él estaría	....
8. usted pondría	....	28. ustedes llegarían	....
9. él gustaría	....	29. ellos explicarían	....
10. nosotros oiríamos	....	30. nosotros diríamos	....
11. usted trabajaría	....	31. tú entrarías	....
12. Luis bailaría	....	32. Rafael temería	....
13. tú partirías	....	33. yo saldría	....
14. él se dormiría	....	34. ellos se aburrirían	....
15. yo me acostaría	....	35. él se levantaría	....
16. Tomás esperaría	....	36. Ramón insistiría	....
17. ustedes traerían	....	37. usted se enfermaría	....
18. ella cambiaría	....	38. ellos olvidarían	....
19. yo preguntaría	....	39. tú olerías	....
20. él bebería	....	40. yo terminaría	....

As indicated previously (page 199), a *past-unreal* condition functions in the same way as a *present-unreal* condition, indicating a situation which is unreal or contrary-to-fact. However, while a *present-unreal* condition refers to present or future time, a *past-unreal* condition refers to past time. In a *past-unreal* condition, the past perfect subjunctive is used in the *if clause,* and the perfect conditional is used in the main or answer clause. Examples:

> Si Juan *hubiera tenido** un automóvil el mes pasado, *habría pasado* sus vacaciones en el campo. (If John had had an automobile last month, he would have spend his vacation in the country.)
>
> Si María *hubiera sabido** nadar el verano pasado, *habría ido* a la playa todos los días. (If Mary had known how to swim last summer, she would have gone to the beach every day.)

Supply the past perfect subjunctive form of the verbs in parentheses, as required in the *if clause* of all such past-unreal conditional statements.

1. Si yo (estar) aquí te habría ayudado.

   (Example: Si yo *hubiera estado* aquí, te habría ayudado.)

2. Si él (saber) la dirección, te la habría dicho.
3. Si usted (necesitar) dinero, se lo habría pedido a Rogelio.
4. Si él (estudiar) más, no habría desaprobado esa asignatura.
5. Si ellos (hacer) más ejercicios, habrían estado mejor preparados.
6. Si María (venir) más temprano, habría visto a sus sobrinos.
7. Si nosotros (recibir) los paquetes, se los habríamos entregado.
8. Si tú (dar) tu autorización, él habría ido en seguida.
9. Si ellas (saber) su nombre, ya le habrían escrito muchas cartas.
10. Si ustedes (levantarse) más temprano, habrían llegado a tiempo.
11. Si Enrique (decir) la verdad, ya habrían terminado las averiguaciones.
12. Si yo (ganar) más dinero, habría comprado un televisor.
13. Si tu tía (enfermarse), ella habría llamado al médico.
14. Si los trabajadores (terminar) pronto su trabajo, ya habrían cobrado.
15. Si Susana (saber) traducir la carta, habría ganado algo.
16. Si nosotros (hacer) los ejercicios, habríamos podido descansar.
17. Si tú (llamar) por teléfono a Luis, él habría regresado en seguida.
18. Si ella (querer) estudiar, habría podido colocarse en esa empresa.

---

* Note here again, as in the case of present-unreal conditions (see footnote, page 194), that there is indicated a hypothetical situation which is unreal or contrary to fact. Thus: Juan NO TENIA un automóvil el mes pasado; pero—Si él *hubiera tenido* uno, *habría pasado* sus vacaciones en el campo. María NO SABIA nadar el verano pasado; pero—Si ella *hubiera sabido* nadar, *habría ido* a la playa todos los días.

Supply the perfect conditional form of the verbs in parentheses, as required in the main or answer clause of all such past-unreal conditions. (See previous exercise, page 200, if necessary, for discussion of past-unreal conditions; also see footnote at bottom of same page.) Follow example.

1. Si él hubiera podido estudiar, ya se (graduar) de médico.

   (Example: Si él hubiera podido estudiar, ya se *habría graduado* de médico.)

2. Si yo hubiera sido su padre, ya lo (castigar) muchas veces.

3. Si José hubiera recibido la noticia, ya se lo (comunicar).

4. Si usted hubiera llegado más temprano, (ver) a su amigo Rodríguez.

5. Si ella hubiera aprendido a coser, ahora (poder) hacerle el vestido.

6. Si nosotros hubiéramos comprado la finca, (tener) muchas frutas.

7. Si yo hubiera tenido su permiso, (usar) su automóvil.

8. Si él hubiera pagado todas las cuentas, ahora (tener) mejor crédito.

9. Si ustedes hubieran trabajado más, (ganar) más dinero.

10. Si Ricardo hubiera entendido bien el inglés, (contestar) al señor.

11. Si tú hubieras sido un buen estudiante, (aprender) español bien.

12. Si ella hubiera ido a la playa, (nadar) varias horas.

13. Si él hubiera tomado las medicinas, ya se (curar).

14. Si usted hubiera prestado el dinero, ya ellos se lo (devolver).

15. Si no hubiera estado lloviendo, yo (ir) a la playa.

16. Si ellos hubieran podido llegar temprano, (ver) a su amigo Pérez.

17. Si nosotras hubiéramos conocido al artista, lo (invitar) a la fiesta.

18. Si él hubiera terminado el ejercicio, ahora (poder) ir a pasear.

19. Si yo hubiera visto a Margarita, le (dar) el recado.

20. Si ella hubiera comprado el libro, (aprender) muchas cosas interesantes.

The sentences below are all past-unreal conditions. (See explanation, if necessary, of past-unreal conditions, pages 199-200 , also footnote on page 200.) In these sentences, supply the required past perfect subjunctive form of the verb in the *if clause;* supply the perfect conditional form of the verb in the main or answer clause. Follow example.

1. Si yo (estudiar) más cuidadosamente, no (obtener) malas notas.

   (Example: Si yo *hubiera estudiado* más cuidadosamente, no *habría obtenido* malas notas.)

2. Si ella (llegar) diez minutos antes, (poder) saludar a su amiga Irene.

3. Si él (contestar) el telegrama, ella (llegar) el sábado.

4. Si (haber) esa medicina, el se (curar) de su enfermedad.

5. Si tú (tener) más cuidado, no (chocar) contra el árbol.

6. Si nosotros (ser) ciudadanos americanos, (poder) desempeñar esos cargos.

7. Si ellos no (estar) tan ocupados, (recibir) a los vendedores.

8. Si Alfredo (asistir) con más frecuencia a las clases, (aprender) más.

9. Si yo (conocer) a esa linda señorita, la (saludar) en la calle.

10. Si usted (venir) con nosotros, (ahorrar) mucho tiempo.

11. Si él me (aumentar) el sueldo, yo (trabajar) mejor.

12. Si Rafael no (beber) tanto, no (emborracharse).

13. Si tú (llegar) a las doce, (comer) con nosotros.

14. Si yo (cuidar) la casa, (permanecer) en buenas condiciones.

15. Si Emilia (tocar) el timbre, ella se (despertar).

16. Si ayer (ser) sábado, ellos (regresar) más temprano del trabajo.

17. Si (haber) suficiente dinero, el viaje (ser) más largo.

18. Si usted (escribir) con más cuidado, él (entender) su mensaje.

19. Si ellos (estar) en España varios años, (aprender) bien el español.

20. Si Mariana (amar) a Samuel, ella se (casar) con él.

The sentences below are all stated in present-unreal* conditional form. By making the necessary changes in the verbs, convert each of these sentences to past-unreal conditional form. (That is, change the verb of the *if clause* of each sentence to past perfect subjunctive form; change the verb of the main or answer clause to perfect conditional form.) Follow example.

1. Si él *comiera* menos, *estaría* más delgado.

   (Example: Si él *hubiera comido* menos, *habría estado* más delgado.)

2. Si yo *fuera* Eduardo, no la *visitaría* más.

3. Si *tuviéramos* más dinero, *estudiaríamos* en esa buena Universidad.

4. Si tú no *fumaras* tanto, te *sentirías* mejor de salud.

5. Si Timoteo no se *emborrachara, podría* trabajar más.

6. Si ellos *supieran* la mala noticia, no *estarían* tan contentos.

7. Si Lucía no *viviera* tan lejos, *iría* a pie hasta su casa.

8. Si tú *pudieras* tomar el autobús de las ocho, *llegarías* más temprano.

9. Si nosotros nos *acostáramos* temprano, nos *despertaríamos* a las cinco.

10. Si ustedes *supieran* cantar, *estarían* en el coro de la iglesia.

11. Si él *tradujera* bien al inglés, *podría* trabajar en tu oficina.

12. Si ellas *hicieran* más caso a la maestra, *sabrían* bailar mejor.

13. Si la guerra se *acabara,* todos *viviríamos* más felices.

14. Si *hubiera* menos analfabetos, ese país *progresaría* más.

15. Si tú me *prestaras* cinco pesos, yo te los *pagaría* la semana que viene.

16. Si tu primo *pasara* los exámenes de Física, se *graduaría* este año.

17. Si Alfredo *fuera* mi hermano, le *prohibiría* boxear con ese loco.

18. Si Juana *fuera* un poco mas diligente, *ocuparía* una mejor posición.

19. Si esa sortija no *tuviera* tanto valor, no *tendrías* que cuidarla tanto.

20. Si este trabajo *estuviera* mejor hecho, *merecería* una buena calificación.

---

* For explanation of present-unreal conditions, if necessary, see page 194, also footnote on same page. For discussion of past-unreal conditions, see page 200, also footnote on same page.

Use of QUISIERA

The imperfect subjunctive of *querer*, QUISIERA, *followed* by an infinitive, is often used in Spanish as a softened statement or polite request. It is equivalent to the English *would like*.

> El *quisiera hablar* con usted. (He would like to talk with you.)
> Yo *quisiera leer* ese libro. (I would like to read that book.)

Note, however, that if a new subject is introduced after *quisiera*, the subordinate clause with the verb in the imperfect subjunctive must be used instead of the infinitive construction.

> El *quisiera* que usted lo *acompañara*. (He would like you to accompany him.)
> Ellos *quisieran* que ella *se quedara* allí más tiempo. (They would like her to remain there longer.)

Replace the infinitive in each of following sentences with a subordinate clause beginning with QUE and with USTED as a subject. Follow example.

1. Yo quisiera *hablar* español muy bien.

   (Example: Yo quisiera *que usted hablara e*spañol muy bien.)

2. Ella quisiera *estar* de regreso por la noche.
3. María quisiera *ir* en seguida a la capital.
4. Ellos quisieran *mirar* el programa de televisión.
5. Nosotros quisiéramos *hablar* italiano correctamente.
6. Yo quisiera *obtener* muy buenas notas en el examen de gramática.
7. El ingeniero quisiera *terminar* la obra la próxima semana.
8. Ernesto quisiera *estudiar* en una universidad española.
9. Ellos quisieran *visitar* los museos de París.
10. Mis hijos quisieran *aprender* química industrial.
11. El quisiera *ser* un buen chofer.
12. Nosotras quisiéramos *regresar* en un vapor.
13. Yo quisiera *gastar* poco dinero en ese viaje.
14. Alfonso quisiera *conocer* el baile andaluz.
15. Ellas quisieran *comprar* un vestido de boda para Luisa.
16. El quisiera *vender* todas sus propiedades.
17. Yo quisiera *viajar* por los países asiáticos.
18. El quisiera *inventar* una máquina de hacer dinero.
19. Yo quisiera *felicitar* a tu hermana en su cumpleaños.
20. Juan y yo quisiéramos *poder* explicarle al jefe lo que sucedió.

Subjunctive After Compound Relative Pronouns

Note that the compound relative pronouns *quienquiera* (whoever), *cualquiera* whatever), *dondequiera* (wherever), etc., are always followed by *que* and the subjunctive if a future action is implied.

> *Quienquiera* que lo *vea*, lo admira mucho.
> *Dondequiera* que usted *vaya*, podrá oír español.

The subjunctive is also used after *ojalá* (*que*)*, to express wish or hope**.

> *Ojalá* que él *venga* pronto. (I hope or wish that he comes soon.)
> *Ojalá* que yo la *conociera* bien. (I wish I knew her well.)
> *Ojalá* yo *hubiera sabido* esto ayer. (I wish I had known this yesterday.)

Supply the required subjunctive form of the verbs in parentheses.

1. Dondequiera que yo (vivir) tendré amigos.

   (Example: Dondequiera que yo *viva*, tendré amigos.)

2. Quienquiera que (ser) podrá competir.
3. Cualquiera que (venir) será bien recibido.
4. Ojalá que mañana no (llover).
5. Ojalá que el profesor (posponer) los exámenes.
6. Ella podrá trabajar dondequiera que (ir).
7. Nosotros no contrataremos a cualquiera que (presentarse).
8. Quienquiera que nos (prestar) el dinero será bien atendido.
9. Ojalá que tú (poder) realizar tus planes.
10. Ojalá que tú (recibir) buenas noticias de tu familia.
11. Cualquiera que (encontrar) ese documento será recompensado.
12. Dondequiera que usted (estar) trate de comunicarse con nosotros.
13. Quienquiera que (estudiar) en ese colegio tendrá que pagar.
14. Ojalá que tú la (encontrar) pronto.
15. Ojalá que ya ella (sentirse) bien de su dolor de cabeza.
16. Ojalá que no se me (olvidar) el discurso.
17. Dondequiera que lo (encontrar) lo reconocerán.
18. Cualquiera que (ser) el precio, lo compraremos.
19. Ojalá que este ejercicio (estar) bien hecho.

---

* The interjection OJALA is very frequently used, literally equivalent to *God grant!* or *would to God*, although the original Arabic reference to God (Alá) has no significance in modern Spanish.

** Here again, since a situation which is unreal or contrary-to-fact is involved, just as in the *if clause* of present and past-unreal conditional sentences (see pages 198-202), the imperfect subjunctive is used to indicate present time and the past perfect subjunctive is used to indicate past time. Note comparable use of past and past perfect tenses in English after *wish*.

REFLEXIVE VERBS · *Special Uses*

The student should note that some verbs in Spanish have one meaning when used reflexively and a second meaning when used non-reflexively. For example, *parecer* means *to seem* or *to appear; parecerse* means *to resemble. Dormir* means *to sleep; dormirse* means *to fall asleep.* (Examples: Juan *parece* muy buena persona —Juan *se parece* mucho a su padre. Yo *dormí* ocho horas anoche —*Me dormí* en seguida anoche después de acostarme.)

Furthermore, many so-called reflexive verbs which refer back to the subject or describe an action performed upon oneself may also be used in non-reflexive form when there is a definite direct object which receives the action of the verb. (Examples: Elena *se lava* las manos antes de comer — Elena *lava* los platos todas las noches. María *se pinta* los ojos — Ellos *pintan* su casa todos los años.)

Choose the correct form, reflexive or non-reflexive, of the verbs in parentheses.

1. El niño siempre (duerme, se duerme) la siesta.

2. Alfonso está enfermo y no (se siente, siente) bien.

3. El maestro de Julia (llama, se llama) Rafael Martínez.

4. Ella (lleva, se lleva) bien con todos sus condiscípulos.

5. Enriqueta (puso, se puso) muy nerviosa cuando vio su mala nota.

6. Ellos no (se volvieron, volvieron) muy tarde antenoche.

7. Yo debo (quitar, quitarme) la ropa al acostarme.

8. Cuando ellos (iban, se iban*), llegó el cartero.

9. Ellos (van, se van) para su país la semana próxima.

10. Ricardo (se despierta, despierta) siempre muy temprano.

11. El tiroteo de anoche (me despertó, despertó).

12. Los pintores (quitaron, se quitaron) las manchas del piso.

13. Debes (quitarte, quitar) el sombrero en el ascensor.

14. Yo (siento, me siento) mucho calor ahora.

15. Ella (puso, se puso) todos sus libros en el estante.

16. Tomás (parece, se parece) a su tío Jaime.

17. Este ejercicio (parece, se parece) difícil, pero no lo es.

18. Ellas (sienten, se sienten) mucho la desgracia ocurrida a Luisa.

19. El (se peinó, peinó) varias veces ante el espejo.

20. La madre (durmió, se durmió) al bebé.

---

* *Ir* means "to go"; *irse,* "to leave".

Relative Pronouns · **QUE, QUIEN** *

The student has no doubt already observed that the relative pronoun *que* may serve as subject or object of the verb. It may also refer to persons or things, singular and plural, without change of form. (Examples: El es el hombre *que* trabaja conmigo. Vi al médico *que* usted me recomendó. Estos son los libros *que* necesito.) Note, however, that after a preposition, *que* refers only to things. (Example: Vi el apartamento en *que* viven.)

If it is necessary to refer to a person after a preposition, then *quien* is used instead of *que*. Since *quien* refers only to persons, it is also used at times instead of *que* to indicate the antecedent more clearly. Note that *quien* (pl. *quienes*) always agrees in number with its antecedent. (Examples: El es el hombre a *quien* vi en el restaurante. Hablé con las muchachas, *quienes* estaban muy contentas con la maestra nueva.)

In the blanks, supply QUE, QUIEN (or QUIENES) as required. Follow examples.

1. Este es el mapa............te compré ayer.

   (Example: Este es el mapa *que* te compré ayer.)

2. Son los estudiantes a............dieron la beca.

   (*Example*: Son los estudiantes a *quienes* dieron la beca.)

3. Esta es la persona de............te estoy hablando.
4. Esta es la casa............compró tu abuelo.
5. Nos encontramos con el señor de............usted hizo alabanzas.
6. Están aquí los libros............tú querías.
7. Francisco es el abogado a............designaron para la defensa.
8. Este es el taller en............yo arreglo mi automóvil.
9. ¿Tiene usted la llave...............yo le di a guardar?
10. Cervantes es el escritor a............nos hemos referido.
11. Estas muchachas son secretarias de............ya te hablé.
12. Veremos a los ladrones a............apresaron anoche.
13. Esta es la maleta...............trajo mi padrino.
14. Era un profesor............estimulaba a sus alumnos.
15. Este es el lápiz con............hago mis dibujos.
16. ¿............son esos individuos?
17. ¿............es el autor de esta novela?
18. ¿.......................trajo Elena?
19. Aquellos son los cuadros............pintó Sebastián Alvarez.
20. ¿A...............está esperando usted, María?

* When acting as subject pronouns, especially in question form, these must be accented: *qué, quién, quiénes.*

EL CUAL, LA CUAL (*los cuales, las cuales*)

In cases of ambiguity where there is more than one possible antecedent for a relative pronoun, *el cual** (*la cual,* etc.) is often used instead of *que* or *quien*. *El cual, la cual,* etc., agree in number and gender with the antecedent and thus indicate, without any possible chance of error, their proper antecedent. They are often used after the preposition *por** and after adverbial phrases such as *después de, además de,* etc.

Vi la película en el Teatro Nacional, *la cual* me gustó mucho.
(Thus, *la cual* here clearly refers to *la película* rather than to *el teatro*.)
Aquí están los paquetes *por los cuales* han venido.

Supply whichever form of EL CUAL is required in the particular sentence. Follow examples.

1. Recibí una carta.............estaba escrita en inglés.

   (Example: Recibí una carta *la cual* estaba escrita en inglés.)

2. Mi carro tiene dos puertas, una de.............está rota.

   (Example: Mi carro tiene dos puertas, una de *las cuales* está rota.)

3. Ese jarrón en................usted puso la flor es valiosísimo.
4. Bolívar libró la batalla de Ayacucho, en.............fue vencedor.
5. Juan tiene dos amigos,.............viven ahora en Uruguay.
6. La caoba es una madera dura con.............se hacen muebles finos.
7. Los gatos son animales domésticos a.............les gusta el pescado.
8. Aquí hay seis lápices, de.............tomaré dos.
9. Anoche ví varios programas de televisión, uno de......no me gustó nada.
10. Ramiro me regaló una camisa.............costó cinco pesos.
11. Me encontré en la calle con mi amigo Luis, a**........no había visto por mucho tiempo.
12. Estos son los bombillos.............valen dos pesos.
13. Este es el invento con................el químico ganó el premio Nobel.
14. Rosalía tiene cuatro hijas, de.............Inés es la más bella.
15. Esta es la pared, detrás de.............se escondió el ladrón.
16. Aquella es la artista de.............se han dicho tantas cosas.
17. Ese es el país.............se habla mucho en esa geografía.
18. Aquí están los libros que buscaba, de................ éste es el que más me interesa.
19. Aquí tiene usted las láminas, entre.............escogerá cinco.
20. Allí esta la sociedad de.............él es el presidente.

---

* *Que*, used as a relative pronoun after *por*, might well be confused with the interrogative *¿por qué?* or the common conjunction *porque*. For this reason *el cual, la cual*, etc., is used.

** *A* and *el* contract to *al; de* and *el* to *del.*

CUYO, CUYA (*Cuyos, Cuyas*)

The possessive relative pronoun *cuyo* (whose) * always agrees in gender and number with the noun which follows it. Examples: El es el muchacho a *cuyo* padre yo conozco. (He is the boy whose father I know.) El es el profesor *cuyas* hijas estudian en Europa. (He is the teacher whose daughters study in Europe.)

Supply the required form of CUYO. Follow examples.

1. Ella es una profesora............cultura es notable.

   (Example: Ella es una profesora *cuya* cultura es notable.)

2. Esta es la artista............manos están aseguradas.

   (Example: Esta es la artista *cuyas* manos están aseguradas.)

3. Este es el autor............libros se venden mucho.

4. Es Tomás Edison,................inventos han sido tan beneficiosos.

5. Esta es la biblia................edición es tan antigua.

6. Ramiro es un deportista............triunfos son muy conocidos.

7. Mi novia,............paciencia es extraordinaria, me perdona.

8. Estos son los huerfanitos ....padres perecieron en el naufragio.

9. El padre José era un sacerdote............bondad es inolvidable.

10. Los Fernández, en............hogar conocí a Luis, se mudaron.

11. Esos árboles,............hojas ya se han caído, son frutales.

12. Ese hombre, ...nombre no recuerdo, me lo contó.

13. El día del accidente, ...fecha exacta no recuerdo, me llevaron al hospital.

14. Antonio,............abuelos viven en Francia, habla francés.

15. Su vecina,............automóvil es rojo y blanco, trabaja en la farmacia.

16. María López,............hermano es compañero mío, se casó ayer.

17. El doctor González es un médico............conocimientos son extensos.

18. Octavio es un compañero por............lealtad todos responden.

19. Aquella casa nueva,............ventanas están todas cerradas, está desalquilada.

20. Este texto,............ejercicios son variados y prácticos, me gusta mucho.

---

* Not to be confused with the interrogative pronoun *whose* (*Whose* book is this?), which is rendered in Spanish by *de quién* (¿*De quién* es este libro?).

HABER as *Auxiliary Verb*

We have already studied the use of *haber* in forming the compound tenses in Spanish. (No *han entregado* todavía esa mercancía. Juan dijo que ya *había visto* esa película.) Note that *haber* is also used to form the past perfect form of both infinitives and participles (*gerundio*). (Me alegro de *haber hecho* todo eso antes de salir. *Habiendo esperado* más de dos horas, nos fuimos.)

Haber is also used to obtain the past form of *deber de* (must) in constructions expressing probability or conjecture*.

> Juan no está aquí. El *debe de haber salido* con María. (John is not here. He must have gone out with Mary.)
> *Debe de haber llovido* mientras estábamos en el cine. (It *must have rained* while we were in the movie.)

Substitute the correct form of DEBE DE HABER for the words in italics. Also make all necessary changes. (The meaning of the sentence, of course, will remain the same in both cases.) Follow example.

1. Luis *probablemente* llamó por teléfono.

    (Example: Luis *debe de haber* llamado por teléfono.)

2. El *probablemente* recibió la carta.
3. Yo *probablemente* perdí los recibos del alquiler.
4. Usted *probablemente* estaba cansado de trabajar.
5. Virginia *probablemente* fue al cine con Roberto.
6. Ellos *probablemente* estudiaron en Alemania.
7. Ella *probablemente* recogió los paquetes de medicinas.
8. Usted *probablemente* olvidó el dinero.
9. Martín *probablemente* gastó toda su fortuna en el juego.
10. El profesor *probablemente* perdió la paciencia con sus estudiantes.
11. Nosotros *probablemente* no lo reconocimos en la calle.
12. Yo *probablemente* me enfermé por descuido.
13. Ella *probablemente* vendió todas sus prendas.
14. El cartero *probablemente* echó las cartas en el buzón.
15. Ramón *probablemente* sabía que la cosecha se había perdido.
16. *Probablemente* él se quedó dormido esta mañana.
17. Usted *probablemente* comió demasiado y por eso se ha indigestado.
18. Pablo *probablemente* resolvió los difíciles problemas de matemáticas.

---

* DEBER DE, whenever used with the preposition *de*, indicates probability or conjecture. However, DEBER, without *de*, is used to express duty or obligation. Both are always followed by infinitives.

210

In the last exercise we studied the use of *haber* as an auxiliary verb in forming the past form of *deber de* (must) in constructions expressing probable past action. Note also that *haber* is similarly used as an auxiliary verb to form the past tense of *debería* (should), expressing an obligation or duty that existed in the past but that was not carried out.

> El *debería haber estudiado* más. (He should have studied more.)
> Usted *debería haberme* llamado* por teléfono anoche.
> (You should have called me by telephone last night.)

Change to past time by introducing HABER. Follow example.

1. Yo *debería hacer* ese trabajo ahora.

   (Example: Yo debería *haber* hecho ese trabajo ahora.)

2. Usted no *debería estudiar* tanto por la noche.

3. Ella *debería leer* más composiciones en verso.

4. Nosotros *deberíamos ir* a comprar más libros.

5. Ese estudiante *debería poner* más cuidado en sus ejercicios.

6. El enfermo *debería descansar* más en la cama.

7. Don Fernando *debería pagar* todas sus deudas.

8. *Deberían llevar* a Luisito al parque zoológico.

9. El maestro *debería poner* menos ejercicios.

10. Nosotros *deberíamos cuidar* mejor nuestra propiedad.

11. Yo *debería estar* allí a las doce en punto.

12. El *debería esperar* más tiempo para casarse.

13. Felipe *debería dar* un paseo por las montañas.

14. Raúl *debería escribir* con más frecuencia.

15. Carlos y Martín *deberían viajar* por los Estados Unidos.

16. Usted *debería decir* la verdad.

17. Ella *debería disfrutar* de unas buenas vacaciones.

18. El *debería entregar* esos telegramas inmediatamente.

19. Nosotros *deberíamos comer* más temprano.

20. Tu sobrino *debería estudiar* con más interés.

---

* Note that direct and indirect object pronouns in such constructions are attached to *haber*. They may also precede the main verb (Usted *me* debería haber llamado anoche) —but the more common practice is to attach them to *haber*. (Usted debería *haberme* llamado anoche.)

a) The conjunction *sino* introduces a positive phrase which is contrary to the preceding *negative* statement; this is equivalent in English to the special use of *but* in similar instances.

> La pluma no es mía, *sino* de ella. (The pen is not mine, but hers.)
> Ella no va a la Argentina, *sino* a Chile. (She is not going to Argentina, but to Chile.)

b) The conjuncion *y* (and) is changed to *e* when the word which follows begins with *i* or *hi*. Likewise, *o* is changed to *u* before words beginning with *o* or *ho*. (Such changes are made simply for reasons of euphony.)

> Hablan francés *e* italiano.   Había siete *u* ocho personas allí.
> Son padre *e* hijo.   No sé si es lobo *u* oso.

Choose the correct form. Follow example.

1. El no quiere estudiar hoy, (pero, sino) mañana.

   (Example: El no quiere estudiar hoy, sino* mañana.)

2. Yo buscaba a Juan, (pero, sino) no estaba en su casa.
3. Esteban no solamente es rico, (pero, sino) también educado.
4. El va a descansar, (pero, sino) yo voy a trabajar.
5. María no quería ir al cine, (pero, sino) al baile.
6. No importa que sea mujer (o, u) hombre.
7. Esteban (y, e) Inés son primos.
8. Nos encontramos con Rafael (y, e) Ignacio.
9. No estuvimos en el campo (pero, sino) en la ciudad.
10. Domingo (y, e) Manuel trabajan en una droguería.
11. Rosalía es una muchacha bonita (y, e) inteligente.
12. Padre (y, e) hijas fueron de pesca al lago.
13. Necesitamos agujas (y, e) hilos de colores distintos.
14. Dame siete (o, u) ocho hojas de papel.
15. Había muchas personas, (pero, sino) ninguna sabía español.
16. No me gusta viajar en barco, (pero, sino) en avión.
17. No quiso tomar vino, (pero, sino) cerveza.
18. El hombre (o, u) la mujer sirven para ese empleo.
19. Antonio no sólo no estudia, (pero, sino) que tampoco trabaja.
20. Tomás va a comprar, (pero, sino) Ernesto va a vender.

---

* PERO and SINO, as employed in this exercise, are always preceded by comma or semicolon.

NOUNS-DIMINUTIVE SUFFIXES

In Spanish, various suffixes are often added to nouns in order to express different degrees of smallness*. The most common of these diminutive endings are *ito, cito, ecito, illo, ico*. If the noun ends in a consonant or accented vowel, the vowel is dropped before the suffix.

mesa	—	*mesita* (little table)	mujer	—	*mujercita* (little woman)
libro	—	*librito* (little book)	joven	—	*jovencito* (young man)
perro	—	*perrito* (puppy)	ventana	—	*ventanilla, ventanita* (little window)
gato	—	*gatico, gatito* (little cat)	pan	—	*panecillo, panecito* (roll, bun)

In addition to expressing degrees of smallness, such diminutives may also express fondness or affection: *viejito* (pleasant old man); *vocecita* (sweet, little voice).

Supply the correct diminutive form of the words in italics.

1. Yo traje una *caja* para María.

   (Example: Yo traje una *cajita* para María.)

2. Recibí una *carta* de mi nieta.

3. Recoge esos *palos* del jardín.

4. Rosa tiene una *casa* de muñecas.

5. Irene es una *muchacha* muy bonita.

6. Yo quiero mucho a mi *mamá* y a mi *papá*.

7. Riega las flores del *jardín*.

8. Me regalaron muchas *flores* de lindos colores.

9. Los *nietos* visitaron a su abuela.

10. Abre las *ventanas* para que entre el aire.

11. La *niña* de Juana juega con su *coche*.

12. Están preciosos los *árboles* de navidad.

13. El *chico* de la vecina siempre está jugando.

14. Sécate la cara con el *paño*.

15. Veo una *luz* en la distancia.

16. Ayer pintamos la *mesa* de la *máquina* de escribir.

17. Corta ese *hilo* que tienes en el cuello de la camisa.

18. Mi *hermano* ya sabe leer y escribir.

19. Dame algunos *panes* calientes con mantequilla.

20. La *muñeca* de Lucía tiene su *cocina*.

---

* Compare in English: book — booklet; kitchen — kitchenette, etc.

ADJECTIVES · ISIMO SUFFIX

The so-called absolute superlative of many adjectives (and occasionally adverbs) is obtained by adding the suffix *ísimo* (*ísima, ísimos, ísimas*). This suffix gives to the adjective a meaning which might be expressed in English by *very, most,* or *extremely*. If the adjective ends in a consonant or accented vowel, the suffix is simply added; if the adjective ends in an unaccented vowel, the vowel is dropped before the suffix*.

fácil	— facilísimo	malo	— malísimo	fino	— finísimo
útil	— utilísimo	dulce	— dulcísimo	feo	— feísimo

Es utilísimo. — It is most useful.   Es finísimo. — It is extremely fine.
Es facilísimo. — It is very easy.   Es malísimo. — It is very bad.

Substitute, for the words in italics, the absolute superlative form of the indicated adjective. Follow example.

1. Ese ejercicio no es *muy difícil*.

    (Example: Ese ejercicio no es *dificilísimo*.)

2. La casa de José es *muy pequeña*.

    (Example: La casa de José es *pequeñísima*.)

3. Josefina tiene *mucho* dinero.
4. Esa tinta es *muy negra*; pero esta otra es *muy roja*.
5. Compré unos zapatos blancos *muy baratos*.
6. Dicen que el vecino está *muy grave*.
7. El señor González es un hombre *muy rico*.**
8. La señora Fernández tiene una hija *muy linda*.
9. La cocina de tu casa es *muy moderna*.
10. El camión de Miguel es *muy grande*.
11. Los muebles de esa mueblería son *muy caros*.
12. Compramos una cinta de seda *muy larga*.**
13. Tu hermana tiene las manos *muy blancas*.
14. El profesor tiene en su biblioteca algunos libros *muy viejos*.
15. Vimos en el parque un niño *muy gracioso*.
16. En el kindergarten había varios niños *muy desobedientes*.
17. Los rascacielos de Nueva York son *muy altos*.
18. Los hijos de Carlos son *muy hermosos*.
19. Tu perro está *muy gordo*.
20. Carmen está *muy flaca* porque come *muy poco*.

* See previous exercise, page 213, for similar addition of diminutive suffix to nouns.

** *Rico — riquísimo*. Note the introduction of *qu* in order to retain the hard sound of *c* before *i*. Similarly, *largo — larguísimo* (introduction of *gu*, see p. 155).

EXCLAMATIONS

Exclamations in Spanish are expressed with *Qué* as shown in the examples which follow. (Note particularly use of *tan*.)

¡*Qué* pálida está! (How pale she is!)
¡*Qué* corbata *tan* bonita! (What a pretty tie!)

Note that *Qué* is accented in both exclamatory and question forms. Also note that exclamatory sentences, as well exclamatory phrases and interjections, are preceded by exclamation marks in reverse.

Change the following sentences to exclamatory form. Make all necessay changes, using QUE (and TAN where needed). Follow examples.

1. Ella es muy estudiosa.

   (*Example*: ¡Qué estudiosa es ella!)

2. Es una noche muy calurosa.

   (*Example*: ¡Qué noche tan calurosa!)

3. Antonia toca bien el violín.
4. Luis aprende muy fácilmente.
5. Son muy raras esas nubes.
6. Es un día espléndido.
7. Es una joven muy linda.
8. Son unas peras duras.
9. El tiene buen gusto.
10. Canta muy bonito Josefa.
11. Es un carro muy extraño.
12. Tiene una casa rara.
13. Ese amigo es muy simpático.
14. Era un paseo muy aburrido.
15. Son ejercicios muy difíciles.
16. Luisa baila muy bien.
17. Son palacios muy antiguos.
18. Era una historia larga.
19. Es una joven guapísima.
20. Una persona muy delicada.
21. Tiene la cara muy triste.
22. Ella estaba muy contenta.

APPENDIX

FIRST CONJUGATION
HABLAR

PRESENT	habl	o	as	a	amos	an
IMPERFECT	habl	aba	abas	aba	ábamos	aban
PRETERIT	habl	é	aste	ó	amos	aron
FUTURE	hablar	é	ás	á	emos	án
CONDITIONAL	hablar	ía	ías	ía	íamos	ían
PRES. SUBJ.	habl	e	es	e	emos	en
IMP. SUBJ. (1)	habl	ara	aras	ara	áramos	aran
IMP. SUBJ. (2)	habl	ase	ases	ase	ásemos	asen
IMPERATIVE	habl		a	e	emos	en
PRES. PART.	habl ando			PAST PART. habl ado		

SECOND CONJUGATION
COMER

PRESENT	com	o	es	e	emos	en
IMPERFECT	com	ía	ías	ía	íamos	ían
PRETERIT	com	í	iste	ió	imos	ieron
FUTURE	comer	é	ás	á	emos	án
CONDITIONAL	comer	ía	ías	ía	íamos	ían
PRES. SUBJ.	com	a	as	a	amos	an
IMP. SUBJ. (1)	com	iera	ieras	iera	iéramos	ieran
IMP. SUBJ. (2)	com	iese	ieses	iese	iésemos	iesen
IMPERATIVE	com		e	a	amos	an
PRES. PART.	com iendo			PAST PART. com ido		

THIRD CONJUGATION
VIVIR

PRESENT	viv	o	es	e	imos	en
IMPERFECT	viv	ía	ías	ía	íamos	ían
PRETERIT	viv	í	iste	ió	imos	ieron
FUTURE	vivir	é	ás	á	emos	án
CONDITIONAL	vivir	ía	ías	ía	íamos	ían
PRES. SUBJ.	viv	a	as	a	amos	an
IMP. SUBJ. (1)	viv	iera	ieras	iera	iéramos	ieren
IMP. SUBJ. (2)	viv	iese	ieses	iese	iésemos	iesen
FUT. SUBJ.	viv	iere	ieres	iere	iéremos	ieran
IMPERATIVE	viv		e	a	amos	an
PRES. PART.	viv iendo			PAST PART. viv ido		

COMPOUND TENSES

INFINITIVE	I	II	III
PRES. PERFECT	haber hablado	haber comido	haber vivido

PARTICIPLE			
PRES. PERFECT	habiendo hablado	habiendo comido	habiendo vivido

INDICATIVE			
PRES. PERFECT	he hablado	he comido	he vivido
PAST PERFECT	había hablado	había comido	había vivido
FUTURE PERFECT	habré hablado	habré comido	habré vivido
COND. PERFECT	habría hablado	habría comido	habría vivido

SUBJUNCTIVE			
PRES. PERFECT	haya hablado	haya comido	haya vivido
PAST PERFECT (1)	hubiera hablado	hubiera comido	hubiera vivido
PAST PERFECT (2)	hubiese hablado	hubiese comido	hubiese vivido

IRREGULAR VERBS

(ANDAR)

PRETERIT   anduve, anduviste, anduvo, anduvimos, anduvieron

IMP. SUBJ.   (1) anduviera, anduvieras, etc. (2) anduviese, anduvieses, etc.

(CABER)

PRESENT   quepo, cabes, cabe, cabemos, caben
PRETERIT   cupe, cupiste, cupo, cupimos cupieron
FUTURE   cabré, cabrás, etc.; COND. cabría, cabrías, etc.
PRES. SUBJ.   quepa, quepas, quepa, quepamos, quepan
IMP. SUBJ.   (1) cupiera, cupieras, etc. (2) cupiese, cupieses, etc.

(CAER)   PARTICIPLES   cayendo   caído

PRESENT   caigo, caes, cae, caemos, caen
PRETERIT   caí, caíste, cayó, caímos, cayeron
PRES. SUBJ.   caiga, caigas, caiga, caigamos, caigan
IMP. SUBJ.   (1) cayera, cayeras, etc. (2) cayese, cayeses, etc.

(DAR)

PRESENT   doy, das, da, damos, dan
PRETERIT   dí, diste, dió, dimos, dieron
PRES. SUBJ.   dé, des, dé, demos, den
IMP. SUBJ.   (1) diera, dieras, etc. (2) diese, dieses, etc.

(DECIR)   PARTICIPLES   diciendo   dicho

PRESENT   digo, dices, dice, decimos, dicen
PRETERIT   dije, dijiste, dijo, dijimos, dijeron
FUTURE   diré, dirás, etc.; COND. diría, dirías, etc.
PRES. SUBJ.   diga, digas, diga, digamos, digan
IMP. SUBJ.   (1) dijera, dijeras, etc. (2) dijese, dijeses, etc.

(ESTAR)	
PRESENT	estoy, estás, está, estamos, están
PRETERIT	estuve, estuviste, estuvo, estuvimos, estuvieron
PRES. SUBJ.	esté, estés, esté, estemos, estén
IMP. SUBJ.	(1) estuviera, estuvieras, etc. (2) estuviese, estuvieses, etc.

(HABER)	
PRESENT	he, has, ha, hemos, han
PRETERIT	hube, hubiste, hubo, hubimos, hubieron
FUTURE	habré, habrás, etc.; COND. habría, habrías, etc.
PRES. SUBJ.	haya, hayas, haya, hayamos, hayan
IMP. SUBJ.	(1) hubiera, hubieras, etc. (2) hubiese, hubieses, etc.

(HACER)	PARTICIPLES haciendo hecho
PRESENT	hago, haces, hace, hacemos, hacen
PRETERIT	hice, hiciste, hizo, hicimos, hicieron
FUTURE	haré, harás, etc.; COND. haría, harías, etc.
PRES. SUBJ.	haga, hagas, haga, hagamos, hagan
IMP. SUBJ.	(1) hiciera, hicieras, etc. (2) hiciese, hicieses, etc.

(IR)	PARTICIPLES yendo ido
PRESENT	voy, vas, va, vamos, van
IMPERFECT	iba, ibas, iba, íbamos, iban
PRETERIT	fuí, fuiste, fué, fuimos, fueron
PRES. SUBJ.	vaya, vayas, vaya, vayamos, vayan
IMP. SUBJ.	(1) fuera, fueras, etc. (2) fuese, fueses, etc.

(OIR)	PARTICIPLES oyendo oído
PRESENT	oigo, oyes, oye, oímos, oyen
PRETERIT	oí, oíste, oyó, oímos, oyeron
PRES. SUBJ.	oiga, oigas, oiga, oigamos, oigan
IMP. SUBJ.	(1) oyera, oyeras, etc. (2) oyese, oyeses, etc.

(PODER)	PARTICIPLES pudiendo podido
PRESENT	puedo, puedes, puede, podemos, pueden
PRETERIT	pude, pudiste, pudo, pudimos, pudieron
FUTURE	podré, podrás, etc.; COND. podría, podrías, etc.
PRES. SUBJ.	pueda, puedas, pueda, podamos, puedan
IMP. SUBJ.	(1) pudiera, pudieras, etc. (2) pudiese, pudieses, etc.

(PONER)	PARTICIPLES poniendo puesto
PRESENT	pongo, pones, pone, ponemos, ponen
PRETERIT	puse, pusiste, puso, pusimos, pusieron
FUTURE	pondré, pondrás, etc.; COND. pondría, pondrías, etc.
PRES. SUBJ.	ponga, pongas, ponga, pongamos, pongan
IMP. SUBJ.	(1) pusiera, pusieras, etc. (2) pusiese, pusieses, etc.

(QUERER)	
PRESENT	quiero, quieres, quiere, queremos, quieren
PRETERIT	quise, quisiste, quiso, quisimos, quisieron
FUTURE	querré, querrás, etc.; COND. querría, querrías, etc.
PRES. SUBJ.	quiera, quieras, quiera, queramos, quieran
IMP. SUBJ.	(1) quisiera, quisieras (2) quisiese, quisieses, etc.

(SABER)

PRESENT	sé, sabes, sabe, sabemos, saben
PRETERIT	supe, supiste, supo, supimos, supieron
FUTURE	sabré, sabrás, etc.; COND. sabría, sabrías, etc.
PRES. SUBJ.	sepa, sepas, sepa, sepamos, sepan
IMP. SUBJ.	(1) supiera, supieras, etc. (2) supiese, supieses, etc.

(SALIR)

PRESENT	salgo, sales, sale, salimos, salen
FUTURE	saldré, saldrás, etc.; COND. saldría, saldrías, etc.
PRES. SUBJ.	salga, salgas, salga, salgamos, salgan

(SER)

PRESENT	soy, eres, es, somos, son
IMPERFECT	era, eras, era, éramos, eran
PRETERIT	fuí, fuiste, fué, fuimos, fueron
PRES. SUBJ.	sea, seas, sea, seamos, sean
IMP. SUBJ.	(1) fuera, fueras, etc. (2) fuese, fueses, etc.

(TENER)

PRESENT	tengo, tienes, tiene, tenemos, tienen
PRETERIT	tuve, tuviste, tuvo, tuvimos, tuvieron
FUTURE	tendré, tendrás, etc.; COND. tendría, tendrías, etc.
PRES. SUBJ.	tenga, tengas, tenga, tengamos, tengan
IMP. SUBJ.	(1) tuviera, tuvieras, etc. (2) tuviese, tuvieses, etc.

(TRADUCIR)

PRESENT	traduzco, traduces, traduce, traducimos, traducen
PRETERIT	traduje, tradujiste, tradujo, tradujimos, tradujeron
PRES. SUBJ.	traduzca, traduzcas, traduzca, traduzcamos, traduzcan
IMP. SUBJ.	(1) tradujera, tradujeras, etc. (2) tradujese, tradujeses, etc.

(TRAER)   PARTICIPLES   trayendo   traído

PRESENT	traigo, traes, trae, traemos, traen
PRETERIT	traje, trajiste, trajo, trajimos, trajeron
PRES. SUBJ.	traiga, traigas, traiga, traigamos, traigan
IMP. SUBJ.	(1) trajera, trajeras, etc. (2) trajese, trajeses, etc.

(VALER)

PRESENT	valgo, vales, vale, valemos, valen
FUTURE	valdré, valdrás, etc.; COND. valdría, valdrías, etc.
PRES. SUBJ.	valga, valgas, valga, valgamos, valgan

(VENIR)   PARTICIPLES   viniendo   venido

PRESENT	vengo, vienes, viene, venimos, vienen
PRETERIT	vine, viniste, vino, vinimos, vinieron
FUTURE	vendré, vendrás, etc.; COND. vendría, vendrías, etc.
PRES. SUBJ.	venga, vengas, venga, vengamos, vengan
IMP. SUBJ.	(1) viniera, vinieras, etc. (2) viniese, vinieses, etc.

(VER)   PARTICIPLES   viendo   visto

PRESENT	veo, ves, ve, vemos, ven
IMPERFECT	veía, veías, veía, veíamos, veían
PRETERIT	ví, viste, vió, vimos, vieron
PRES. SUBJ.	vea, veas, vea, veamos, vean
IMP. SUBJ.	(1) viera vieras, etc. (2) viese, vieses, etc.

RADICAL CHANGING VERBS

(PENSAR)
RES. IND.   pienso, piensas, piensa, pensamos, piensan
RES. SUBJ.   piense, pienses, piense, pensemos, piensen

(PERDER)
RES. IND.   pierdo, pierdes, perdemos, pierden
RES. SUBJ.   pierda, pierdas, pierda, perdamos, pierdan
Like *perder*:   defender, entender, etc.

(CONTAR)
RES. IND.   cuento, cuentas, cuenta, contamos, cuentan
RES. SUBJ.   cuente, cuentes, cuente, contemos, cuenten
Like *contar*:   acordarse, acostarse, almorzar, costar, encontrar, recordar, rogar, soñar, jugar, etc.

(VOLVER)
RES. IND.   vuelvo, vuelves, vuelve, volvemos, vuelven
RES. SUBJ.   vuelva, vuelvas, vuelva, volvamos, vuelvan
Like *volver*:   llover, morder, mover, etc.

(JUGAR)
RES. IND.   juego, juegas, juega, jugamos, juegan
RES. SUBJ.   juegue, juegues, juegue, juguemos, jueguen

(SENTIR)   PARTICIPLES   sintiendo   sentido
RES. IND.   siento, sientes, siente, sentimos, sienten
RETERIT   sentí, sentiste, sintió, sentimos, sintieron
RES. SUBJ.   sienta, sientas, sienta, sintamos, sientan
MP. SUBJ.   (1) sintiera, sintieras, etc. (2) sintiese, sintieses, etc.
Like *sentir*:   concernir, discernir, digerir, etc.

(DORMIR)   PARTICIPLES   durmiendo   dormido
RES. IND.   duermo, duermes, duerme, dormimos, duermen
RETERIT   dormí, dormiste, durmió, dormimos, durmieron
RES. SUBJ.   duerma, duermas, duerma, durmamos, duerman
MP. SUBJ.   (1) durmiera, durmieras, etc. (2) durmiese, durmieses, etc.

(PEDIR)   PARTICIPLES   pidiendo   pedido
RES. IND.   pido, pides, pide, pedimos, piden
RETERIT   pedí, pediste, pidió, pedimos, pidieron
RES. SUBJ.   pida, pidas, pida, pidamos, pidan
MP. SUBJ.   (1) pidiera, pidieras, etc. (2) pidiese, pidieses, etc.
Like *pedir*:   corregir, despedir, elegir, repetir, servir, vestir, etc.

(REIR)   PARTICIPLES   riendo   reído
RES. IND.   río, ríes, río, reímos, ríen
RETERIT   reí, reíste, rió, reímos, rieron
RES. SUBJ.   ría, rías, ría, ríamos, rían
MP. SUBJ.   (1) riera, rieras, etc. (2) riese, rieses, etc.

223

ORTOGRAPHIC CHANGES

(BUSCAR)

PRETERIT	busqué, buscaste, buscó, buscamos, buscaron
PRES. SUBJ.	busque, busques, busque, busquemos, busquen
Like buscar:	acercarse, sacar, tocar, etc.

(PAGAR)

PRETERIT	pagué, pagaste, pagó, pagamos, pagaron
PRES. SUBJ.	pague, pagues, pague, paguemos, paguen
Like *pagar*:	entregar, llegar, negar, rogar, etc.

(CRUZAR)

PRETERIT	crucé, cruzaste, cruzó, cruzamos, cruzaron
PRES. SUBJ.	cruce, cruces, cruce, crucemos, crucen
Like *cruzar*:	almorzar, empezar, lanzar, etc.

(COGER)

PRES. IND.	cojo, coges, coge, cogemos, cogen
PRES. SUBJ.	coja, cojas, coja, cojamos, coja
Like *coger*:	escoger, proteger, recoger, etc.

(DIRIGIR)

PRES. IND.	dirijo, diriges, dirige, dirigimos, dirigen
PRES. SUBJ.	dirija, dirijas, dirija, dirijamos, dirijan
Like *dirigir*:	corregir, elegir, exigir, etc.

(DISTINGUIR)

PRES. IND.	distingo, distingues, distingue, distinguimos, distinguen
PRES. SUBJ.	distinga, distingas, distinga, distingamos, distingan
Like *distinguir*:	seguir, etc.

(LEER)

PRETERIT	leí, leíste, leyó, leímos, leyeron
IMP. SUBJ.	(1) leyera, leyeras, etc. (2) leyese, leyeses, etc.

(HUIR)

PRES. IND.	huyo, huyes, huye, huímos, huyen
PRETERIT	huí, huiste, huyó, huímos, huyeron
PRES. SUBJ.	huya, huyas, huya, huyamos, huyan
IMP. SUBJ.	(1) huyera, huyeras, etc. (2) huyese, huyeses, etc.